The Catalyst

Shayna Maidle

Unsafe at Any Speed

Anti-Venom for the Soul

The First Time (Best Lesbian Erotica 1997)

"the SM fiction of choice among pansexuals."

-Susan Wright (editor, SM Classics)

"The Marketplace series was like water to a thirsty woman. I drank them. I inhaled them. I think they will become, if they aren't already, basic texts — the ABC's of BDSM for fiction — much like Capote's In Cold Blood is the classic for that genre of crime novel."

-Claire Thompson (author, Sara's Surrender)

"If you haven't read the...Marketplace series, you have been missing out on some of the best S/M erotica around." "(Antoniou) gives her characters an incredible depth and provides them with unique individual voices. I believe in them. In fact, I expect to run into them on the street."

-Girlfriends Magazine

"some of the best S/M erotica around."

- Blowfish

"Queens-bornAntoniou is heiress presumptive to some of the erotic territory staked out by Pat Califia and John Preston...Antoniou's writing moves with assurance between genders and sexual orientations, relentlessly exploring the dark side of sexuality."

-Michael Rowe (Writing Below the Belt)

"If you like smut with a plot, engaging characters and snappy dialogue, this (series) is for you."

- The Servant's Quarters

"Reads like cool silk on whip reddened flanks. Gay, bi, or straight, master, novice, slave, switch, Daddy, boy, fetishist, hedonist, and submissive will all respond to these erotic pages. Compelling, and charged with electricity, pleasurable as leather rain."

-Kitty Tsui (author, Breathless)

"quite simply, the best SM novels in decades."

- Cuir Underground

"Laura Antoniou… elevates the genre of SM erotica...The tales ring true, the dialogue achingly real, and the sex is as hot as you'd ever hope for."

-Kate Bornstein (author, My Gender Workbook)

The Catalyst
and Other Works

by Laura Antoniou

The Catalyst
and Other Works

by Laura Antoniou

Mystic Rose

Fairfield, Connecticut

Cover by
DM Foster - www.dark-arts.net/bound2serve

Foreward by Midori

The Catalyst and Other Works
Copyright ©2004 by Laura Antoniou

Published by

Mystic Rose Books
P.O. Box 1036/SMS
Fairfield, CT 06432

ISBN 0-9645960-8-3

First Edition, first printing 2004

Contents

Foreword   5
Introduction   9
Writing My Body   11
Unsafe at Any Speed   11
My Writing Life, or, Everything Old is New Again   17
Defending Pornography (for real this time)   23
Sex Toys   27
The New Brand   32
The First Time   38
Alternate Worlds & Realities   43
Electra, on the Rocks   43
Shayna Maidel   50
To Serve in Close Attendance to Nobility
Samurai Tradition in an SM Context   69
The Way of Heaven   76
One Drop   84
The Little Urban-maid   97
GenderFucks
Stories About Boyz and Men   112
Anti-venom for the Soul   112
Succession of Honor   119
Everything Under Control   125
Looking for Bubba   131
Brian on the Farm   142
Steamgauge   153
Musclebound, first chapter   162
Grrls, Women, and Goddesses   167
Some Women Do   167
In the Name of Art   171
We Never Speak   179
Coprolalia   183
Don't Get Me Wrong   186
Mandarin Style   197
The Catalyst   207

Foreword

I know what you want.

You want to get to the *'good stuff.'* You know that Laura delivers on the *'good stuff.'* Let me tell you up front that what's in this book is steamy, hot, sexy and provocative. So, at this point if you want to skip my accolades of her writing and my confessions on how I got off on reading them, I totally understand.

So, go ahead, skip ahead right now.

* * *

OK, now it's just you and me. Since you have chosen to continue reading this I will assume that you are either a masochist who enjoys denial play or you like a good, slow tease. If this makes me your mental smut Fluffer before the main event of Laura's words stroking and probing your gray matter, wet and hard stuff, I don't mind.

A few weeks ago I received a very anonymous looking Fed Ex package containing a document. No notes or letter accompanied this. A simple e-mail a few months ago was the only warning I had. But I knew my mission. Read it - test it's jack-of-worthiness and write this forward. The mysterious document simply launched me directly into Laura's dirty mind. As I opened the package I grinned like the proverbial post-canary cat. I knew that I held in my hot little hands a much-coveted item. I will confess to the gloating phone calls. Guess what I have? I whispered digitally to a famous erotic photographer friend of mine in New York. Last of the limited edition Hello Kitty vibrator? she quipped, knowing my taste. No, better than that! The unpublished manuscript of Laura Antoniou's next book! I could barely contain my evil villainess cackle. Her reply? You Bitch! Some of my lovers and tricks offered sexual favors for a sneak peek. Let's just saythat I thoroughly enjoyed the black-market value of the stack of papers among my circle of friends. That's the kind of power that Laura's words have.

Reading this book is like getting a little peek into Laura's mind. And there's so much to her mind, sexual, primal, political and even the goofy. Truly a Renaissance perv, she doesn't simply reside in fantasyland. She's got an axe or two to grind and she's going to tell you about the unjust realities of the world that limit our potential for pleasures. She'll rant and rave and then share the very desires and dirty fantasies that polite society would rather silence her for. They are primordial, hungry, violent and raw. She's got serious cajones, not just to write down her dark visions, but then to go ahead and publish it, admitting to the world the desires that so many of us keep locked up, even from ourselves. The word is out. She's unflinchingly kinky. It's a good thing she's not planning to run for President.

As you read this book I wonder if you'll have the same questions I did. I wondered which character she identified with. I wondered which, of her own and our mutual friends, carnal adventures inspired the tales. I wondered if she had to relieve the pressure in her clit after writing a tale as I had to after reading it. The next time I share a Cuban cigar with her in the dim light of some leather bar I'll make sure to ask her. Yes, there's a really juicy story behind that, but I'll leave it to Laura to tell that to you in a future book.

Like you, I like to tease myself with prolonged pleasure. (After all, that is why you're reading my introduction and not Laura's smut immediately, right?) So, after receiving the fresh-from-the-printer manuscript I stashed it into my carry-on luggage and hit the road on my usual travels. Brazenly, I read everywhere. I read on the long flights to leather events. This is why my basic carry-on kit includes a mini vibrator. You never know when the urge to get-off may strike you. I like to be prepared. I read it on the beach in Vancouver, BC. I read lounging near naked on the deck of a 50' yacht on the blue waters of the British Virgin Islands. My hand roamed downwards to my own private ocean to relieve the mounting heat caused entirely by Laura's writings. I passed the chapters around so my fellow crewmates could also enjoy the chapters in their cabins.

The original document that she sent me is pretty decimated now. Waters of the Caribbean and sticky fingers are hard on paper. Even with such material challenges, I deeply (and with lavish lubrication) enjoyed the tales and essays.Some even inspired me to devious sex acts with my lovers and playmates. I told them that if they had any problems with my sudden sexual hungers and inspirations they should send their complaints directly to **Laura**. If they're smart, they'll send her thank-you notes. In fact, if you find your loins catch fire after this, drop her a line and thank her for her dedication to the perverted pen.

Now you may turn the page and get turned on.
Enjoy!

Midori

* Note on Midori: Consider her an agent provocateur of pleasure and ambassador of kink. Some call her Fetish Diva. Midori is a San Francisco based sex and kink educator. She globe trots, sharing the secrets to pleasure wherever pleasure is sought. She's a rope artist and author of the book Seductive Art of Japanese Bondage , and many other works. Any resemblance to her of any particular character from Laura's writing is purely coincidental.

Introduction

I've been writing for a long time. To my surprise, I've even found an audience which has followed me from my awkward beginnings to the point where I am constantly answering "when's the next book?" e-mails. Very gratifying! Most writers never even get that much.

But it also continues to surprise me how segmented my work can be. Readers tell me they are shocked to find me in places they never imagined. Fans of my essays are surprised I've done short story work. Short story fans express amazement I've written novels. And my novel readers, now the largest segment, often express astonishmment I've done anything else.

Lesbians still write to me asking when I started to write "straight" fiction. Straight people wonder why I've written so much "gay stuff." And of course, gay men turn pale when they find out I've written quite a bit for them as well.

So, it was about time to gather samples of my work from everywhere I've dipped my four typing fingers. (Yes, I know some of you are shocked I'm not a touch typist!) With this collection, you'll find my first short story collection, The Catalyst, and my most famous bit of self examination, Unsafe at Any Speed - known as my "anti-SSC rant." But there are also a couple of unpublished pieces, two Marketplace stories, some of my gay male fiction published under other names, and some of the lesbian fiction I put in my own books when I couldn't get enough stories to finish them. Everything from Jewish lesbian vampires to gay cowboys to alternate universe Japanese high fantasy with a female dominant/ male submissive perspective. Oh, and an article on using the samurai paradigm in your SM relationships, just because I get a lot of requests for copies of that one.

There is a mild attempt to divide the works here into sections, but don't take them very seriously. Almost everything I write has some personal exposure in it; the pieces in Writing My Body are just moreso. And there is a sense of the fantastic in all erotica, but there's more magic in Alternate Worlds & Realities, from the prosaic magic of gender fluidity to ghosts who inhabit lovers. Anyone who has read my novels will know I like writing gay male sex scenes, but that I've had some sucess in writing excusively for that audience is what is reflected in Genderfucks. And of course, I write lesbian and woman-focussed stories as well, and some samples can be found in Grrls, Women and Goddesses. Finally, I have included the complete collection titled The Catalyst. Those of you who knew me back then and stayed with me this long deserve a special thank-you.

Some of this work still pleases me. Some of it is remarkably dated for such a short writing career! And some of it makes me cringe. Believe me, I looked through reams of stuff I'd written under a variety of names, trying to be fair in representing myself. But some things are best left to the stack of yellowing paperbacks and flimsy magazines in my office. Trust me. When you read something here that makes you cringe, thank me for not including stuff that was far worse.

Is this the end? Have I stopped writing? Hell no! But after I churned out 600 pages for my last novel, I needed a break. Now that this is out, I can focus on my next novels. I hope you will be patient and stick with me a while. But in the mean time, enjoy a look at how I got to a place where people will actually read a 600 page erotic novel.

Laura Antoniou
2004

Writing My Body; Glimpses of the Persona

Unsafe at Any Speed
Or, Safe, Sane and Consensual, My Fanny

(Originally presented at the University of Washington's Center for Human Sexuality, reprinted in *Pucker Up.)*

My fantasies have never been safe ones. Even back when I was a child, I remember coaching a playmate into behaving the way I imagined was proper for this little psychodrama we were about to enact. "You get to be in charge," I said, pushing from the bottom as only a six-year-old novice can, "and you're really mean. You tell me to do things that are impossible, and when I can't, you punish me and laugh."

What can I tell you, my tastes grew up with me. The amazing thing to me now, twenty-five years later, is how succinctly I captured the essence of SM play, the role of the "dominant" as the active, playacting partner, and my own role as natural, all response, passive - but only under the structure I created.

Later on, I discovered that to my mind, power and sex were interlocked. There were no sexual feelings without dreams of rape, suffering, beatings, torture. No imaginary relationships with partners of equal standing with me - only people who used me, or people I used. Dating in high school was a silly mess- a tangle of mostly-forgotten fumblings in order to demonstrate my passing heterosexuality and/or my ability to feel something other than hungry and silly when I got stoned. The real-life power and danger that was my home and the man who married my mother were much more like what I always knew sex would be. Forbidden. Secret. Painful. Confusing. Awesome in the true sense of the word, capable of creating emotions so strong that words couldn't be put to them, that there was no

11

sound a human being could make in order to express the terrible passion of it.

Unsafe.

Insane.

Non-consensual.

Fantasies aren't reality, I know, I know, I know. Except when they are. Except when you make them into reality. And fuck this, I didn't come out of years of fantasy, rescuing myself from a toxic parent and guilt-tripping myself through anti-sex feminism, politically correct lesbianism and socially-programmed homosexual activism so that someone else can make my goddamn sex life into a slogan.

Safe, sane and consensual - what do those words really mean?

Assimilation, that's what. The politics of appeasement, the hope that "Gee, if we look and act just like everyone else, if we can only convince the dominant culture that we're really harmless, and just like they are, except for where we put our dicks and clits and tongues, and what we like on our dicks and clits and tongues, why we'll earn our civil rights and everybody will live happily ever after, except for the boy-lovers who give us all a bad name anyway."

Originally, safe, sane and consensual (hereafter referred to as SSC) came out of the mostly gay men's SM movement, probably GMSMA, but possibly elsewhere. I've heard several different versions of "who came up with our beloved slogan." The first time I heard about it was in connection with the expansion of the National Leather Association, in connection with a desire to create some sort of unified national network of leather-perverts. SSC was something everyone could stand behind. For a group of marginalized outcasts, it became a rallying cry.

A rallying cry!? Hello? Like Live Free or Die? Remember the Alamo? Black is Beautiful? Who Killed Karen Silkwood? No Nukes?

Safe. Sane. Consensual.

Well, OK, it's as good as any. But why not: Happy, Healthy and Wise? Rational, Intelligent and Sensitive? Open-minded, Empathic and Cheerful? Willing, Hot and Horny? These are all laudable attitudes too! So some rallying cry - who could argue with it? And what's more to the point - what social interaction should not be safe, sane and consensual? Shouldn't all sex be that? Shouldn't all relationships be that?

But OK, it's a slogan. Slogans don't mean shit - after all, what did "Just Say No!" and "Just Do It!" have to do with any kind of reality you know? Slogans give people something to chant, something to put on their banners, something to distinguish the Us from the Them. And I guess SSC beats "Horny and looking for kinky nookie right now, are you a top or bottom and what are you wearing?"

But it's become so much more than merely a slogan. Now, it's a way of life. Every SM organization has to include this little catchphrase in their statement of purpose - if they ever get around to having one. It has to be on every banner when they march. It has to be included in titleholder speeches, in club banquets, on colors and in newsletters. Every entrant into SM on one level or another is assured, ad nauseam, that "everything will be safe, sane and consensual." The only activity they condone is SSC. Why, all good SM is SSC. SSC is good. Isn't it good that we all practice SM that is SSC?

I'm walking through a play party, black and red showing left, a bag of toys stashed behind the couch. There's a cutie I'd love to diddle, but right now, she's busy getting a back rub. Well, that's OK. I'll watch this scene over here - two people methodically going through their toy bag, as he uses them one at a time on her. They chat - doesn't she like this? Giggle, oh yes, she does. Smack - isn't that nasty? Giggle, ouch! You beast. Giggle. Let's try that one! It's made out of an old mop head. More giggles.

Fighting off a yawn (how rude), I wander past two girls earnestly discussing their upcoming scene. Red means stop. Yellow means slow down. Blue means I want to talk to you about something. Green means you can go faster, harder. I don't tell them about fisting, piss and cocksucking, why feel older than I am? But I want to tell them about muffled yelps, screams, and the moment before the tears start to flow, that terrible moment when you know that one more sharp pain and you won't be able to hold them back. I want to tell them about watching someone's control slip away, clutching a crotch to find that there's pussy cream mixing with drops of panic-piss, about the redness of a face when the sobbing has become regular. I want to tell them about the pleas of the damned, the cries when someone doesn't know when it's going to stop, or how, only that they want their mommy, they want their master, they want to surrender and fall to the ground and feel a boot at the back of their neck. But I smile and nod and don't say a fucking thing.

There's a whipping going on, so I go to watch that. Oh yeah, this is better, thwack, thwack, thump, thump. Heavy red marks, muscles straining, grunts, and then the whip lands around the ribs and I hear the bottom snap, "Wrap!" and the top bites her lip and tries to aim better next time. Someone in the background snorts in derision. I guess their bottom had better manners, or maybe their aim is perfect and they never, ever wrap.

That happened to me once. I grabbed her by the hair and pulled her head back onto my shoulder and brought the whip handle against her throat. "Don't you think I know that?" I asked her, knowing that in one second, if she gave me the wrong answer, I was going to set her free, rub her wrists and go upstairs for coffee. "Do you think that I'm not looking? That I'm an idiot? Do you think I'm your fucking whip slave, that you can use that tone of voice with me, and alert me to what I'm doing?" She did the right thing, I whipped her some more. But later on, I pushed the envelope very, very far. I used my knife. It took a while to get her into the proper place. It took longer to get me back.

What is happening to my sexuality?
It's cold, it's passionless, and what's worse, it's dull.
John Preston was right. SM has become a nice, sweet alternative to heavy petting, and the leaders of this SM "community," want us to be the Elks or some other animal-named civics association, gathering to sell expensive clothing and raffle tickets, congratulating ourselves on how nice we all are.
This used to be about sex. The literature of my people was pornography, filled with cries for mercy, drama enacted on people without prolonged negotiation, partners engaged in a dance in the middle of a bonfire. Now, it's three-hundred page manuals about how to make sure nothing bad will happen. And twelve page play party rules, which state that the utmost care must be taken to make sure that no one is frightened or offended, that no bodily fluids are spilled, and no cries shock the neighbors.

Nothing is Safe

I have a new friend who had an old problem. Engaged as a co-top in a scene, she was present when a well-trussed-up bottom had a seizure. There was nothing in what they were doing which was related to the event - it was just one of those medical anomalies. Like a flash, they bottom was freed from bondage, 911 was called. There was knowledge of CPR - there was plenty of wise emergency care. The bottom got better. Went home under their own power. Check that out with a doctor - find out if there's a problem we didn't know about, OK?
My friend was disturbed by this incident - as anyone would be. It's no joy to be present when someone starts going limp. But her initial reaction was that something had gone wrong with an SM scene - that someone had almost died on her. That suddenly, the awesome responsibility upon her as a top was revealed. She told this as a cautionary tale.
Bullshit.

People have seizures. People faint. People have mysterious heart conditions that rear up and kill them at sixteen years of age when they're playing basketball. Do coaches then rise up and solemnly discuss how all coaches should be heart specialists, because of the great responsibilities of training potentially fragile athletes? If I'm driving my car and a friend in the passenger seat has a heart attack, am I at fault for not being a surgeon? For not having nitro on hand? If I'm passionately screwing away at the advanced age of 97, and suddenly, my entire brain explodes in one final orgasm that snuffs me out like a candle dipped in blood, will that sweet thing beneath me be responsible for not knowing about that massive embolism waiting for the right moment to end my lifelong perversity?

What goes on when people over-fetishize safety is that they're relapsing into that old frame of mind that what we're doing is BAD. It's dangerous, it's scary, it has the potential to get out of hand. That's why we have to surround ourselves with rules, and make a slogan into a mantra, why we have to police ourselves and each other with a sterile obsession aimed at making our love, life, and play into the safest, sanest and most consensual drama ever enacted on a relationship stage.

Well, life ain't safe. I get up and every day I do things that place my body and life in danger. I take showers - and we all know how many people bash their brains out in the tub every year. I stand on rickety chairs to change light bulbs. I drive. I walk through dark Manhattan streets in the meat packing district in very queer clothing. I drink. I go to gyms and abuse my body and sit in saunas - people die in them you know. I eat meat. I eat sugar. I ride horses. I shovel snow. I write and edit pornographic books under my real name in a conservative administration. I join the ACLU. If I want to, I can take up karate, I can go skiing, or buy a motorcycle. This is deadly stuff.

And life ain't sane, in case you haven't noticed. Any world where kids are born unwanted, and people die from hunger, where tobacco is subsidized and day care is not, where television preachers are wealthy and artists are not, where one gender is dominant and one skin tone, where rapists get out on bail and pot smokers get thirty year sentences - this is NOT a fucking sane world. So, who gets to judge my relative sanity? Doctors? Lawyers? Other perverts?

As for consent - well, there's the real issue, isn't it? Except that, surprise! It's just another shadow term, all substance and no real meaning. I can hear the whines - "But it's BAD to do these things without consent!"

No fucking kidding. It's bad to conduct medical experiments on people without consent, yet I don't see the AMA adopting the slogan, "Healthy, Helpful and Consensual!" All sex should be consenting - yet I've yet to see a dating service advertise itself as "Fun, Sexy and Consensual!"

The trouble is, SMers are allowing themselves to be defined by what they are not. We think, "Oh, so many people believe that we're all murderers and rapists, and we have to explain that we're not!" Uh - so, a slogan for the gay civil rights movement should be "Normal, Nonthreatening and Not After Your Children?"

What's worse is the growth of that slogan into the labeling device it's become. Whenever someone is found to be unpopular or threatening, all it takes to get them out of "the scene" is to start a whispering campaign about how unsafe, insane and non-consensual they are. Now, when the boys want that big old dyke and her bullwhip away from their sash parades, all they have to say is "She's endangering people" - UNSAFE! or "She's not projecting a proper image for our community" - INSANE! or, "The people watching have not given their permission to be shown this type of behavior" - NON-CONSENSUAL! And boom - they don't have to say that no big old dyke with a whip is gonna lead their parade. They have good ol' SSC to rely on, and no one wants to argue with that.

Fact is, I'm tired of being told what's OK for me. I'm fucking tired of multiple safewords, and sometimes I'm tired of safewords all together. I don't want to negotiate everything to death, I want to be surprised, or surprise someone. I want to be afraid - I want to cause genuine fear. I want sweat, piss, cum and blood to drip - and not just because it's warm and late and the sex is nice. There are times when I just want to walk through a room, grab that girl, slap her hard and make her cry. Push her down and fuck her mind over twice as hard as her body.

Sometimes, I want to be that girl.

And the harder the SSC gets pushed at me, the harder I feel like pushing back. Passion, that's what I'm into, passion and blood and honor, so powerful that it pounds through my veins and blinds me, so terrible that I can't look away. Danger, Dementia, and Denial. I want to hear that panic, scream "No, Please!" and struggle through the haze of pain and pleasure and all that stuff that goes on between the moment we touch eyes and the moment when we both collapse and try to catch our breaths and break the silence.

My fantasies have never been safe ones. Don't fuck with me, unless you understand that.

Note: People have asked me if my position has changed at all since I wrote this, and yes, it has. Now, I would write, "I'm fucking tired of multiple safewords and safewords all together." Otherwise, I stand by the rest of it.

My Writing Life, or, Everything Old is New Again

(First published in *The Burning Pen, Sex Writers on Sex Writing,* edited by M. Christian.)

I'm a pornographer, by choice, by trade, by political affiliation. I'm somewhat prolific, with porn of every variety having issued from my word processor at one time or another. You might have read my Marketplace series of novels, about a modern-day real-life slave market, or perhaps seen an anthology or two - or six - of mine. You've possibly read me having no idea it was me, in little digest-sized magazines full of "true" letters and stories or on the shelves in the gay men's erotica section or even in a publication intended for straight men.

I was going through some of my work to prepare for writing this essay and found a few memorable moments in fiction. See if any of them sound familiar.

A young person brimming with promise becomes an apprentice to an older, wiser, sardonic, and mysterious teacher whose demands often seem cruel and whose history contains elements of suffering for the sake of a higher goal.

Two women meet at a bar, take a liking to one another, and for their first night together, the more dominant one teaches the other to polish her boots the right way. Mention is made of lashes earned for boots polished the wrong way....

17

Two strong, hotheaded youths are matched against each other in battle for the idle entertainment of their master, who wagers on them and murmurs, "I will have the winner," much to the amusement of his guests.

A low-ranking trainee is set upon by her higher-status roommates, who taunt her for failing to show proper respect and then leave her hog-tied on her bed while they go laughing off to dinner.

A lengthy session with a nine-foot single tail, three pages to get through 10 lashes, each of which draws blood, until the recipient staggers against the chains and slumps, only to hear, "Ten more…"

Recognize any yet? How about this excerpt?

"Garret put the finishing touches on his Lord's right boot, and his hands were shaking. When Renton had noticed a flaw in Garret's usually brilliant shine, the lad had received a vicious kick in the ribs. Although Renton had retired in a good mood, it seemed that his slave would bear a constant stream of abuse nonetheless. If Garret thought ill of such treatment, neither his face nor his eyes gave him away…."

Something from one of the Marketplace books, right? Or perhaps from one of my gay male S/M novels or short stories?

Actually, all of these situations and the excerpt are from a novel I started a little bit earlier than my more recent works. It's unpublished, actually, and will never be published. But then, how many works do you think survive rewrites starting at age 13?

Now, did I think this was porn when I was writing it? No, I thought of it as high fantasy, that sort of standard sword-and-sorcery, going on a question to get the ancient relic kind of thing. In fact, its original title was "The Sword of Truth," which I changed to "Where's the Magic?" during a sudden fit of adolescent despair that last about 100 years.

John Preston, in his essay "How Dare You Even Think of These Things," mentions a similar experience as a teenager, writing a fantasy about a handsome, manly lord type riding through the fields of his estate and gazing at the muscular bodies of the men who worked for him and deciding which would be chosen for his pleasure that night. I wrote that sort of stuff too, but probably at age 15 or later, and all of those stories are gone now, consigned to flames in a panic-stricken night when I thought that when I ran away, someone would find them and... I don't know what. Know I was a pervert, I guess.

But my fantasy novel was different. It had a plot. (Albeit a convoluted, monstrously derivative and not very well-thought-out one.) It had character development. It had magical stuff! Somehow, all of these changes added up to making something of greater merit than the sum of all the parts that would make my heart pond when I wrote them.

It's difficult to piece together exactly what I thought when I was writing this stuff. The first draft, underneath the clumsy construction and awful dialogue, still shows signs of a measured buildup of mystery and attraction to danger and power. Through two alter-ego characters, I made a case for both the "How can you live this way?" view of the outsider who sees black uniforms, strict discipline, and a fetish for obedience as alien, and for the military leader who sees the world as a series of superiors who must be obeyed and inferiors who must be controlled.

And it's pretty clear whose point of view I favored, too.

But in the rewrite, I see that I had started to strip away some of the more blatant, sexualized pieces of fetish behavior for a more subtle approach. I had always struggled with my erotic impulses. I couldn't deny them and didn't really want to. But neither could I reveal them and I knew that very early. I can see that I had started to embed them deeper into the story, to make a big deal out of - oh, for example, a scene where one character backhands another. I think I had begun to realize that if I set the rules of my fantasy world to include such things without comment, then no one would know how much it thrilled me to think about them.

In later years, I took the world of this aborted novel - all 300 pages or so of it (even back then, I had a problem with length) - and I turned it into my world for an Advanced Dungeons and Dragons role-playing game. As I read through the pages, I wondered, was this world of mine always so shallow? Wasn't there more?

Yes, indeed there was... created for small groups of friends to help me in my erotic imaginings, whether they understood what they were doing or not. Through my college years, my simple world built up around a simple story became much richer and more personally fulfilling. With the help of other sexually maturing friends, my world began to fill with things I had dared not write about. Consensual adult incest, intergenerational sex. Group sex and polyamorous relationships - long before I had ever heard that word. Pain play. Sex with professionals because they did it better, not because they were available at a tavern. And all of it packed into pretty standard action-adventure stories with a little bit of the "Kill the monster/Take the treasure" thrown in to appease the traditionalists.

It was during that time that I found a lover who also had as rich a fantasy world as I had made, and finally, I revealed the truth behind all this plotting and magic. It was an excuse to tell the story of an attraction to power and the loneliness and hunger that comes when you get that power, the drive to serve one greater than yourself and - of course - every ritualized beating and boot polishing and whack across the face that brought us through the tale. We spoke porn to each other and acted it out, and I discovered that the real thing is ever so much more fun than just writing about it.

Now, years later, I find myself 300 pages into the fifth book in a series about attraction to power, the need to serve, etc., etc. and in an ironic twist, now I am overburdened with plot, which I must sometimes suspend in order to include the very scenes that were my excuse for plots when I first starting writing!

What has happened here?

What was I always really writing about?

At first, it was easy to point at the obvious fetish pieces, ranging from my adolescent daring in suggesting that same-gender attractions might actually be preferred in a military setting, especially one in a world without reliable birth control, to the mulitpartner, bondage- and S/M-inclusive, possibly incestuous groupings that popped up from time to time.

But the real story that hooked these scenes together - or gave me an excuse to imagine them and write them - is also familiar.

I see the main character, bitter because of a lost opportunity, who nonetheless excels in her field and dedicates herself to making someone to replace her.

I see the confusion of someone who has been both drawn to and frightened of power, who both struggles with new concepts of right and wrong and embraces them with all the desperation of one of those "gifted children" who will do just about anything to impress a distant parent.

Power struggles abound in every rewrite, getting more and more subtle. Blatant threats in the early version become veiled, silky, dangerous in that understated way of someone who doesn't have to bluster to threaten. There are people sworn to service who hate the ones they are sworn to serve nonetheless. There are slaves taken in battle and as war prizes who grow to have affection, respect, and even love for their owners - much to the discomfort of those owners. (Was I unable to completely imagine such a thing? Or was I so sure that any moral person would not want to be loved by someone who could not freely choose to be with them?)

Everyone who had power found that it came with a cost attached to it. The warrior-king who could not be slain by any weapon except the one in the hand of his second in command was forbidden to love. The woman raised to believe she would be a champion found out there would be another after her who would actually take on the task she was trained to do - and that she would have to make this person ready to do it.

It was all a romance - a soap opera with elves and swords. Melodrama in the classic sense of the word, because what is a teenager if not melodramatic? Questions of good and evil came up, as they will when you are writing fantasy, and I delighted in making my evil characters honorable, my fun-loving ones amoral - if not apathetic. Even back then, I didn't want things to be too easy. Honor and loyalty, pain and betrayal, deep love and hate that can't be mentioned out loud, quests and adventures, looking for the magical thing that will solve it all - romance.

And what am I writing now? A soap opera with whips and chains. About a character who misses a chance at becoming something he has always dreamed of and instead finds himself training others to be that which he desires for himself. A lengthy question adventure through the modern S/M fetish world as a woman searches for the magical solution to her identify and desires, looking for that perfect happy ending and finding it's not that simple. Master Trainers who look at the pain they cause and mutter things like "omelettes and eggs..." and then get back to the work they have to do. Honor and loyalty, pain and betrayal ... etc.

And still I am caught between wanting the sex and power and S/M all spelled out because that's what turns me on (and, presumably, the other readers), and wanting it to be such a given, built into the structure of the world, that readers can understand that it will happen - but there is no need to read through 20 pages of it when three will do. Not unless it advances the plot and shows some of those wonderful character conflicts and resolutions.

OK, so I am writing the same story. (The lead character even has the same name, although the spelling and gender have changed.)

But believe me, it's much better without the elves.

Defending Pornography (for real this time)

(This article is reprinted from *The Harvard Gay and Lesbian Review, Summer 1995.*)

If pornography is part of your sexuality, then you have no right to your sexuality. - Catharine MacKinnon

Lesbian written pornography ... is an expression of self hatred. - Andrea Dworkin

With statements like these descending from their lips, it almost seems unnecessary to dispute Dworkin and MacKinnon: they obviously have the wherewithal to shoot themselves in various appendages and make enemies by the score. And that's before we start gathering other mots, such as their implied and stated contention that sex is what heterosexual men do to heterosexual women, and that all other forms of sexuality are mere representations or substitutions for the same; that essentially all men are born rapists and all women their victims; that women cannot be trusted to enter into a voluntary contract that involves any form of sexual expression; and on and on. These women are obsessed with sex, specifically of the violent and nonconsensual variety as enacted by men against women.

When Dworkin stood to testify before Congress and its Meese Commission in 1986, she claimed that 65 to 70% of all women involved in the sex industries—such as prostitutes, film stars, models, and presumably writers of a certain kind—had been victims of incest or child abuse, though she supplied no evidence to substantiate this assertion. She suggested that so-called snuff films were so commonplace, it began to sound as if you could pick one up at your local Blockbuster. When MacKinnon wrote an impassioned story about the horrible atrocities being committed in prison camps in Bosnia, her lurid tales of sexual abuse and torture were almost lyrical in their attention to detail.

The writings of MacKinnon and Dworkin could be dismissed were it not for the fact that much of the world—including whole governments, such as that of Canada—have taken their arguments seriously and even codified them into law. This opens up a curious mystery. Usually, when a woman with some academic credentials behind her stands up and rails against the heterosexist, patriarchal, violence-loving, oppressive, angry-white-male culture, she is left alone with her women's studies classes, published in under-distributed journals, abandoned by the mainstream to wait for tenure and retirement. But these two get their faces on every roundtable discussion, testify before every commission, get discussed in state legislatures, and find their words written into Canadian law (and make it necessary for me to become an international smuggler to sell my wares)!

What made MacKinnon and Dworkin such a uniquely successful feminist force to be reckoned with? Was it MacKinnon's sparkling prose? Dworkin's high media-Q factor and star quality?

Of course not: it was the smut. It was their focus on pornography, the writings of whores, the land of the solitary vice, that made the terrible twosome famous and feared. What they discovered, after years of putting in their time on various feminist fronts, was that the pornography war was the only one which the aforementioned hetero-patriarchal government and culture responded to. It was their big chance to get something done. No amount of writing and talking on their part could actually raise working women's salaries, create childcare opportunities, or make abortion safe and available to poor women. Congress wasn't holding hearings on the question of domestic partnership laws or the rights of lesbians to qualify for health care or the rights of young queers to safe sex information. People were looking for a scapegoat for every perceived moral and ethical failing in our culture, and pornography fit the bill. And MacDworkin—to borrow Nadine Strossen's name for them in *Defending Pornography* (Scribner, 1995)—was ready to fall into step. Here, at last, was a battle they could win.

This victory was not achieved without political compromise. As Strossen points out in her book, MacDworkin and the entire pro-censorship faction of the left-feminist movement has allied itself with the far Right, especially with groups such as Phyllis Schlafly's Eagle Forum and Beverly La Haye's Concerned Women for America. The two factions would probably rather slit their wrists than share a potluck supper, yet there they are, to-gether in as unholy an alliance as anyone might imagine. Strossen is right to emphasize the importance of this alliance with the Christian Right, and knows just how damning it is, even for middle-of-the-road types who might be tempted to pick up and read a book with a title like Defending Pornography.

But for all her good intentions in "defending" porn, what we really have is a solidly written and well-researched book that makes a thoroughly convincing case as to why censorship is bad. What it does not do is say why pornography is good. Where is the promised "defense" of pornography?

As a woman making a living in the field of erotic writing—as a pornographer—I was eager to see how Strossen would defend my literary niche. God knows I have a hard enough time doing so myself—when I bother. My defense rests on two legs: one, this was the first writing someone paid me to do; and two, writing and editing pornography have given me—and my readers, I trust—pleasure: the pleasure no one talks about when we talk about pornography, Noel Coward's "solitary vice." (And not so solitary, if you're into reading your lover bedtime stories, but that's another point entirely.) I wanted to hear from a woman—a scholarly woman—how great it was to have a literature of one's own, a place of fantasy where mind and body could be teased, aroused, and pleasured.

Instead, what we get from Strossen is an old-time defense of free speech, complete with a recitation of the First Amendment. Now it's easy to attack censorship, and even easier to poke fun at people who find salacious meanings everywhere. Strossen offers lots of examples of the latter, such as the censorship of crates of classical art because some contained voluptuous vessels of Venus, or the professor who saw in an exercise video an example of the exploitation of women in the media. The book Hot, Hotter, Hottest was stopped at the Canadian border but turned out to be a cookbook for dishes with jalapeno peppers. Also held up was Doing It Debbie's Way, an exercise video by Debbie Reynolds. The final kick in the head was the delay of two of Dworkin's own books, jam-packed as they were with scenes of women being degraded or used as "sex objects." What this defense of pornography amounts to is a slippery slope argument of the kind, "If we allow censorship of one thing, what next?" If, for example, we allow the censorship of *Leatherwomen*, then what might be next, *Rubyfruit Jungle*? My question is, where does that leave Leatherwomen? The implication is that the only reason Leatherwomen deserves protection is to provide a line of defense for the literature that we truly value, and Strossen takes pains to show how much of our literature and culture could be sacrificed if the censors had their way, citing examples of books that would be banned not only by the far Right but by pro-censorship "feminists," as well. The implication is that porn is only a necessary evil in the battle for free speech.

When Strossen does get down to actually defending porngraphy, she points out that, contrary to the claims of the MacDworkin factions, the vast majority of porn is egalitarian and rather adolescent, depicting women as sexual aggressors who enjoy sex, are orgasmic, and seem to be having fun. Porn that doesn't fit this mold—which I gather would include a lot of what

I write—is dismissed as the exception that proves the rule. Nor does Strossen have much to say about the suppression of gay and lesbian literature, which has been the chief victim of the MacDworkin-inspired Canadian statutes.

She does get around to quoting both Pat Califia and John Preston, but her chief concern is not to defend the literature at the margins but instead the larger world of plain vanilla heterosexual porn, and from there the still larger world of literature and the arts in general. In the end it is the preservation of works with "socially redeeming value" that seems to matter, not works that might be defined by some as unmitigated filth.

I take Strossen as typical of a larger cultural inability to defend pornography in and of itself, not as just the price of free speech but as a positive good, as something both usefull and fun, something that can be dangerous and scary and that can also help us learn about our fantasies and demons—and as something that can get us off. Standing up for free speech and attacking censorship are always worthy goals, but they should not be mistaken for the actual defense of pornography, even in its more exploratory or extreme forms, as intrinsically worthy of being defended.

Sex Toys

(Never before published)

One of my mother's earliest and most persistent tactics to seduce me toward more outward displays of femininity lay, figuratively, in her offering of a new bed.

Not that mine wasn't perfectly serviceable. It had a mattress, it was raised sufficiently off the floor to allow for the stowing of secrets underneath and most importantly, it had a special, soft pillow of which I was inordinately fond. She had a disturbing tendency to suggest that it be dressed in pink, an endless array of pinks that I steadfastly rejected, culminating in one perfectly dreadful term in which I was stuck with a riotous yellow room and a matching bedspread upon which Snoopy danced. But otherwise, the bed was hardly something I had seen fit to complain about and it did not need replacing.

Except when she mentioned that special phrase, which would allow even my pink-hardened mind to fix upon.

Canopy bed.

Ah, a canopy bed. I longed for one of those vast constructs in the middle of my room - an elegant structure that could be draped in gauze or sheer cotton or - dare I even think it - a light and view blocking sheet that would grant me privacy even inside my own space, a room within a room for once more comfortable than a closet. The ability to look up and see the closer darkness of my own little chamber above me. And at last, four sturdy posters.

One for each limb.

Can my thoughts have drifted into that potential even at an age when Snoopy was an appropriate decoration for my room? When posters of slender, long haired boys and elegant long haired ponies still decorated my walls and my grandmother's annual porcelain guardian angels - each with my August birthstone embedded in her gown or scepter or crown or wings or nose, for all I cared - were all arrayed on a shelf?

They did. My less frequent solitary activities involving various dolls and their always silent adventures - I couldn't dare say out loud the words and deeds they enacted for me, lest some passing adult denounce me as the violent and depraved child I obviously was, under that layer of baby fat and poor eyesight - were always full of the kinds of activities that I have imagined and half desired were possible. My fantasies were fueled by age-appropriate books about Roman and American slavery and non-age appropriate reading filched from my mom when she wasn't looking. A particular book about a group of men who abduct a movie star for their own private amusement and torment and another about children who turn on their summer baby-sitter provided my Barbies with an endless stream of imaginary abuse. Or Action Jackson. I was an equal opportunity sadist. Masochist.

But the bed. Ah, the bed. If I had such a wondrous thing, it was not inconceivable that somehow, someday, one might have limbs splayed wide upon it for - well - for things I couldn't say aloud. I knew it was possible to be bound to anything that had four anchor points, and my own steel frame could be used for this purpose, as I was to discover in desperation and adolescent curiosity. But to have the four posts at each corner - to be able to casually loop rope or chain or leather straps or robe belts or neckties around visible points - that would be perfect. I just knew it.

So every once in a while, I would quiet the powerful voice inside me that wished for dark, wood furniture and a captain's bunk with real drawers underneath and try to act a little more like the alien creature my mom seemed to think I was, and I would wait for the arrival of that damn canopy bed. Sublimation in the name of acquisition.

In college, I picked up an array of "blow-in" cards in all the student publications and found my way into the world of mailing lists, whereupon I was the recipient of everything from vacation come-ons to offers of cemetery plots. And, in the mail, I found a hard plastic object that was to enslave me for the first, but not final time in my life. It came from Citibank. It had a twelve hundred dollar spending limit. And I had my own apartment at last.

To be sure, I had a bed, too. It came with the apartment and was a perfectly serviceable queen-size bed, appropriate for two, my first bed that I could fit a lover into, if I had one. I had even added three additional pillows to my favorite one from childhood, to create that inviting mound at the top of the bed. There were two people I was interested in bringing there, and one was like Barbie and one was like Action Jackson, because I was still an equal opportunity sadist. Masochist. One who slept alone, but I knew, just knew, that if I only had the right bed, my life could be filled with my very own action figures, suitably articulate in all their limbs and at last fully complete below their navels.

I had, in my near poverty, saved a few dollars and purchased a cheap "brass-like" headboard which clamped more or less securely onto my queen-size bed frame. But the brass coloring flaked off if you touched it harshly, and the bars bent with the slightest of pressure. It mocked me with its instability, its fakery. It was the sole reason I couldn't invite a new toy home to play.

Armed with my new purchasing power, I went shopping. I knew exactly where, too. For many years, I had passed the windows of this store, full of nothing but beds in glossy, golden brass. Solid looking bars, huge, phallic corner posts adorned with heavy balls. Curly back boards with an infinite number of anchor points. And yes, real brass. Something that wouldn't bend under the pressure of a clenched fist, at least, not easily.

The sunlit color of the beds when I finally walked in dazzled me. I saw little dancing dust motes in the corners of my eyes as I brushed past salesmen and sat on each bed in turn, recalling a scene from a white covered novel that had caused such a sensation the previous year. I had picked it up at a B. Dalton, long before that name became just another corner in a suburban mall, a thin book carefully displayed without any indication about it's contents. I had read parts of it in shock - did they allow such stories to be written and sold in bookstores you didn't need to enter in desperation? And I remember feeling disgusted and thrilled by a scene in a department store - Macy's, maybe. Would I dare to lay back on one of these beds and grasp the bars over my head and spread my legs? Would I if someone told me to?

I lost myself in fantasy as I examined each bed. None had canopies; that was all right. It was never the canopy, after all, but the posts which were the point. Up close, the affordable ones seemed as cheap and glossy as my headboard, disappointingly meager and certainly not suitable for frantic struggles. And many of the classic styles proved only to remind me of my youth, spent rejecting all things too girly. Porcelain knobs were not acceptable, nor were glass balls. Swirls proved too much on the femme side as well - I drifted to bars. And then, a salesman who finally figured me out brought me into the back, away from the glossy window styles and toward a smaller grouping of gunmetal gray beds that made my heart pound and my hands sweat.

This - this was still brass?

I caressed the smooth, cool bars, walking around the three styles he had, letting him talk about metal and finishes and quality and strength and durability, his empty flattery and his eerily dead-on assessment of my tastes. When I revealed that the room this bed would be in was painted blue

- (at last!) - he seemed triumphant as he pointed out how nicely this blue-gray metal would look, how elegant, how cool.

I had the power to choose any of them. I wondered if he would lay down on one and spread his legs for me, whether he had tested these sturdy looking bars against his own arms after the store closed and no one could see these models, so far from the glittery, fast moving ones set up in the windows.

By then, I was used to finding the good stuff way in the back.

I chose one that was a combination of gray and brass-gold, heavy and strong and beautiful; a blend of feminine and masculine. The head and footboards curved at the top, wide, sensuous bars that bent like a body over the edge of the bed, held up by blue-gray bars studded with golden anchor points - although I am sure he used a different word to describe them. It cost more than my semester at school. I handed over my new card, even had to sign the back, for this was my first purchase on credit. And as I arranged for delivery, I thought I'd have this paid off within a year. It was to take several, of course. If I had been told that, I would have still bought it.

I was flushed when I left - in debt for the first time in my life, not to a bank, but to my imagination. There, behind me, as I raced up Utopia Parkway in a car that was worth less than my new bed, was my investment in my erotic future. Now, I had no reason not to place those invitations, to Barbie or Action Jackson, or to any number of playmates, regardless of wardrobe or accessories. I had every reason to hold someone by the hand as I introduced them to my new altar, my proving ground, my playground.

But who was to be asked for the inauguration? Would it prove to be something that would set the standard for all my future adventures? Should it be one or the other, Barbie or Jackson? And whose limbs should be spread to the outermost points on this new playing field; mine, or someone else's? Was it gauche to invite someone home, hand them ropes and lay back? Would I have to discuss it first, something tedious and shameful and annoying? It suddenly mattered that my knots were clumsy and my tastes easily as ill defined as my bondage techniques.

I tried to imagine my potentials. Jackson, writhing on his back, his dark skin against the white sheets. (I would need new sheets. Perhaps baby blue flannel with little grazing sheep was not appropriate for this massive, masculine bed.)

Barbie, kneeling over me, with that ironic smile on her face and her body tantalizingly out of reach.

No, Barbie face down, my hand between her legs while she moaned.

No, Jackson face down, and me with something that he would hate to see, but love to feel.

No, no, wait - Barbie and Jackson, together! While I directed the action, comfortable in a papa-san chair - (hm - more shopping to do). Yes, yes, I could do that, too. Leaping in joyfully when it I couldn't stand it any more. Or letting them take fair vengeance for the pain and humiliation and pleasure I had compelled them to. Oh, yes, that was it - and we would soon become a single erotic team, mutually sharing fears and fantasies, pledging to each other in secrets and trust and plots of intricate dimensions, taking our turns caressing the corners of the bed, wrapping ropes and straps and neckties around limbs and bars and combing our bodies in every way we could imagine. Maybe we could find a Ken to match with Action Jackson as well, to maximize on every possible combination. I already knew, deep in my heart, that Jackson would want that. But he would be downright eager to do it if it was suggested by the two women he was sharing his body with.

A veritable circus of flesh and activity, all around my new bed. I would need more accessories, I could see that at once. Leather cuffs and blindfolds, maybe a hood. Dildos, yes, and a better vibrator than the one powered by two batteries. Perhaps Barbie could be persuaded to make another trip to the Pink Pussycat and this time I will not blush when the saleswoman says Orgasmatron. This time I will buy one. I will hand over my credit card, used only to purchase sex toys, and I will openly declare that my search for live pleasure and companionship had begun in force. Perhaps I will buy a whip, too. When my chosen lovers came to my private pleasure dome, they would want for nothing that their erotic imaginations desired. I was free. I was sexy. I was available. And I had the bed! Nothing could stop me.

I was pulled over for speeding. As the policeman wrote the ticket, I laughed until I cried. I had the bed. What was fifty miles an hour compared to the rest of my life?

The New Brand

(First printed in *The SandMutopia Guardian.*)

The mirror is positioned by my side as I sit at the computer. All I need to do is glance over my left shoulder and there they are - two sets of raised wings, one faded into a beige crest of raised and mottled flesh, paling against my natural skin tone, the other a dark, angry crinkled mass of scar tissue, wrinkling up as it dries, waiting for me to rip it off and expose the pale, blood spotted skin beneath it.

One is three years old. The other is one week and three days. They are brands.

Branding is perhaps one of the most misrepresented body modification acts in SM literature. I clearly recall the branding scene in *The Story of O*, even to the dimensions of the marks - three inches in height, half that in thickness, and nearly half an inch deep.

I look at mine - yes, it's about three inches long. But the width, at the time of the branding? I measure my old brand with the ruler on the desk. The part that touched me is less than 1/16 of an inch. The finished, old brand, spread to a width of 1/4" - the new one is just slightly less than that. It looks like it might spread a little more. The depth of each brand - except for one strike - was about an eighth of an inch, if I recall. The depth was the first thing to blur on the new one, and I never measured the first. I was too busy caring for it, ruining it, and caring for it again.

Funny how they never mentioned O doing that. Maybe one of the other babes took care of her brands, huge and impossible as they were. The "S" must have been especially ugly over time, as the curves filled in to make blotches on her rear end.

But she's a character. I look over my shoulder and see the real thing and it makes me tremble with a delicious joy. They look so cool.

I got the first because Raelyn needed someone to burn. Well, that's not exactly true, I'm sure she had other volunteers. But when I got the call - Raelyn is coming, we need someone to take a brand, it was almost automatic for me to say "yes." Raelyn had done my big cutting, executed a splendid rose on my shoulder with that casual pleasure that made the entire event energizing and empowering for me. If she needed a body for a demonstration, she could sure as hell have mine. But what to do?

It had been only a short time ago that my period in service had ended. I was at a limbo period in my life, wondering about things like orientation, my future, my dreams and goals. I knew, somehow, that a part of my life was beginning to close - not only in a close and emotional sense, but in my public participation in "leather community" events. It was all closing, not only behind me, but around me, and I was doing some study on life changes to try and ease myself through it. As the time for the demo approached, I still hadn't a single idea about what I was willing to have burned into my flesh. But the day Raelyn called to ask me about the design, I had been flipping through an illustrated book by Joseph Campbell, and my eyes fell upon a sand painting. Along the borders were small silhouettes of birds in flight - you know, the little squiggles kids put in their drawings. These were placed at the four cardinal points along the border of the painting, and the text revealed them to be messengers, carrying prayers - and sometimes souls - to various destinies.

Sounded good to me. It could act as a symbolic ritual to mark the end of one leg of my journey, and point the way to the next. It also fit the guidelines that I had been given - simple, not too wide, and able to be recognized after the brand spread. When I met Raelyn, I drew her a quick sketch on a piece of cardboard, and she clipped a piece of metal and bent it to the shape I drew. Testing it against the board, it made a very slight hissing sound, and the brown card burned black and emitted a thin thread of dark smoke. Yes, that was one wing - and with a dexterous switch of sides, and some more fire applied to the brand, there was the other. Finally, the head of a nail would be used to dot the two unjoined wings at their base. In the drawing, that had been a diamond shape - the nail head would have to do. The finished brand looked lovely - graceful, simple. I nodded and went off to do a little za-zen breathing exercises, shaking out my arms and shoulders and bracing myself for the pain.

I had been told that the pain would be great. This is not something you casually say to me - my eyes have been known to light up when someone warns me like that. Also, as a masochist, I'd taken a bit of pain before. For someone to suggest that this would/could be much worse gave me that deep-in-the-pit-of-the-stomach doubt. Could I take this much?

But being in a butchy swagger mode, I refused the offer of bondage. I'd long grown out of the need for bondage to hold me still for pain. I wanted this, it was happening of my own accord. But taking Raelyn's advice, I braced myself in the wooden chair provided, wrapping my ankles around the front legs, throwing my right arm over the back and locking my fist around one of the slats. From the audience came a friend of mine, Naria, hot and butch and gleaming with anticipation - she braced her body against mine to further hold me in place, just in case the sharp pain made me leap involuntarily. Ordinarily, I might have objected. But try to make me object when a stunning butch is bracing her shoulders against me. Not bloody likely.

The torch was lit, and the brand held up for my final approval. I took one more series of deep breaths, in through the nose, out through the mouth, and nodded. I don't remember Raelyn saying anything, only knew that the heat from the brand was arcing across from her to me, and then I felt it touch my skin.

I'm glad I had a witness right in my lap.

It's often described as a kiss - and to me, it was. A hot, searing kiss, like the kiss of a whistling cane strike. It was so pure in its intensity, so beautiful, I was at once swept from the moment and plunged into a kind of ecstasy that defies description. My head tilted back, and I let out a sort of sigh, and when I opened my eyes, the brand was gone, and the smell of my burnt flesh was all that remained. I looked down at Naria and said, softly, "I don't think I need you anymore," and heard the whistles and murmurs of the women watching.

The second one was just as good, and the nail tip was almost too swift. The whole thing was over before I knew it, and when I looked over my shoulder, there, with blackened edges, were the raised wings I had sketched. I was filled with wonder at the sight - there was an actual impression in my own flesh! I could run my finger over it - it barely hurt at all - and feel where the iron had touched! Women ooohhed and aahhed, and Raelyn pressed the cooled brand into my hand, and when I left, I found other friends and showed them my new acquisition. More than a few thought I was nuts. One stranger asked me, "Whose sign is that?" meaning, "Who do you belong to?"

"It's mine," I responded. Every permanent mark on my body is my own.

Years later, and I'm reading at Grand Opening, this wonderful sexuality shop in Boston. Things have changed for me - back when that brand was new, I was a newly professional writer, with two books to names not my own. Sitting down at Grand Opening, there is a standing room only gathering of people who have come to hear me read, to get my signature. I sign six different titles that night, and read from something new. And who should walk in but Raelyn! Hugging like the old, happy acquaintances we are, I find out that she's due back at this very store to do some cutting, piercing and branding the following weekend.

Before the end of the evening, I'm already thinking it's time for another kiss. It's easy to see why - I've made my break from the past that was troubling me, and I've done only good for myself since. And as I sat there in Boston, there was with me a person who was symbolizing another great change for me, a leap that made the shaking free of my past seem trivial. I was planning an ordeal for her in my mind, and planning a relationship in my heart. Surely, this was worth a new mark. I'm not a believer in magic - but coincidence doesn't begin to describe some of the circumstances in my life. When I got home after that visit, I looked for the old branding iron - and it was in the first place I looked. I called Raelyn, and scheduled a visit.

This time, everything was different. This time, I knew what to expect. My appointment was scheduled for last, a Sunday evening moment in time after an entire weekend of body modification. I arrived a little early, just in time to see a handsome young man take the last of a series of chevrons on his outer thighs. Three men were holding him down, and he clenched his teeth and growled with almost every one. But they were so beautiful, as he was beautiful when he took them. There was good energy in the room - people with stunning tattoos and glittering piercings were watching, admiring, sharing.

This time, when I took my chair, I kept both feet on the floor and let my arm fall loose into Raelyn's lap. On my right, the girl sat, and I ran my fingers through her hair. I wanted her there to witness this, wanted her to feel what I was doing. I didn't have the words to explain to her, don't have them now - but I knew that being there was important.

I wondered, briefly, if the first time had been a fluke. Maybe I had been so jazzed up I had not really noticed what was going on. But when Raelyn told me - this time I heard her - that she would warn me before each strike, I smiled and nodded, and invited each one.

Oh, the purity of that biting pain. No, it's not pain - it's more like a shock, like being hit by lightning that licks through your body, to clutch at your heart before working its way down through your loins and the further down your legs until your toes curl. Yeah, just like when you come. I wiggled my toes in my boots and sighed.

So nice.

I smiled as Raelyn reversed the brand and reheated it, and this time, I kept my eyes open, so I could see Kim, sitting across from me, her own eyes wide with gleeful shock, and I sighed when the metal was taken away and felt the silky hair under my fingers and felt that all was right with the world.

And then, the final strike, the nail head. I nodded, "Ready," and Raelyn pressed it to my skin. Slowly, that electrical feeling of pleasure wound through me, and then I realized that it wasn't stopping. The nail was still in me, still wearing through my flesh, and I smelled myself burning and whispered/growled, "Oh, you bitch…", as my head lolled back. The room seemed to reverberate with laughter and Raelyn looked a little surprised as she took the metal away at last. That final strike was a deep one. But fine, oh, so fine.

We treated the fresh brand with a layer of aloe, and I slept deeply, feeling good about it. To my surprise the next morning, however, it had already begun to spread. My first brand stayed small and dark and deep for nearly a week - but this one wanted to flower open. Fascinated, I've been watching it, tending it. Within two days, it was already building up a scab that was ready for stripping.

You have to understand, I heal beautifully. To encourage my first brand to stay, I had to unlearn everything I'd known about wound management; I had to struggle to pick at it, to not douse it with antibiotic ointments, bandage it, etc. This time, I was looking forward to the kind of mayhem I needed to keep the burn from closing up. But even as I worked it and washed the droplets of blood away, I was amazed at the cleanliness of the skin beneath, the eager way my body gave up the thin scab. This is a brand that wants to stay.

I have to compare the two. One, I took knowing I was about to undergo a trial, when I was saying good-bye to a role I had found compellingly sweet. I was a little frightened, wary, and sad. That one took its sweet time to open, and hurt in its healing. This new one, I took in anticipation of joy, marking a separation between a pleasant life of work and predictability, and the hope of a life of adventures and passion. I was eager, relaxed, and confident. And although my bicep aches a little, and I hiss when people thump on it thoughtlessly, the burn is clean, and wide, and already beautiful to my eyes.

It's not easy to embrace a mark that won't go away, at least not for me. But it's also not easy to have the kind of ecstatic experience I know when I feel the kiss of the metal - I find that I want it again, and again. It gives me some satisfaction to make myself wait for the right time, though, and to give meaning to the joy and the pain. Yes, my brand are marks of ownership - they establish myself as the guardian of my past and future.

Note: I have three of them now. Considering a fourth.

The First Time

(Originally printed in *Best Lesbian Erotica 1997*, edited by Tristan Taormino.)

The first time I was bound, she wound strips of a mutilated white cotton nightdress around each wrist, chiding me for my rude behavior. How dare I make fun of her exquisite gowns, delicately edged in lace, gathered slightly below the bodice and sweeping to cover my feet while floating above her own delicate ankles. I'd laughed at them, these gently worn, sensual garments of such feminine intensity that I could not even imagine them near my skin, unless they were clinging to her body, her body then pressed next to mine. But wear such a thing? No, not I.

When she picked up the scissors, I laughed aloud and shivered in mock fear. When she made the first cut, just below the neckline, I started to reach for her, to stop her from destroying such a pretty thing. But her arms tightened and all the concentration in her eyes pinned me to the bed. I had to watch her tear through the thin cotton, making ragged, long tears that rapidly became the neat strips of anonymous white material, ethereal yet stronger than I might have guessed.

I pulled one hand away, testing her fortitude, and she slapped me with an imperious look. It was delicious. I let her pull my hands together, wrapping them around with one strip, and then across with another, and then relaxed back onto her rich linen sheets and hand embroidered pillowcases.

I let her touch me, smiling and sighing between the giggles, and reached for her as if to fight, aching for the strips to be tighter, to keep my hands above my head so there was no way I could impede her progress as she continued to make her points with maddeningly light slaps to my body.

I reared up once, to kiss her, and she pushed me back as easily as I could push her slight body around and yes, I let her.

I wanted to see what she was going to do.

Because no one had bound me before.

But we were young and shy and the boldness we showed on stage and in the dark corners behind the scenery vanished into the awkwardness of authentic intimacy. She reared back herself, and during the silence we both made our decisions. We were apart before long, and she remained a sharp reminder of the dangers of straight women, the perfidy of femmes. And she made me hunger for shadows of her for years, until at last I laid myself down for a woman in a gown, and sighed in perfect release and abandon.

Or, maybe it didn't happen that way at all; maybe I imagined it.

Because the first time I was bound, it was to my own bed, by a man younger than I, an aching, beautiful boy, expertly instructed and coached by the one who knew exactly what she wanted. He danced and ran and shook his body in delight, never still, never at repose, even when he snuggled up to me in the coldest moments of the night. He grinned when I sought his eyes and told him it was time, and he eagerly handled my toys and used them in a careful progression, making me crazy with need and then falling on me with a passion so pure it had to be exactly as he claimed - virginal. We gave each other a sacrifice that year, cutting into ourselves and handing over the warm, moist parts that were our secret passions.

I bared myself for him, and he bared himself to me. He struck me with all his youthful strength and crammed folded towels in my mouth to muffle the cries, and held onto me later on, when his body twitched in a sleep without rest. He didn't tease, couldn't know how to tease, and so he satisfied me fully, and made me feel that I might actually have a way to fulfill this desperate need in me.

I knew precisely what he was going to do; I was his instructor.

I needed to be in charge; no one had ever bound me before.

And so he knew where the tools were, and knew exactly the kinds of stimulation I wanted, where, how often, for how long. No one could know me better than he, because I had told him everything he needed to know. I was in absolute control of my tender young faggot, my sweet lonely lover, and was able to surrender to my passions, if not to him.

Or maybe it didn't happen that way at all.

Because, really, the first time I was bound, it was by a stranger. A tall, powerful woman who could have lived my life twice with time to spare. She buckled worn, leather cuffs onto my wrists and locked them in place and slapped me, hard. I could not look at her while she completed the rituals which transformed her from the rough voiced seducer of a crowded and smoky bar and into the sleek, silken seductress who could charm the most frightened young woman into a very dangerous game. I knew the proper words to say and the proper games to play, but still I went with her to a place I did not know, leaving no one behind to call for me, or know whose hands I had given myself into.

She stripped my body and tied me up tight, and for the first time, I truly felt the pull against restraints placed on me by another, the weight of my own body, the limits of my own strength. And she stroked my face tenderly before striking me again, and again, and kissed the blood from my teeth and lips, so I could see it on her when she drew away. In a too-late moment of indecision, I tested the bonds and found them locked onto me, impossible to slip or lift off. And I knew what it meant to be truly helpless, at anothers mercy. Alone, with a person who was known for being merciless.

I had no idea what she was going to do.

I was terrified, because no one had ever bound me before.

She brought weapons before me, silky, dangerous weapons like herself, and let me be romanced by them before they launched into brutality. Opening my bruised mouth, she commanded words from me, and got only sounds, and her fury was so magnificent that I knew she was beyond human. She demanded worship. And in the end, she got it. At a price so great, I was never to see her again.

No, it didn't happen that way at all.

The first time I was bound, it was by words alone. "Stay there," and "stand still," and "don't move," uttered with a playful, casual simplicity, punctuated by stinging cuts which threw ripples of distraction all along nerve endings. A light voice and soft hands, and a test which was designed for me to fail. I ground my teeth and set my body and keened out lengthy screams which echoed in my skull but actually came out in hisses and gasps. And the more I obeyed, the harsher it was, until the agony exploded and waves of nausea swept through me. Drunkenly stubborn, I locked my limbs in place - I would stay there, stand still, and not move, until rivers of blood covered my body, until my lungs couldn't draw another breath, until the star-bursts of pain behind my eyelids became one bright red light and I fell to the floor and didn't know anymore.

And I did fall, but not to the ground. Instead, I spiraled inward, and my obedience to these commands left my body no choice but to ignore those petty, spiteful stings. They faded into distant jabs which distracted me from myself, and when they rose in a flurry of angry impotence, I ceased to mind them at all.

I didn't know what was happening.

I had never been bound before.

Not much later, hands beat against my locked arms and fingers and bent me forward and at last I moved, and the sizzling, crackling awakenings of my body finally made me cry out. I could barely hear him, cradling me, his once cynical voice trembling with shame and horror and fear, as he asked over and over again, why I had not moved. I knew then that he could hold me no longer, and so I let him soothe me, and did not remind him whose bonds had held me so fast. I knew that he hated me then, and I allowed that hate to fill me with the much belated pain, and freed myself minutes after he left me for the last time.

No, it couldn't have happened that way.

No, really, the first time I was bound it was after years and years of bondage, when I was handed two pairs of cuffs and told to put them on. When I passed the rope I cut the night before under the bed legs and lay down in genuine state of fear. Not fear of her, but fear that because I had never been bound, that I shouldn't have been there, hadn't earned my way to that strange bed and those accurate hands.

And with the two items I had brought and the one she had, she taught me what it was like to be tied, to be spread so wide that there were no safe places on my body. She taught me that the place I had gone before was not accessible through her, and when at last the tears came, I gave myself to them wholeheartedly, never losing myself, never turning away.

The cuffs were snug and light, and when I pulled against them, I did nothing but press my body wider for her. And in time, when I was turned and moved, it was her voice that held me and the bondage seemed almost superfluous. I struggled against the ties and sighed in agony as they refused to give, and in one blissful moment, reared against them, fingers curled and my entire body tensed to tear them from their anchor points. They held. What a luxury to be so tightly bound.

"Luxurious, ain't it?" she breathed into my ear.

And I cried again, clean tears which poured through me, soaking my face, my hair, the sheets beneath me, because I was so grateful for that moment.

You see, I'd never been bound before.

And when the bonds were gone, I found that they had stayed with me anyway, and I slept in them and wore them for quite some time. The marks were not to fade from my body for months, years maybe, but the cuffs are still there, waiting for the rope under the bed.

But maybe that wasn't the way it happened at all.
Maybe it's still to come.

Alternate Worlds & Realities

Electra, on the Rocks - Following the Paradigm Tides

(First published in *The Second Coming,* edited by Pat Califia and Robin Sweeney.)

My first memories of fantasy were bound inextricably to suffering, humiliation, pain and subjugation. I didn't know those words. I did know how to spell my name. I was a child. I did know, however, that these core thoughts were not meant to be shared with others, certainly not with adults. They became a hidden, buried part of me, around which I constructed masks. These simple masks later became roles, all of which served to hide what I have always believed is my essential nature.

All through my life, the fantasies of pain and passion wove their way through me, infiltrating my dreams and nightmares, inserting themselves in my thoughts at odd times, surfacing in my writing even as a kid. There's no doubt in my mind that I was born programmed to receive them, a permanent cable decoder in my brain descrambling all the messages of power and pain and dominance and submission and relay them directly into my emotional growth, my sensual awareness, my sexual awakening.

Now, after 30 years or so of receiving these messages, I'm seeing an underlying programming, something grown out of my experiences, something taken from a mixture of education and need. There are roles I've played all my life, some with more passion and truth than others, roles people play because that's our way of coping. Dutiful child, diligent scholar, sardonic rebel, sarcastic undergraduate, sullen employee, enthusiastic volunteer, one part after another, and always that edge of distance that made me doubt my sanity and reality. That was how I saw the relationship - somewhere underneath the role, there was a person who was not fully relating to her circumstances, her family, her friends, the rest of life. A role gave me a context in which to interact, a plan to follow. It wasn't real.

I knew when I was real - it was when my body dripped sweat from fear and pain and anguish and indecision and determination and terror and the will to take one more, push harder, until something, someone broke.

I was real the first time a woman touched my face after she slapped me, and then kissed me, hard, and it was the first time a tongue in my mouth didn't feel like a nauseating violation.

I was real when I burned with the glowing aprés-beating pains that made me aware that my flawed body was really an amazing thing that made me feel alive and hot and desirable.

I was real the first time my hand pushed past that last ring of tight flesh and there was a human being leaning back and laughing, poised on my wrist, my hand pounding with the beating of their heart.

I was real the time I passed a blade along smooth, unmarked flesh, parting the skin and drawing up the blood, and fighting the urge to bend and lick, to suck their life right from them until I could hear that heartbeat again, feel their pulsing in my body and be with them utterly.

This reality, the sadomasochistic reality, kept me going. It was where I explored everything fascinating about human nature, conflict and resolution, passion and control, anger and conditional love. I ignored the nagging voice in me which I still call the chastiser, which continually wondered why I was doing this, what I was seeking. In every physical experience, I found another piece of brick to structure my support tower. If I had enough play time, I was sure that I wouldn't need anything else. If I had one more ecstatic experience, or if I could just extend it - I would be real that much longer. I pushed myself, always looking for the heavier "scene," the new kink. If it worked, I wanted it to last longer, for the whole night, for the weekend, for the extent of the relationship. I was real, and that was all that mattered.

I did whatever I had to do to keep this physical wall going up. If I lacked a woman, I would find a man. If I lacked a top, I would become one. Lacking the clothing to suit a lover, I would buy it, make it, fake it. Lacking the endurance for a particular act, I'd cut my body off with too many drinks or an interesting drug, or just through grinning wildly and turning it all off, until the thumps and stings were like echoes in a canyon, insubstantial except for faint reverberations, and I'd take an evil kind of pleasure in knowing that eventually top du jour would give up and I would win. I shut off the chastiser that kept asking what on earth I was getting out of this except for bruises, cuts, aches, and those incredible moments of timelessness when there were no masks on me and I was alone in my pleasure and pain.

Reality, my reality. Physicality mingled with an intellectual distance, an almost scientific detachment. It was empty in a primal way, never leaving me feeling fully satisfied. I remember crying one night, sobbing and asking over and over again, why it wasn't enough, these beatings and bondage, the rituals of submission and dominance, why I kept searching for more. I couldn't even begin to explain what exactly was missing. Maybe it was the stability of monogamy, I supposed. Maybe it was a strong, definite sense of a single, clear orientation that everyone else seemed to have. Perhaps it was that ultimate of relationships, that of mistress and slave, which would satisfy me - but even when I sought that, it seemed hollow, meaningless. All I knew was that something was always missing - and I couldn't put a word to it. Not then.

Now I know - I lacked a *context*. I lacked the proper lens to bring my physical experiences into focus, to bind them to my emotional needs and my growing sense of an underlying hunger within me that I never named. My internal programming was cut off from the vital key to making me feel complete, because I had been too busy using it as a way to hide. What I lacked was a role. I'd used them all my life as a masking method of cutting myself off from people - but in an ironic twist, lacking one made my sex life fairly shallow. Not to mention enormously frustrating.

The first time I heard about Daddies was from a man who told me about gay men and Daddies and boys. I remember sitting there, astonished at the way my mind snapped to attention, my lingering aches and pains vanished, at the way my clit started to tingle. I was at once aroused, disgusted and ashamed. "How romantic," I remember saying.

Let's keep this about gay men, I remember thinking.

I'm the last one to raise my bad childhood as a big issue. I'm very unsympathetic to victimization as an excuse for a thoroughly fucked up life. And I've had enough therapists, amateur and professional, explain to me how my attraction to pain and power is but a result of abuse at the hands of (please fill in the blank, I have no intention of going into details). But that last piece of baggage in me, that last piece of "isn't this all sick?," was right there in my face. That moment in a Greek diner, everything frozen for that second, the cheeseburger, the limp fries, the droplets of water on my glass, the tinny sound of Frank Sinatra coming from a booth across the room - my voice went on while my brain halted. I couldn't believe what was happening while I calmly discussed something that my rational mind told me should have made me sick to my stomach.

It's just a role, I consoled myself. It's about men, and their fathers. It has nothing to do with me.

But it had everything to do with me. From that moment on, it never left my mind. I turned it over and over, looking for the impulse in me that was turned

45

on, self-analyzing until I realized that there was just no bottom line except that I responded to that image, that idea of a role, in a way I had never responded to anything dreamed up by lovers, tricks, or even my favorite erotic authors. I struggled against my attraction to it because of those lingering doubts, and only occasionally wandered into territories where I could play with the powerful words and the dangerous concepts which were so scary. It was only a matter of time before I gave in.

In another time, another world, I saw one small, strong butch girl fisting another one, and all the while the room was shaking with the cries of a woman screaming for Daddy, begging, pleading, insisting that Daddy fuck her, harder, faster, deeper. I sat on the floor, unable to rise, to leave, to speak, even to reach down and touch myself and make sure that the seam on my jeans was really that hot and damp with this new passion, just utterly captivated by the enactment of the forbidden.

I hate getting fucked like a girl.

But oh, that night, in my mind, I threw away every piece of girl clothing I had in my closet, burned every pair of pantyhose, every waist cinching skirt, every black pump, and I bought myself boots and a vest and chaps, and as I did this little makeover, I bent over for Daddy, 'cause I wanted to get fucked faster, harder, deeper. And I wanted Daddy to hold me until I cried and beat me until I couldn't stand it, and love me unconditionally, and I wanted to be the best boy, ever.

Hello, paradigm shift.

After years of making myself fit the circumstance, I'd found something that resonated inside me. This was the click that made everything else make sense. It was the key to freeing me from the limitations of the physical - the role which felt natural, however odd it seemed externally. The physical nature of what I was doing took a slight turn away from things which I had no connection with, and toward what made me stronger. I slowly learned to stop looking for the longer scene, the harder one, the stranger one, and began to follow, rather than push. The long-standing confusion about erotic attention, punishment and pain for pleasure's sake became untangled, sorted out and made sensible. I had a context to put it all in - a model to follow, to compare with, to alter to suit me.

Slowly, the change pushed me to recognize parts of me which had previously come out only in writing or in late night "I've had a few too many" honesty sessions with friends who were all too polite to mention it the next day.

For example, my drive to service was always strong, yet I had struggled with it for years because of a nagging sense that I didn't just want to be someone's cook/maid/whatever in exchange for a good beating every once in a while. With the shift into a Daddy/boy relationship, there came a greater sense of availability for service. I no longer felt used - I felt like I was doing something useful.

The romantic and extreme notions about honor and loyalty which I'd kept hidden came out bit by bit, as I found that expressing them to a partner who identified as a nurturer rather than an owner was cleaner, safer, easier to manage. The embarrassment I felt about them - awkward notions, uncomfortable in this modern world of easy alliances and casual betrayals - faded as I realized that I could accept such gifts - no, expect them! - from my dominant partner.

My fantasies about being owned and utterly mastered paled in comparison to the reality I had found in a Daddy/boy relationship. They were still there, but they faded slowly over the years, until I realized that much of what I'd felt was that original drive for an experience that would just stretch out the purity of my SM encounters. It was a fantasy construct from minute one, where I created a godlike partner who would somehow grant me fulfillment simply by declaring a particular relationship was in existence. I came to peace with my fantasies and wrote about them, worked them until I could stand free of them. But it was only by finding the proper role for me - one which gave me the tools I needed to put meaning to what I was doing - which freed me to do that.

This context allowed me to fully explore my needs, desires and fantasies. After the initial sense of vertigo, after I had come to terms with that last bit of self-judging doubt about whether I could step away from the past and embrace what never was there for me as a child and make it into an erotic and emotional masterpiece of adult relationship management, my discovery of the boy inside me made me feel whole. It enabled me to toss out a lot of old baggage, a real brain sweeping which is still working to my favor. It also gave me a sense of stability which had been altogether lacking in every previous relationship I had ever had.

In retrospect, it doesn't seem like this was such a big deal. Roles are the most common part of SM play. When we explain SM behavior to the unknowing, we start by explaining tops and bottoms. We illustrate fantasies by exploring roles. But I had never realized how vital a proper role was for me. Only after I embraced that boy and accepted a Daddy could I shake loose the vestiges of toxic parenting that were still steadily burning away at parts of me from the inside.

And it wasn't just the whole "father" thing I learned to deal with, but aspects of gender and identity, bringing me in touch not only with my butch nature, but my tangled attractions to other butches and to femmes. It gave me somewhere to put my basic switchable nature, too - as a boy, I knew that one day I would be grown and take on a boy of my own. This appealed to the traditionalist inside me, too. One simple role - and it changed my life.

I've been thinking about that a lot over the past three years, as parts of my life, visions, fantasies and realities came out bit by bit in the books I've been writing under the name Sara Adamson. I use literary license of course, mixing truth with fantasy, exaggerating experiences and feelings for the sake of drama and neat endings. But when I reread the manuscripts, I can feel myself poking through, my feelings and dreams laid bare in ways that I tell myself only I can really see. And now, I stand at the verge of yet another shift - only this time, I feel it happening.

There was a voice inside of me which came out in the unfinished story *The Triangle* (that one written under the pseudonym Lady Sara), the voice of the switchable butch boy, hungry for daddy and cruising for girl/boys with big eyes. Arrogant and posturing, too tough for my own good, stupid at times, stubborn and scared, but at the same time secure in the knowledge that there was a plan ahead of me. I remember what it was like, feeling that everything was all figured out. I had a Daddy - one day I would be a Daddy. As the bottom inside me grew and changed, the top inside me was soaking up knowledge, getting a feel for power, gaining experience and understanding. The role had been found, satisfaction answered, happiness achieved.

Now, I'm realizing that this ain't necessarily so.

Fact is, right now I don't feel like much of a Daddy. Oh, there's one lurking inside me, but it's not the urge I feel when I'm in charge. Something else triggers those feelings of passion which make me respond to a bottom. Part of it is my sheer sadism - but most of it is a drive to train and own another person.

Even writing that down makes me feel a tightening at my spine, brings heat to my palms.

Paradigm shift, revisited. Unexpected, at least by my rational brain. But like the boy who remained dormant until the right notes were struck in my experience, so the master has slumbered inside me, flowing out of my fingers at a keyboard while I denied its presence.

It's hard to nail down the differences in my mind, especially in those places where Daddies and owners cross paths. It always seems to be an exercise in semantic time wasting to sit down and illustrate the differences between tops, mistresses, daddies, masters, owners, caliphs, or whatevers - and I don't think my personal definitions would be useful to anyone who isn't interested in me specifically. But I do know that in my mind there is a difference. It has to do with how much of someone I want to carry - it has to do with how much I want to use. It's selfish. It's sometimes cruel, always demanding.

Part of me wonders if I'm trying to recapture that old dream of a relationship deeply rooted in the cultural mythology of SM. In my head, I hear the chastiser reminding me that I should not dare to take on what I had never given. I hear the growl of the more arrogant youth, who topped and found it to her liking, crying that she's paid her dues, give her the reward her patience has earned her. She's a hungry bitch, that one, and she's outstripped my old friend the chastiser over and over again, until my doubts have slipped from me and there's only the sense that I am becoming someone new. The youth has grown, and wants to take the keys for a while - Daddy can wait. I'm pushing a new envelope, and touching the borders of a role which will once again remake me, and find me peace. At least, I hope that's where this will lead.

I do know this; it feels real.

And that's all I need for now.

Shayna Maidel

(Previously published in *Ritual Sex* edited by Tristan Taorimino & *Things Invisible To See* edited by Lawrence Shimel.)

Kiva sighed as she took the freedom rings from around her throat and hung them from the hook on the back of the closet door.

"It's not going to be that bad," Shari consoled from across the room. "It's only for a few days. And really, I've wanted to meet your family anyway."

"As my roommate," Kiva groused.

"As your special friend. When you're ready to come out, I'll be ready too." Shari was as patient as ever, her dark, sapphire eyes showing nothing but acceptance, security and love. It never took long for those eyes to make Kiva smile, and she eventually did, her lips tight in a sharp grin.

"Well, wait until you experience the High Holy Days at Temple Hillel," Kiva teased. "Every stereotype of Jewish culture, right there in front of you, and half of them coming from my relatives. Women in fur coats, trying to make matches while comparing the cost of cars, weddings and jewelry."

"I just wish I could bring my *tallis*."

"Me too, baby. But I don't think Rabbi Feldman will be very up on women in *tallit*. And I don't expect he'll have some interesting interpretation on the *vidui*, and I don't think we'll be hearing a woman sing the *Kol Nidre*, either."

Their regular synagogue was a very liberal congregation, with a heavy gay and lesbian membership. Shari, since her conversion, was a much better Jew then Kiva when it came to observing the customs. Yet, because of Shari's fervor, Kiva had rediscovered the beauty and serenity of the Sabbath, and the comfort of the seasons and their celebrations. Time could easily get to be abstract without those reliable markers.

"We'll make-do, sweetie," Shari said. "*Bubeleh*." She giggled.

"Don't start with me," Kiva warned. With another long suffering sigh, she pulled a dark skirt out of the closet and began to fold it. "Just don't start. I'll sic my mama on you, and she'll have you married and pregnant before Sukkot."

"Oh! *Kayn aynhoreh* on that!" In a fit of giggles, Shari almost fell off the bed. When she recovered, she noticed that Kiva hadn't joined in or offered a pithy comment. Instead, the darker woman was holding an old gray wool shawl, embroidered with fine stitching and worn around the edges. She had it bunched up under her nose, breathing in the scent of old perfume and smoke and piety.

"I wish you could have met her," Kiva said, breaking the silence. "I wish I had."

Kiva folded the shawl carefully and put it in her suitcase. Maybe this year, she would wear it in front of the rest of the family, and solve the mystery of what Baba Chanah had done with it before died.

But then, maybe she wouldn't. Kiva drew in more barren air and compressed her body to expel it, falling into the rhythm as she continued to pack. She was a little out of practice. Baba Chanah had told her not to allow these things to fall away, but it was so easy to forget. Especially when she had the headache of a family reunion after all these years. And during the Days of Awe, of course. The fast was going to make her very touchy. All this, she had explained to Shari months ago, but Shari was firm. It was time for Kiva to go home, even for a visit, and time that she met the family. It was only fair - Kiva got to meet Shari's parents last year, during Christmas, when they had to deal with their daughter's conversion and her new lover.

But fair doesn't mean bubkes when you have a family like mine, Kiva thought. And without Chanahleh there to smooth things over...

There were definitely times when lacking the ability to cry was a blessing.

"I've come to tell you a story, Akivaleh," Baba Chanah said as she slipped into Kiva's bedroom. Kiva pulled her head off the pillow and smirked.

"Baba, I'm eighteen years old. Don't you think that's a little grown-up for bedtime stories? And what are you doing up so late?"

"You don't think an old woman like me hears things, like young women sneaking into the house at three in the morning?" Baba Chanah humphed in her elegant, knowing way and sat down on the edge of the bed.

Unlike her sisters, she had not grown rounded in her age, staying slender and almost a little bit fragile, her pale skin tight over her long fingered hands. She was always a small woman, but strong, and when the sisters gathered in family emergencies, it was always Chanah who was consulted and heeded. Kiva's mother had once told her that Chanah had always taken care of the entire family, men or no, and always would.

"I'm sorry I woke you," Kiva said immediately. She meant it.

"Tcha, tcha, I don't need all this sleep. I need to tell you a story. Now, will you be quiet and listen to your old Baba, or talk, talk, all night?"

Kiva sat up and drew her legs under her. If Baba Chanah wanted to tell her something this much, it must be important. She looked into the older woman's sharp eyes and wondered if Baba Chanah felt she was going to die. She was never ill, never weak. But she was much older than she looked...Kiva bit her lip to hold back the wave of pain that swept through her and took Chanah's hand.

"Is it about the family?" she asked. "Is it about you?"

"Yes, of course!" Chanah patted Kiva's hand reassuringly. "It's time you were told about Michal."

"And this couldn't wait until morning?"

"Tcha! It's morning enough! Now listen:

Back in the old country, under the Tsars, our family lived in a village where nothing stands now, in a place where people do not remember that a Jew was ever there. And Michal, the girl with the strong name and a temper to match, was the oldest daughter of Akiva, for whom you were named, and who was the finest weaver for miles and miles.

"You never say anything about the men, Baba Chanah."

"Ah, men. They tell their own tales. These tales are ours, Akivaleh. Now, listen!"

As I was saying; Michal was the eldest of three daughters and two sons. There are men for you, all right? And this was back in the days when we Jews lived only by the whim of the Tsar - one day, we are valuable, and the next we are nothing. There might be peace for a year, for three, or five, but then the Cossacks would stir up the filthy peasants who hated us and they would burn and steal, and drive us away from our homes, what little land we had. They would cut down men in the street and take the young girls and do as they wished to them. They burned down our synagogues and spat upon the learned men and the Torah. And there was nothing to do, no place to go! There was no police precinct to complain to, because the police were the peasants, ready to take what was ours. We had no - no - civil rights? - not like here in *goldeneh medina*.

For many years, my mother's village was quiet. A little beating here, a little fire there, some ruffians breaking windows and stealing chickens, that was all.

Now, also from this village was a loose woman, a *kurveh...*"

"Baba Chanah!"

"Well, she was! You're not a child, you can hear such talk."

"Mama would die if she heard you say that!"

"Your Mama, dear heart, should be so lucky that she gets a story like this one from me. Are you going to listen now?"

"Yes, Baba."

"This woman who had a reputation, nu? But more then that, she had a profession, and she didn't come to the synagogue, and no one spoke to her. Except for Michal, who had been her friend in their childhood and never forgot that, even when this woman turned her back on our ways and went to ply her trade among the goyim. And not a few of our men as well, I might add! But they never talked about that, only that she was *shtupping* the *goyim* for rubles. Never mind the giggles, Akivaleh, just listen!

It happens that one day, Michal goes into the fields to the secret place where she meets her old friend, and instead of gossip and young women's thoughts and dreams, they share terrible news. This outcast, this woman, had heard (don't ask how) that men were coming to this village, soon, tomorrow maybe! They were going to do this pogrom, do you know what that was? Of course you do, you're a good girl, a good scholar. They were going to burn the village and chase all the Jews out, maybe even kill them.

And now, Michal knew. But there she was, with her younger brothers and sisters, her mama, and the whole village to think of, what could she do? She was only a girl. If she warned them, they would not defend themselves - there were no shops to go buy guns, and our people, sadly, were not great fighters in those days. *Chachemim*, yes, but Lions of Judea, no. They could only run away, and hide, and hope that the troubles would be over soon.

Michal did what she thought was right; she ran home as quickly as her legs could carry her, through the fields and down the roads, and to all she passed, she cried, "The Cossacks are coming! The Cossacks…

"What, what's so funny? This is a serious story I'm telling!"
"I'm sorry, Baba. Please, go on."

And the word spread through the town. Many people put their candlesticks and holy items under boards in the floors of stables and in their houses. They hid their valuables - what little they had - and they sent many of their daughters on wagons to another town to the east, where there was no trouble that day. But Michal's mama would not separate her family - together they would stay, until the troubles were over. Carefully, they took up their shawls and the smaller children, and some milk and bread and *cholent* in an old iron pot, and they went off into the woods, where no one knew the trails. Akiva (for whom you are named) was a wise woman to do this, but foolish as well. They left the morning of the pogrom, and slipped into the trees and vanished, a family together.

When the animals came the following day, they did the things they are known to do, and worse. They smashed windows and they smashed people. They carried off furniture and books and chickens and children, the girls for… hurting… and the boys to go into the army. And they burned down not only the synagogue, but the three shops and the mill and the spinning house where all the women of the village went. And when they discovered that many people were missing, they became enraged and set out into the fields and onto the roads, and yes, into the forest, to look for them.

They did not like being outsmarted, these Cossacks and their peasant slaves. Now, they wanted to kill as many Jews as possible, to teach them a lesson.

Deep in the woods, as dusk fell and no one from the village came to look for them, Akiva became worried and sent Michal back along their trail to try and find out what had happened. Michal didn't have to search long to realize that the woods were full of drunken peasants looking for the escaped Jews! She hurried back to her mother and her brothers and sisters, and took two children up in her arms. Leading the way, she brought them further and further into the woods, never losing the sounds of these terrible men coming after them. It was a nightmare, one shadow on another, strange cries and noises, and so many kinder to look after. Soon, they all became tired, and Michal had them take shelter near a stream. As they drank their fill, Michal looked at her mama and said, "I must go and get help."

Akiva didn't argue, only kissed her daughter and sent her on her way. You might ask, what help was there? As I said, there was no police, no

FBI, no men to come save them. And this Michal knew also, yet she thought that there was one chance.

Through the woods she went, now to the north, now to the east, now to the west - each way, she looked and listened, and kept moving - always ahead of the searching men, always watching that some drunken *momzer* doesn't come and catch her.

And then suddenly, she sees a clearing. And in that clearing is a house, built in the old way, with logs and straw on the roof, and round windows without glass. There is no path leading to the heavy door, because that house doesn't sit still for much time in one place. But there were three large rocks by the door, because the house didn't sit on the ground. No, on both sides of the house were big, fat legs. The legs of a chicken!

"You like laughing at old women?"

"Baba! You're mixing Russian folktales with Yiddish ones!"

"Tcha! This is a story in Russia, yes? And she is being chased by Russians, right?"

"You didn't tell me this was a fairy tale."

"Because it is not a fairy tale, Miss Smart Mouth. Are you going to listen or not?"

"All right, Baba Chanah. So, she meets Baba Yaga."

No, not Baba Yaga, as though there is only one. One of the Baba Yaga's, perhaps a young one, perhaps an old one. To her eyes, as she climbed the stones and reached for the door and it opened by itself, to her eyes, Baba Yaga is a baba, a little grandmother of a woman, with bad teeth, and round black eyes like saucers and hair like a bird's nest. Baba Yaga reached out for Michal with one huge hand like a shovel and brings her into the hut on chicken legs and sits her down by the fire and gives her a nice cup of tea from a kettle that sings old Volga songs. Michal takes the tea and sees that her chair is made of bones, but she drinks the tea and said, "Hello, Grandmother. Peace be unto you."

You see, even being chased by those *momzerim*, she was still polite.

And Baba Yaga laughed in the way of old women, and sat down in a chair piled high with the skins of unclean beasts and picked her crooked teeth and nodded. "Greetings, child of the Chosen People. I have never received a visit from your folk before!"

"And I have never met one of your folk before," said Michal.

"What is it you wish, Daughter of Sorrows? A charm to win the heart of the Rabbi's son? A potion to rid a woman of an ill-gotten babe? A cow that gives golden milk, or a the horn of Cheslav the Wicked, which brings the dead back to life once during a battle and once during a wedding?"

55

And Michal shuddered to hear of such things, because she was a good girl. She said, "No, Grandmother, I have no need of such things, thank you. But I am in need of something to save my family with." And so she explained about her mother and brothers and sisters hiding in the woods with the Cossacks and the peasants getting nearer.

"My magic can only help one person at a time,' said the old witch, rubbing her bony hands together. 'Tell me what I can give to you so that you might save them instead."

Michal thought and thought, but couldn't come up with the answer. All she could think of was asking for some great weapon out of the past, but she was a young woman, she knew nothing about any weapon save the Ark of the Covenant, which she would not even mention before this *goyisher* magic woman. And in despair, she cried, "I wish I had the power - the strength and cunning to protect my mother and all of my family from harm, forever!"

And Baba Yaga laughed again and spun in her chair and cracked her knuckles like gunshots. She sprang up and leaned over Michal, her breath like spoiled meat, and said, "By your God, I swear that I will give you this power in exchange for a kiss and an oath!"

"I will not swear before God to do anything without knowing what it is," Michal said wisely.

"You will have the power you seek forever," promised the old witch. "But you must consume what is forbidden to your people in order to do so!"

Michal's stomach turned at the thought of eating pig. (For that was what she thought the old women meant.) But to save her family? Yes, this she would do.

"I swear that I will consume as you direct if this power is true," she said.

"Then come for your kiss, Daughter of the Book!"

And Michal closed her eyes and leaned forward. But instead of kissing her on the forehead (as her mama did), or on the cheeks (like Russians did) or on the lips (as lovers did), Baba Yaga kissed Michal on the neck.

After that, Michal could hardly remember what happened. She saw herself putting the teacup down and thanking the old woman for her gift. She remembered walking out of the hut and patting one of the fat chicken legs absently as she turned to the south. She knew it was night, but she could see as clear as day. And although she knew that there were still men running through the forest looking for her and her family, she was no longer afraid.

When she came upon one, who was carrying an old sword and a pistol and a bottle, she almost ran away. And as he came to her, unsteady and filthy, grinning like a wolf, she wanted to fall to the ground and cry and shake.

But instead, she waited for him, her entire body full of something, she didn't know what. Not until he touched her did she move.

His neck was broken in a blink of an eye!

Yes, Michal, the daughter of the weaver woman, had taken a grown man up and broken his neck -snap! - like a dry branch. And instead of letting him fall, she caught him, and pulled him to her, because like Baba Yaga, she wanted to give him a kiss. But not on the forehead, or the cheeks, or the mouth. Michal kissed him on the throat, and took into her the most forbidden *trayf*!

"Are you saying that Baba Yaga made Michal into a vampire?"

"Are you going to listen to the rest of the story, or ask questions?"

"Baba Chanah - why do you have to tell me this in the middle of the night?"

"Shush and you'll learn."

Michal was terrified of course. She had heard legends of creatures that drank blood, but they were things of the Christians, the *goyim*, not of her people. (Well, there's Lilith, but she's a demon, so she doesn't count. Besides, she really wasn't Jewish.) Michal wanted to run away at once and kill herself, but she knew that her family was depending on her. So, she dropped the body of the man who would have raped and killed her, and went in search of her mama.

During that long night, Michal did what she had to do to keep her family safe. And when the dawn came, she roused them and took them back to their village, without explaining what had happened to her or how it was that they were never found. "It was surely God's will," she kept saying.

But when they got back to the village, matters had become even worse! For all the Jews were being forced to leave, at once, and they no longer had a house to return to, nor mule nor chickens. They had to join another family as almost beggars, and go onto the road alone in the world, after a night of horror.

"But Baba, the sun was up."

"The sun shouldn't be up in the daytime?"

"But Michal was a vampire! Didn't she have to sleep in a coffin or something?"

"*Gevalt*! Didn't she have enough *tsuris*, without this Dracula nonsense? Obviously, the vampires in Russia are different than the Romanian ones, what can I say? Oh, Michal didn't like it out in the sun, but it was a fashion to wear a shawl in those days, even if you were a pretty, young, unmarried woman, a nice *shayna maidel* like you."

"What about crosses?"

"She was Jewish, Akivaleh, what do crosses have to do with her? That's *goyisher mishegoss*."

"OK, OK. So, they're on the road, fleeing the village."

That night, Michal slips away, and goes into another part of the woods, off the side of the road. Before long, what with going this way and that way, and this way and that way, she finds her way to the hut with the chicken feet underneath. This time, Baba Yaga is outside, picking mushrooms.

"You must undo this gift," Michal said right off.

"Oh, but you swore," the old witch said back, taking a large pink mushroom and munching. "Have I not given you the power to keep your family safe, forever? And is not the price that you must eat a forbidden thing? Or drink it?!"

Michal wanted to say that she was wrong for asking for the gift, but when she thought about how many families back in the village were missing people, girls and boys gone forever, and she knew that no bargain she made to save her family could be a bad one. She was resigned to live with it - but forever?

"Before *Hashem*, it would be an *averah* to live more years then Moshe," she said finally. "I beg you to limit my life to 119 years only. Surely that will be long enough."

Baba Yaga considered as she munched and munched. "Forever is forever, Daughter of the Hebrews, as you well know. But I will give you this; before your 120th year, should you find a daughter of your mother's blood who will accept your place, you may die a true death and be judged as your God wills. But if you wait for one day past the start of the 120th year, you shall stay as you are forever, and be cut off from your people when your Messiah comes!"

"And if there are no girl children of my blood?"

The old witch cackled. "When there are no daughters, there are no babies! But I will allow this - if there are no girl children to pass this gift on to, then surely it will pass away."

Michal bowed her head. She knew she would get no better than that. And she returned to her family and stayed with them and guided them to safety, eventually, in Poland.

"A lot good that did," Kiva said bitterly. "Think of what you had to do to get the family out of there!"

"Well, I was only doing what Michal told me to do before she died, *alecha ha-shalom*. When I had to became the guardian of the family." And Baba Chanah sighed and patted Kiva's hand. "And now, I'm thinking that 119 years is a long time for a woman to walk the earth. Eighty one was enough for Michal, and I'm thinking that eighty-seven years is long enough for me. And Akivaleh - you are the only daughter of my blood."

Kiva eyed her old aunt with tired skepticism. "Baba... none of this makes any sense, you know. You're only talking about two generations going back to pre-revolution Russia. And you're sixty-seven, not eighty-seven."

"And this is so, *bubeleh* - according to the records in this country. We age slowly, we Sovetski women. Especially the cursed ones." She sighed and patted her niece's hand absently. "I am the only daughter of Michal's youngest sister, Leah. So many died in Poland. I was our protector, but only of those of our blood - so wives, husbands, they were taken - it was our blessing and my curse that we were able to survive, some of us, and come here to be safe again."

"Wait. I'm losing track here. You're not my aunt?"

"I'm your grandmother, Akivaleh."

"Does mama know?"

"Of course she does! What child doesn't know her own mother?!"

"But ...why lie about it?"

"That was my idea - when Baba Michal finally went to her rest, I thought we could change the records and make it seem like I had no daughters. I could just join my child with her cousins, and say that they were my sisters. Perhaps the curse would end there! But blood tells, and your Mama was supposed to be the one I asked to become our next strong woman. But Akivaleh - you know your Mama, my sweet Leah, my tender Lily. Nice, she is. Bright, oh, she's bright as a button! And very kind, full of charity! But strong? Strong, she's not. So, anyway, here we are. And Akivaleh...you might be the one to end this forever! We don't need guardians anymore, in this new country. We have a nice family - all boys! And, honestly, I don't think you're planning on having any babies, are you?"

"Baba Chanah!" Kiva blushed and then rapidly paled. "What...what do you mean?"

"I mean that you're a nice young woman who's not interested in men, nu? And to think, I'd be happy that my own granddaughter is a *faygeleh*! But, that's what you get for having children. In this case, it's a blessing from God, I'm sure. You'll be the guardian, and when your time runs out, the bargain with Baba Yaga will be over, and we will be free." She brushed her hands briskly together in her "That was easy!" gesture and smiled.

Kiva lowered her gaze at her newly discovered grandmother and chewed her lip. "So, you're a vampire."

"Yes!"

"And you want to make me one, because you think I'm a lesbian. And when I do become a vampire, you can die. After that, I'll live until I'm 120 years old and then, because there won't be any more women of your blood in the family, I'll die."

"Yes!"

"Baba Chanah," Kiva said softly, "have you ever heard of Prozac? It was a long night for both of them.

"Kiva! Kiva, sweetie, over here! There's my baby!"

Kiva sighed and shifted the garment carrier on her shoulder. She pointed at the waving figure covered in fur and mouthed the word "Mom" to Shari.

"I guessed," Shari said, smiling. They nodded and waved as they made their way through the checkpoint and toward the baggage claim area where the excited woman and two beaming men stood waiting.

"Kiva, Kiva, look at you! My little *bubeleh*, so thin, so pale! Look at her, Henry, she's thin as a stick! Are you starving in your fancy schmancy condo in Chicago?" Lily Birnbaum held her daughter at arm's length and then drew her in for a flurry of kisses. "Oh, it's so good to see you, my baby, my poor skinny baby!"

"It's a co-op, ma," Kiva sighed. "Ma - Ma, it's OK, I'm fine!" She laughed and kissed her mother gently on the cheek. "You know, I'm not alone - this is Shari, my roommate."

Shari darted forward and shook hands with Lily. "It's great to meet you, Mrs. Birnbaum. Kiva's told me all sorts of things about you."

"It's good to meet you too, Shari, welcome to New York. Well, come on, let's get these poor girls someplace warm - Kiva, you're as cold as ice! I've got some nice chicken soup for you - your favorite, with the noodles, just like when you were little! Did she tell you how she made us always put the noodles in the soup instead of matzah, Shari! Oh, how she liked her noodles!"

Meeting the men was a brief clutch of hands, and the girls were swept into the car and onto the roads in a flurry of nostalgia. During the ride, Kiva smiled and clutched Shari's hand carefully, and tried to remember to breathe.

"You didn't tell me about the noodles," Shari whispered accusingly.

The house was full, not only of people, but of scents, rich, heavy scents of long simmered soup, pungent aromas that made your mouth water, like the garlic touched drizzle that spoke of fat, green pickles, aged in barrels. In preparation for the fast, lunch was catered from the local corner deli. In addition to Lily's soup, there were hills of burgundy colored corned beef, peppery pastrami, pale roast turkey, slow cooked brisket. And the hills led up to a veritable mountain of potato salad and cole slaw, and were surrounded by islands of potato and kasha knishes. Tributaries of sour and half sour pickles led you to bowls of pickled tomatoes, stuffed derma, kasha salad with bowtie noodles, and then finally to a lake of chopped liver, wide and deep enough for the skewered herring - not the cream sauce one, but rich with marinated onions - to swim in - if they were in any shape to swim.

Men were everywhere. Shari was introduced to Uncle-this, and Uncle-that, and this cousin and that cousin. She had always understood that Kiva was the only girl in her generation, but never really though of how isolating that could be. Wives were present, yes, and even one girlfriend for one of the younger boys. But no sisters, other than the three who led this clan. No girl cousins. When she did spot another twenty-something girl, chatting at the other end of the room, she asked who that was.

"My Uncle Mike married a divorced woman after his divorce," Kiva explained, politely turning down an offer of a taste of chopped liver, nicely spread for her on a cracker. "That's Trudy, her daughter by her first marriage. No blood there. Unfortunately for Mike, no Jew, either. Trudy was baptized, and although Aunt Eileen did convert to marry Mike, Trudy hasn't yet. Gee, let's move away from the food again, OK?"

They had discussed the fast before. Last year, the day long fast for the atonement of the sins of the Jewish people was meaningless to Kiva, who didn't eat much anyway. Oh, she could, if she wanted to - put some mass in her mouth, chew and swallow it. But it was rarely worth the cramps as her body tried to figure out what to do with this foreign matter. It also wasn't very palatable any more, no matter how she used to love it. No, in order for the fast to be meaningful, she had to abstain from what really served as her diet for at least a week.

Now the only trick was to hide this special fast from the rest of her family for the two days before Yom Kippur.

"Eat, *bubeleh*, eat!" That was Aunt Sarah, now known to Kiva as not her mother's sister, but her cousin.

"I had some in the kitchen," Kiva gamely lied, patting her flat stomach. It had been like this for hours. She eyed Shari with a different kind of hunger, and the two women surreptitiously touched. Shari's warmth, her vitality, her sheer force of life made Kiva hunger in ways that her body could not process. From this desire too, she was abstaining. It was a vacant

61

hope against hopes that some sacrifice would serve to open the proper gates this time. She sighed and turned down an offer of some more chopped liver.

"Your roommate, she's not seeing anyone, not engaged?" Sarah whispered, passing the liver off to someone else. "Two nice girls like you! Listen, you go to temple, I'll introduce you to my friend Paula's son, Harry, he's a graduate of Yale! I'm sure one of you will get lucky!"

That night, Shari slipped into Kiva's bed, Kiva hearing every move as her lover eased back the sheets and tiptoed across the room. They were sharing the guest room, the one with one single bed and a folding cot that smelled of mothballs. They had considered moving them together, but decided not to tempt fate.

"I miss you," Shari whispered unnecessarily as Kiva gathered her into an embrace. "Maybe you were right, this is too hard. I'm so sorry, sweetheart, I didn't realize - there's be so many people here - and that we'd never get any chance to be alone -"

"Shhh, it's OK," Kiva consoled, letting her lips touch Shari's forehead. "It's almost over. Tomorrow starts the fast, and we'll be heading home right after it's over." They touched, slowly, their hands exploring, cool and warm, soft and hard, until Shari moaned and broke away.

"This is the hardest for me," she said, turning away. "I want you so much it hurts."

Kiva smiled her thin smile and touched Shari's back with one cool finger. "*Aishet kayyil...*" she murmured. *A woman of valor...*

"...I have found. Her worth is far beyond that of rubies," Shari responded automatically. She turned halfway to kiss that finger, went back to her cot. Finally, the two women rested, each in her own way.

It was still daylight when they entered the temple, surrounded by well dressed men and women, some of the men carrying decorated tallis bags, others looking vaguely lost. In her white blouse, with Baba Chana's shawl around her shoulders, Kiva looked more pale than ever, and Lily had agonized over it all through the ride and into the actual temple.

"You shouldn't fast when you're sick," she lectured, eyes whipping back and forth to greet friends and rarely seen acquaintances. "The rabbi said so, last year."

"I'm fine," Kiva insisted. In fact, she did feel a little weak. But that was the point, wasn't it? The daylight shining through the windows gave her a pounding headache - she practically had to let Shari lead her to a seat and settle her. She tried to ignore the steady stream of humanity that passed her by, their pulsating heat, the rich scent of their bodies, the sound of their heartbeats echoing against the walls. When she saw the ushers herding people to their seats and the white-clad cantors ascend the bima, she almost felt like sighing. It took a while to figure out how to do it, though, so she passed.

It was so familiar, not only to her, but to the memories bound by blood which lived inside of her. The relief that the Days of Awe were almost about to close, the anxieties of communal sin about to be washed away by communal repentance - all the burdens of humanity against humanity examined and stripped and held up for judgment. And now, on this holy of holies, the burden of humanity's crimes against the Ineffable. Not so much crimes of blasphemy and law breaking - but that of the making of vows which should not have been made.

The shortest cantor was the one with the biggest voice. As he pulled his pristine kittle in place around his rotund body, the entire congregation stirred and then stilled.

"Kol Nidre!", he sang, his voice quavering in that beautiful, haunting melody which compelled silence and attention. He was surrounded by two other men, holding Torahs, for this was not a prayer as much as it was a legal statement.

Shari had learned that much in her religious studies. The Kol Nidre asked that forgiveness be granted for vows made and not fulfilled, and that any vow made falsely or under duress will be considered null and void. These vows could not have been made specifically to other people - they had to be vows before or to God. There were all sorts of theories about where the Kol Nidre came from, and why it was part of the ceremonies of Yom Kippur, but it had occurred to Shari that it might have real meaning for Kiva.

"Who knows?" she had said, urging consideration of her idea. "At worst, you'll be hungry for a while. At best..."

Kiva didn't think about what might happen for the best. She cleared her mind and allowed the words of the Kol Nidre to penetrate her, fill her, and as it was repeated two more times, she swayed with its passionate rhythm and resonance. Slowly, the sun began to set and the evening services continued, just a hint about the marathon of prayers and reflection which would come the next day.

The afternoon sun was merciless as the millionth repetition of the *al chet* had Kiva staggering to her feet and beating her chest with genuine anguish. This list of community sins, cried out in the plural, as the entire congregation confessed to them, was a central part of the Yom Kippur daytime services. It was even repeated within the solitary prayers. She dimly realized that many members of her family were shocked, not only by her appearance, but by this apparent religious fervor. To Lily, religion was fine, a good thing to have - but not in abundance. Luckily, Shari situated herself between them and Kiva, and made it difficult for any of them to reach over and ask what was going on.

Shari gives me strength, Kiva thought, sinking back down into her seat. I need her so much! She glanced at the swelling body of the woman in the row in front of them, and then reeled back a little and closed her eyes. The pulsing heat of her, the hypnotizing scent, it was worse than being tempted with food. Food didn't fulfill your soul - food didn't give you the purity of oneness, that moment when a heartbeat becomes yours.

Just a few more hours, she thought, clenching her fists tightly. Then, I'll slip away and … or maybe not! Maybe this will end it all - the gates of heaven will open, and this injustice will be over! God will see that a deal made by a frightened girl with a crazy old witch should never have gone this far!

A tiny part of her mind stubbornly avoided the issue of what kind of God would allow this sort of thing to happen to begin with.

The service droned on, through the story of Jonah, through still more recitations of the *al chet*, and then, finally, the late afternoon saw the part of the ceremony called *Ne'ilah*, the Closing, representing the closing of heaven's gates, open for only so long.

Souls gathered in that temple, earnest prayers of release and relief, mingled with mumbled echoes of bad Hebrew tinged with annoying hunger pangs, thirst, and caffeine and nicotine withdrawal symptoms.

Kiva's withdrawal was making her itchy - her mouth and stomach ached, her head pounded. She needed to get out, and soon. But still, she prayed and sent her prayers into the setting of the sun, toward those gates which could surely send her case directly to the Creator, the Originator, to her *Shekinah*, the female essence of God. Hear me! she begged, not even realizing that she had fallen back into her seat.

When she felt Shari's hand on her shoulder, she started and almost leapt up. "Come on, honey, everyone's outside!"

Kiva licked her tongue across the top edges of her mouth and this time did execute a perfect sigh. Her lips were cracked, and there was a unique, sharp agony buried deep in her jaw that tingled and pounded at the same time. Shari was looking at her with compassion, guilt and worry written all over her face. "It's time to go," she said softy. There was nothing else to say.

Kiva got to her feet and stretched. Food or no, it was night, and she was stronger at night. Carefully, she made her way down the stairs, into the back seat of her mother's Buick, where she waved off the panicked suggestions that she need medical attention.

"Food!" Lily declared, throwing the car into gear. "She needs some nice, hot food! Chicken soup, with noodles, we have some at home in the fridge."

The very thought made Kiva's stomach lurch - or, what passed for such a reaction these days. The heavy, cloying smell of chicken fat, the pale golden color, the thin liquid, the high temperature - she closed her eyes and gripped Shari's hand, wrapping her fingers in icicles. Time was running out. If she didn't find a way to get out of the house, she would start losing it. That much she knew - her limitations had made themselves clear many times before. On two occasions, it was Shari who had saved her - Shari, with her beautiful, unselfish, unwavering love, Shari, who held her up and never, ever doubted or condemned her - Shari, whose pulse seemed so loud, drowning out the engine, the wind, the sounds of Kiva's aching soul.

Past the front door, she burst upstairs, Shari in close pursuit. An echo - "We'll be down soon!" seemed like jackhammers in her ears, and the startled cries and tsks of the relations were like the retorts of gunshots. Once in the room, checking the window, no, the fall wouldn't be that bad, she could hit the ground running. What a damn shame old Michal hadn't bargained better, the ability to become a bat or a wolf would be nice at moments like this. She threw the window open and groaned as her body shuddered in a great spasm of hunger/hurt.

Instantly, Shari's arms were around her. "Don't, don't," Shari murmured, her heat wrapped around Kiva from behind. "Lover, love, stay, don't leave me. God, I want you so much, Akiva..." Little kisses, sweet as a Rosh Hashanah apple, dripping with the honey of her tongue - Kiva turned in the embrace and wrapped her arms around her lover, unable to resist.

Their hands were everywhere at once, sweeping over their backs, curling over arms, twisting in hair. Their skirts rode against each other, and slid up, as their thighs crushed together, their bodies melded. Always like this after a period of abstinence, but worse now, because Kiva was lost in hunger, lost in the bitterness of a bargain left intact, a price so heavy it couldn't be spoken of.

"I can't do this to you again," she whispered, groaning, into Shari's ear. She nibbled on that earlobe, sucking it, a tease that made her teeth ache. Even as she spoke, she felt the shift in her mouth, and the preparation of her body to receive what would sustain her. "Three times, isn't that what they say? Let me go, I can't - I can't-"

"I'm not afraid," Shari whispered back. "I want you, now. I want you in me, lover, I want all of you." She pressed her own short, grinding teeth against Kiva's throat, and Kiva shuddered and whimpered in sympathetic agony. The sweeping power of her body's response made her growl, and forced the final change - that inner *click* that told her she was

65

ready to feed. She grasped Shari's hair in one hand and swept the other fingers across her chest, tearing pearl buttons open, revealing Shari's beautiful breasts, nipples taut with excitement.

"I love you," Kiva growled. And she bent forward, scent and heat and need driving her, until she could feel the touch of needle to flesh, feel the sweet heaviness of the impression, taste the heaviness of the skin's own sheen - and then the door opened.

"Kivaleh! What is going on in here? You don't answer - *Gevalt!*" Lily Birnbaum stood in the doorway, still clutching a mug of her bracing chicken soup, her mouth open, and her eyes sharp. Next to her was Aunt Sarah, and then behind her was Aunt Reba. The triptych of their astonishment might have been amusing had it been caught at that moment and gone no further.

Kiva and Shari, caught in the act, stared back at the three old women at the door. They were still entangled, their skirts hiked up past their thighs, Shari's blouse gaping open, Kiva's rumpled and loose. And worse - far worse for Kiva, who swayed as she realized what was on her lips, she had done more than tease Shari's flesh - a little trickle from one successful puncture was stark against the white of her throat and her blouse. A drop - a single, cursed drop! - was shooting through her mouth, screaming for company.

"Close the door!" Lily snapped, stepping in. Still, her grip on the mug was unwavering - not for nothing had she managed Passover Seders and High Holy Day meals for over thirty years! Her "sisters" stepped in as well, and were busy shaking their heads in amazement.

"And just what is going on here?" Lily demanded, her voice just hitting the lower range of her scale.

Shari grabbed the sides of her blouse and shrieked as she realized that her throat was a bit messy. She turned away, blushing and shoving her skirt down over her upper thighs again. Kiva drew herself up, hard when she was so dizzy and one of her shoes had fallen off. The pounding of her hunger and the pain from her disappointment had made her bold. How dare her not-strong-enough mother barge in on them like this? And why did she care what this ungrateful family thought about her anyway? To hell with being the guardian, to hell with it all! She had been about to have amazingly tasty sex with the woman she loved more than she had loved life, and she couldn't even do that?!

"I'm a vampire, mom!" she shouted, baring her still extended - and now truly agonizingly hurting teeth. "Just like Baba Chanah was, and Michal before her! To save this stupid family from the Russians, from the Nazi's, from those pathetic skinhead creeps that attacked cousin Nate when he was a kid! That's right, a stick-my-teeth-in-someone's-neck-and-drink-their-blood vampire! And you're driving me crazy with your 'eat this, drink that, you're so skinny and pale' - dammit, I'm undead! We're not supposed to look like the very picture of health!"

Aunt Sarah made tsking sounds as she shook her head. "So, that's what Chanah did!"

Aunt Reba nodded. "That old fool, *alecha ha-shalom*. She couldn't tell us? What did she think we'd do, tell the world?"

"Always with the mysteries," agreed Sarah with a sigh.

Shari turned back, her breasts recontained and the trickle now smudged into a pinkish smear on her neck. She looked at an equally confused Kiva and then back at the three women at the door. "You - knew?"

"Of course we knew, what are we, idiots? Children? You think we don't know what's what in our own houses?" Lily asked indignantly. "Am I some stupid *yutz* who doesn't even know what her mama is doing? Apparently so, because here I don't know what my own daughter is doing! Akiva, why did you do such a thing to this nice girl, your roommate!? Don't you know, this is only for *mamzers*, the scum outside? What did mama tell you, nothing at all? What a way to treat such a *shayna maidel*, and to do this on a Holy Day, besides!"

"I'm not - but mom-" Kiva stumbled over her words and sat down, missing the bed entirely and sliding to the floor. She looked up at Shari for help, advice, anything, and Shari pressed her lips together and nodded.

"Kiva wasn't hurting me, Mrs. Birnbaum," she said carefully. "I wanted her to, um, do what she was doing. I've done it before. You see, we're more than good friends - we're lovers. I don't mind when Kiva takes a little blood from me - she can have it all, if she wants." She looked down at her befuddled and starving lover fondly and then back at the relatives. "I love your daughter, Mrs. Birnbaum."

"Lesbians?" Lily's fingers loosened, and all that good soup spilled over the worn shag carpeting, the cup bouncing harmlessly aside. "You're a *faygeleh*?" Her voice scaled up two more octaves, and the sisters behind her began "tsk-ing" again. "I don't believe it - go raise children! This is how they treat you - they run off and become homosexual!" She threw her hands up for good dramatic effect and shook them accusingly at the sky. "Curses aren't enough, you have to do this? Go raise children!"

With that mighty wish aimed at the Almighty, Lily Birnbaum stalked to the door and threw it open. "So, be a lesbian! If that's what you want! Don't give a thought to your mama, who loves you! I'll just go back and cook some more now, don't pay any mind to me!"

"She knows about-?" Kiva waved her hand limply over her mouth. "She knows?"

"She'll get over it, this lesbian thing," Sarah counseled, picking up the mug. "Oy, what a mess. One of you girls will clean this up, OK? It's OK to call you girls, right? Of course, right. Just don't go marching with those drag-boys, yes? You stay at home and just keep out of trouble. And don't worry about the family. You come down later, when - you're feeling better."

The two young women nodded, in shock, and Sarah took a breath to start advising them some more, but caught an elbow from her sister.

"Don't talk, go," Reba snapped, pushing Sarah out the door. "Lesbians!" the girls could hear her say, as the door swung. "And such nice girls, too!"

To Serve in Close Attendance to Nobility:
Samurai Tradition in an SM Context

(Originally printed in the *SandMutopia Guardian.*)

Attendant to nobility (samurai)
Ask for your master's umbrella
The dews beneath the trees of Miyagino
Are thicker than rain

-poem from Kokinshu, 1091 CE - earliest known reference using the word
"samurai"

      For far too many westerners, the image of the samurai is bound
unmistakably with half-remembered stereotypes of rigid, fanatical warlords
who haphazardly order their robotic followers to slit their bellies for the
slightest reason.

      Yet within the samurai history and literature is a wealth of sage
advice for daily living, a remarkable source for strategic thinking, and a
proud tradition of service and loyalty which could serve as an admirable
alternative to the western images of master and slave, owner and owned, the
basis for many relationships in the SM/leather community.

      The word samurai itself is often translated as meaning warrior,
but the correct word for warrior is actually bushi. (Bushido = the way of the
warrior.) Samurai comes from an older word, saburau, which roughly means
"those who serve in close attendance to the nobility." The very essence of
samurai existence and thought, when it is not concerned with winning battles,

is that of service. Service to one's lord (daimyo), and service toward one's retainer.

There is no single "samurai code" to consult, because the tradition was developed over hundreds of years, with disparate leaders instructing their retainers to practice or shun different things depending on the time, the political upheavals in Japan, and/or their personal beliefs. But even a cursory study of some of the legacies left by famous samurai lords and generals will reveal precepts which are easily applied to a special kind of relationship, one which is not adequately served by the more common descriptions. My attempt here is not to create rules for such a relationship, but to encourage the consideration of this style as an alternative to the usual master/slave, daddy/boy, owner/owned pairings. My study of these traditions can at best be called cursory, so I apologize in advance for my lack of scholarship.

Samurai Bottom - Hold the Belushi, please.

A samurai style relationship in SM would be one based primarily on honor, loyalty and respect. It would not necessarily have anything to do with love or sex, although nothing stands to rule those things out. Above all, it would be a relationship between adults, both of whom have responsibilities, both to each other and to the greater world. This would be the first major breakaway from the western tradition. A slave is often considered the lowest on the social rung of society. But even the lowest grade samurai is considered a part of an elite group, whose responsibilities and traditions are vital to the stability of the society.

A lot of the precepts of samurai ethics are based in Confucian doctrine, which stresses austerity, humility, clear thinking, and an adherence to authority. Also included is a reverence for study and continual selfimprovement, and a directive to be disciplined in all things:

"Those who desire to govern their states should first put their families in order. And those who desire to put their families in order should first discipline themselves." - Confucius

This is obviously a good basis to begin the structure of any relationship. But underneath it is the principle that a leader or master must possess the very discipline that they will expect from their retainers; they must be in control of themselves even to a greater extent than their potential followers, providing a role model for behavior and discipline. And it also assumes that anyone may have the potential for leadership, as long as they are self-disciplined and organized. That would be another aspect of the experience of a samurai bottom; that one day, they may be expected to use the skills they have mastered in their service in order to become leaders (masters/daimyos, etc.) themselves. In fact, the samurai tradition is perfect for people who want to have submissives of their own yet still maintain a submissive relationship with someone else.

Much of the advice culled from the writings of the samurai warlords and leaders is advice to those in service. The reason is simple; in the structure of that culture, each leader was almost guaranteed to have a direct superior, to whom he owed the same measure of loyalty and respect that he was due from his retainers. Even the most powerful of military generals would have to show submission to the Emperor (although the actual political value of that submission decreased over the centuries).

Everything in a samurai's life revolved around service to the lord, even to the choosing of what to wear and how to conduct one's affairs at home. There were always questions: how will this action reflect on my master? Will this purchase be judged appropriate for a person of my level? Will my behavior be noted and praised, or will word get back to my lord that I am rude and boorish, uneducated or unjust? A samurai would never sit quietly when their lord was spoken of harshly or with disrespect, the status of their new enemy the only factor upon which to determine their action. A low status person might be rebuked verbally, or punished instantly, if the samurai had jurisdiction over them. An equal might be challenged instantly to a duel. (And so might a superior, depending upon the nature of the insult and the conditions of the meeting.) Sometimes, a samurai might just have to leave the presence of such hostility, proud and silent and with all the dignity possible. But they would never forget it.

Service to their lord is not only their responsibility, but their pride. A samurai bottom, therefore, should seek only the finest of persons to serve, hoping that one day they will achieve the presence and ability of their master. It is an honor merely to be in the master's presence, as seen in this behavior guideline from Hojo Nagauji (1432-1519):

"When one has been addressed by the master, even though he is seated at a distance he should quickly answer, 'Yes!', draw forward immediately, approaching on his knees, and make his response with full respect…"

Nagauji also suggests showing respect to the master's equals and associates, especially when they are leaders themselves. He says:

"To be without deference…would be outrageously rude. To be samurai is to be polite at all times."

There are plenty of what I call "scouting codes," instructions to be truthful, reverent, clean, punctual, and to pay attention to details. But an awful lot of attention is paid to ethical instruction, advising retainers to learn about and practice justice, and to hear differing opinions and keep silent until they know enough to comment. These skills were to be honed

71

because it would make them more useful to their lord in any capacity, so that should the lord wish a service, they could instantly fulfill it. But should they be ignorant of a particular matter or skill, they are counseled to admit it quickly, so as not to waste any time. That situation is acknowledged as potentially embarrassing, but not as bad as actually committing an error, which causes one to lose face. Yet even then, retainers are advised to take their punishment and not dwell on the error. In the Lun Yu, quoted at length by Takeda Nobushige in his Ninety Nine Articles, it says:

"When one makes a mistake, he should not be hesitant to correct it. Making a mistake and not correcting it, this is the real mistake."

Retainers were not permitted to pass judgment on their masters, and in fact, there is an old riddle about samurai behavior which is meaningful here.

It goes, "Which samurai is behaving more in the spirit of Bushido, the one who serves an even tempered and just master, or the one who serves an angry and cruel one?"

The answer is the samurai who serves the harsh master, because their loyal service to an unjust lord gains them greater merit as samurai. But SMers wishing to use some of these concepts don't necessarily have to find themselves angry, unjust masters in order to gain samurai brownie points. (After all, historically, most samurai didn't have much choice in who they got to serve.) But the lesson in that riddle does have meaning in the little injustices which occur as part of any human relationship, whether they're as slight as a forgotten special day or as meaningful as a broken promise. If the samurai bottom could compose themselves with patience and reflect upon the spirit of their loyalty, these common elements of the relationship can become spiritual tests to overcome, training for dignity and self-discipline.

(Of course, it goes without saying that the samurai top must strive to remember those special days and keep their promises!)

Together, top and bottom can be striving for a kind of perfection, knowing that it is unobtainable in life, but searching for it nonetheless.

A samurai bottom should be willing to be used in whatever manner their lord wishes, but a wise lord will use them well. It is important to note that the tradition carries a strong sense of pride, so although a samurai bottom will certainly be a footstool if that's what their top wants, it is probably best not to casually use such an arrangement in public, where they may be shamed by it. Not by the act itself, mind you, but by other people's perception of the act. Another important distinction.

The punishment of a samurai is a serious matter. Every kind of punishment is embarrassing, a blow to pride and to their status. There is much more advice to lords on how and when to discipline their retainers than to retainers about how to take it. (With dignity, son, with dignity.)

In a samurai gathering, should a lord grow angry and wish to humiliate their retainer, the dignity of that retainer while being rebuked or punished will be seen with pleasure. (Whereas a show of cowardice would be utterly embarrassing.) But in front of people who might think that your proud warrior was indeed a slave whose use was most appropriate as a footstool, such a command would demean the bottom and, by extension, the lord who ordered such a thing.

Samurai bottoms will always be looking for ways to be useful to their tops in public, behaving much like military orderlies, a companion with whom one does not chat or joke, an aide who is always ready with the coat, the door, the lighter, drink, or car. They will be instantly obedient to the oddest requests, and generally avoid distraction. And after an evening of service, the samurai will be grateful for having been given the chance to serve, and should not expect rewards, although a reward might be forthcoming. Hojo Shigetoki says:

"When one is serving officially...he should not think of a hundred people, or a thousand people, but only the importance of the master...To think of receiving the blessings of the master without fulfilling (one's) duties is no different from trying to cross a rough sea without a boat."

To sum up: a samurai bottom serves with pride and dignity, offering authentic service to a person who is deserving of it. They will seek out positions of honor through being useful, quick, even tempered, polite, and strong. They may expect to be improved by their service, to be challenged by it, and that they will be treated fairly and with respect.

They may also expect to learn how to top, whether that means the actual physical skills or the emotional and mental patterns which allow a person to be respected and followed. That is why I have also included the following section.

Samurai Top - Beyond Shogun

Many Japanese leaders, in their advice to heirs and other important members of their clans, provide excellent guidance for the would-be samurai top. For example:

"A leader with intelligence and a firm heart will be able to put others to use. People's ways are variant, and to use one to whom one has taken a liking for all things - for example, to use a military man for literary matters, or a man untalented in speech as a messenger, or a slow witted man where a quick wit is necessary - may bring about failure..." - Shiba Yoshimasa

This seems like common sense, yet it responds directly to a frequent situation in SM relationships, where a top tries to mold a bottom to a role or task for which they are not suited. The samurai top, knowing that their resources are limited and should be used to maximize their utility, will not waste time making a pet out of a warrior or a bodyguard out of a cook.

The samurai top is responsible for caring for the retainers in many ways, and their appearance and behavior reflects back onto their lord. That is why Imagawa Sadayo noted in his regulations:

"It is forbidden to be excessive in one's own clothing and armor while one's retainers go about shabbily."

But he was also careful about how he treated his retainers in matters of justice:

"It is forbidden to be indiscriminate of one's retainers good and evil actions and to distribute unjust rewards and punishments."

None of this "making up a reason to punish you" stuff for the samurai top. Punishments are punishments and rewards are rewards.

In theory, everything which belongs to the retainer belongs to their master, but the sages are strong in reminding future masters that they should never take advantage of this right. Asakura Soteki says:

"A master should not unreasonably make requests for the possessions of his retainers, such as their horses and falcons, or their swords...paintings...(etc.). Generally speaking, for retainers to possess valuable articles is the same as if their master possessed them. If in spite of that, however, the master still desires something, he should offer double its appropriate price..."

This reinforces the idea that the retainer has responsibilities and a life of their own. (And, incidentally, attracts a better class of retainers, who will collect such possessions and keep them in the clan for future generations.)

It is imperative that the samurai top be respected by the retainer; fear or worship would not be acceptable substitutions. In fact, almost all the leaders agree that one should worship the god(s)/Buddhas (depending on the age), and revere one's parents, but show abiding loyalty and respect toward one's lord. Soteki adds,

"It is not good to be feared by one's own retainers... It is fundamental to value one's retainers deep devotion."

Perhaps Kuroda Nagamasa had the most to say about the correct behavior of a leader. In his own Regulations, he describes what authority is and isn't:

"Generally speaking, the master...should discharge his duties with love and humanity, should not listen to slander, and should exercise the good...When one understands 'authority' to mean taking an attitude of intimidation toward everyone, acting in a high-blown manner even when meeting with the clan elders, using rough words for matters of no consequence at all, refusing to listen to the admonitions of others, persevering in one's own mistakes, and forcibly shoving through one's own opinions...he will likely be pulled along (a destructive path) by his own actions... What may be called true authority is brought about first in bearing oneself with the correct etiquette and in making clear the distinction between right and wrong, reward and punishment. If one will act this way, and be neither prideful nor intimidating toward others, the retainers and the common people will not respect him simply out of fear, or despise and make light of him, and he will be endowed with a natural authority."

Which is not to say that anger and fear-creating rages were not appropriate from time to time. The samurai is justified in losing cool over matters such as the desecration of shrines and over lack of respect paid to one's lord. Both samurai top and bottom might very well be known for an extreme sense of right and wrong, and the strength and will to stand up for what they believe is right regardless of what others might think or say. And just as the bottom will not sit quietly when disrespect is offered to their top, so will the top be mindful of the treatment of their retainer, for any insult offered to them is offered to the top. It's demanding, and it is rigid, and it's a code of honor which is (sadly) entirely lacking in much public congress. Shiba Yoshimasa, in The Chikubasho, notes that:

"A person's character and depth of mind may be seen by his behavior."

The samurai tradition, applied to an SM lifestyle, is a perfect forum from which to test and display one's character.

Notes:

A study of Zen principles would also benefit those who might want to try a samurai relationship, but there wouldn't be enough room to go into even the basics of Zen in these pages. You're on your own.

Books about the samurai tradition are not common; I utilized my local Asian bookstore until the clerks got tired of seeing me. Much of the writing is not easily accessible. Of course there's the *Book of The Five Rings*, and the *Art of War* (which is really Chinese, but had great influence not only in Japan, but in every "civilized" nation which makes war), and the romantic *Tale of the Genji*.

Westernized fiction about Japan (such as *Shogun*) isn't as bad a culture-defenders would have it, and if nothing else would be a good place to start. I owe a great deal of the quotes in this article to *Ideals of the Samurai*, by William Scott Wilson.

The Way of Heaven

      The Lady General, Asano Ochina, Mistress of the Four Provinces, Conqueror of the Battle of Kiyoshi and Special Retainer to the Lord of the Sunlit Isles, bowed her head down to the woven mat and held her position until the barely perceptible movement of her Lord's little finger. Although no one else in the room was permitted to keep their arms, her swords glittered from their polished scabbards on her back and in her sash.

      "I like this little," Lord Nuri sniffed, leaning delicately toward his companion Lord Kaneto. "This upstart peasant female owns the puissance of a lord twice her age and four times her breeding! The Prince is too much swayed by her."

      "Oh, yes, that is surely so," Lord Kaneto flirted back, lowering his eyes demurely.

      "And yet, she had served us well upon the fields of battle," interjected young Princess Asa, who was the Great Lord's adopted cousin. The three of them watched as the general's back straightened and she was acknowledged by her Lord. Her armor moved underneath layers of brightly colored woven and knotted silk, bands of crimson and gold overlaid with the crescent moon and clover symbol of the royal house. Her long black hair was bound behind her, and a wide band was wrapped around her forehead, battle style. No other fighter ever dared to enter the court dressed in such an outlandish way. Even the lowest ranking soldier knew to change into formal kimono and sandals. But not the Lady General.

      "Her victories only serve to make her more dangerous," Nuri snarled. "One day, she will rise up and betray the Lord, mark my words."

      "You are a fool," whispered the elderly Lord Senji. His bones creaked like armor when he shifted his posture so the younger retainers could hear his carefully modulated words. "You must observe everything,

76

else know nothing. Observe; does she not show him great deference in her every move, in her very choice of inflection and her every breath? Do her eyes never leave his person, ever following the plumes of his breath, her body taut with eagerness to obey? Does not the Great Lord always take his Lady General into private session after her report, in order to hear what is meant only for his ears? And does not the Great Lord always return from such meetings refreshed and full of strength?"

"This is so, Old Lord," the Princess murmured, "but what is it you are suggesting?"

"That the Great Lord is pillowing with his general?" Kaneto muffled a snicker. "Oh, surely not! With a commoner?"

"A further outrage!" Nuri hissed. "She will perhaps try to entice him into a dalliance!"

"You know that is impossible," Lord Senji chided. "Has not the Great Lord already accepted the Lady Echiko to be his wife? No, nothing can come of this, save the continued loyalty and love of his General." He glanced at the two of them conferring at the front of the room, oblivious to the surrounding audience of retainers, guards and petitioners. "No, children," the old man sighed, "there is no danger from the General. He has tamed her with his passion, bound her to him through his power. She loves our master and will serve him loyally to death."

Princess Asa nodded and turned her nose away from the gossiping lords, ignoring the slight curl of contempt in Kaneto's lips.

Lord Nuri straightened his own back and composed his handsome face. "She is a viper," he assured Kaneto.

"Oh, she surely is," Kaneto agreed.

"And finally, Lord, here are the agreements of the provincial governing lords, and their written oaths to you. They will arrive in the capital before the first snows to offer their obedience in person, and beg leave to present you with such gifts and tributes as you desire."

Ochina's voice was low and gravely, the voice of a woman long used to raising sound above the din of a battlefield. Her weathered face framed dark eyes, like pools of still water in moonlight. Even under the exaggerated wings of her formal battle armor, her shoulders looked broad and strong. Her hand, extending the rolled sheaf of papers to her lord, was brown and marked with winds, reins and hilts, and crisscrossed with old scars.

Lord Yoshinake took the scrolls with one clean, smooth and manicured hand. Although his palms and fingers were also marked by the sword, he had not seen battle from any position closer than scenic overlooks.

And why should he? He had been fortunate in finding and obtaining the service of the greatest general in the Isles, and with her strength and his wisdom had nearly succeeded in uniting all of the provinces and kingdoms as they were when the land was new. It was only a matter of time before he would become the first Emperor of the unified Sunlit Isles in centuries.

"We are pleased with our General," he intoned, nodding gravely. He was a young man still, barely into his third decade, a child when his father died and left him the swords and fan of the clan. His hair was ink black and swept up onto his head in the style favored by royalty, his cheeks clean and his skin pale and soft. But he was a serious and calculating lord, full of plans and insights, and he had earned the respect of his retainers.

"We shall now retire into privacy to hear that which is for our ears only," he said, nodding to the room. As one, his court bowed, and his bodyguards sprang up to make way for their lord. He rose while his court was still bowed into rows of colorful backs and smiled briefly at the sight of their heads all bobbing slightly above the floor. His general waited until her lord was walking to rise herself and followed him at the correct distance.

"A viper!" Nuri repeated.

"As you say," murmured Kaneto, fanning himself.

Yoshinake Tetsuo, Lord of the Sunlit Isles, Protector of the Shrines of Kiso, Bearer of the Sacred Regalia, and Prince of the Blood, immediately threw himself down onto his belly when the doors behind him slid shut. He lay there, trembling and quivering like a minnow trapped in a receding tidal pool as the sounds of his personal guard echoed away into the distance.

"You are so like a worm," Ochina commented.

"Oh, yes, my lady," he eagerly offered back, not daring to raise his head.

Ochina kicked him once, hard, catching him in the side, near his ribs. "You're forgetful, oh Prince."

"My general! My glorious general!"

"Do you know why you are like a worm, oh Prince?"

He stiffened and his fists tightened in the effort required to answer her. "I squirm upon the very earth before you, my general?"

Ochina kicked him again, this time catching him in the thigh. "No, you cretin. It is because you are blind, and useful only to catch greater prey. Speaking of which, have you accepted Echiko?"

"Yes, my general!" Eager to be recognized for doing something right, the Prince raised his head, just a little bit. "As you instructed me, my general! She arrives in sixteen days!"

"Good," Ochina murmured. She walked the length of the room, and shrugged her shoulders under the armor. "You may approach me, my royal wormling."

Tetsuo leaped to his feet and tried to contain himself as he crossed the mats to where she stood, rigid and waiting for his ministrations. Carefully, he untied the silk ribbons of her over mantle, and then the straps and ties of her body armor. With the ease of a man who has seen this done thousands of times and learned from the royal valets themselves, he acted the perfect personal servant. With a calm demeanor which did not betray his nervousness, he used his own stand to lay her armor aside, carrying each piece with care and delicacy.

"I remember when you lacked these skills," Ochina chuckled. "I suppose that you do have some use after all."

She turned toward him, her final layer between them the leather underpadding, soft with use where it was not stiff with repeated washings in sweat and blood. He blushed sweetly, like a girl, and she flicked one finger in his direction. With trembling fingers, Tetsuo carefully untied the knots which held the padding together, and without brushing her skin with his bare hands, drew it off.

Her hard body, brown where the layers of silk and armor failed to cover her and harder and pale where it did, made him moan, a tight sound barely held in check as he scurried to lay the padding down and return with a light cotton robe. He noted with familiar pangs of sympathetic pain her calluses and her scars, the bruises from her latest engagement and the white lines that mapped out past ones.

"You are a goddess," he murmured, slipping the cool cotton over her shoulders.

"Wormling," she snorted. "At least you can finally be left on your own. Show me your devotion, oh Prince." She seated herself on his mats, pulling one leg up in a vulgar fashion never displayed before such an august presence, and poured herself some of his wine. It had been a waste of time to have him serve it; he never could hear the musical tone of the liquid as it filled the small porcelain cup, and without that understanding, she might as well do it herself. In fact, the casual grace that she displayed in such a simple act shamed him even further. Peasants were not supposed to have such a touch for artistry.

But instead of dwelling on his faults, Tetsuo knelt before her and parted his own robes. His sash was heavy brocade, wound through with precious thread of gold, but he cast it aside without a thought and eagerly parted layers of silk to reveal his artfully folded loincloth. When he unwound it, his tumescent manhood, awakened since the first appearance of his goddess, stirred over the clean, round spheres that housed his future generations. But cast through the head of his royal cock was a device no household servant had seen.

It was a large ring, carved of ivory. It was not a complete circle, but gapped, leaving two points separated by a finger's width. The entire ring could be contained in the circle he made with his thumb and forefinger. On one end of the ring was a knob, carved from the original tusk, and depicting a chrysanthemum bud. The other end of the ring came to a sharp and narrow point. Covering the point now was a golden ball with a pin through it.

The ring actually went into his organ, through the little slit at the end. He remembered himself, bound for his own safety, his mind flooded with entreaties to his ancestors and all the gods (should they exist) that the pain would be endurable and that he would show no discomfort. He did his ancestors proud in that respect, although he privately doubted that many of them approved of the nature of the pain he endured. But that was not his fault; these were different times. It was no longer the custom of a Prince to actually do battle in the field. He must have his mettle tested in more esoteric endeavors.

Ochina had affixed this ornament herself, hammering the gold around the point with the edge of her chop. Tetsuo could have easily removed the appliance had he wished, but he could have never duplicated her own design in the soft gold if he marred it in any way.

The Lady General gazed at the displayed royal genitalia and nodded. "You have been good, my princeling," she said generously. "And you are still as pretty as a girl."

He beamed with pleasure, another thing his court never saw. "Thank you, my General!"

"Come closer," she commanded.

Eagerly, he shuffled forward, and displayed his pretty body for her pleasure. His bare chest shone with scented oils, his body was clean of the few hairs that grew when he did not order his barber to remove them. He was strong and healthy and in his prime, and the sedentary life at court did not prevent him from engaging in regular exercise with swords and bows, or long rides through the countryside, hunting and taking the air. His nipples seemed somewhat larger than those of other men, but that was also because of his goddess. Even now, she reached for them first, testing them with tight pinching and a light slap of her rough fingertips. Tetsuo sighed with pleasure.

"These shall have to be schooled again," she said softly. "They are unused to attention. I have brought with me wooden pegs which we shall employ later. Eventually, I shall have made matching rings, so that you may be decorated here as well."

Tetsuo opened his eyes and bit the inside of his lip. "My General...nothing would please me more...yet...my General surely knows...it will be very difficult for me to hide such rings! I will have to dismiss my dressers entirely, and forbid all from my bath, and never strip to the waist during competition!"

Ochina nodded, a slight smile on her lips. "Yes, that is true," she acknowledged. Her eyes flashed across his body appreciably. "But by that time, you will have already firmly established your... eccentricities. Your court will believe this to be some new fad of yours, and you will create fashion. It is already said in Jito-Myo that the most civilized of men will never bare their generative organs to less-than-equals." She smiled again and moved her fingers down to stroke the length of his shaft, which swelled at her touch. It was also clean and sweet smelling, the skin as smooth as heavy silk. She stroked it absently, like a pet, until it rose and jutted out, and Tetsuo sucked in a quick breath to prepare for the usual response to such behavior.

Her hand swept away from the royal cock and then back, slapping it sharply, so that it swung to one side, striking his upper thigh and rebounding back. Tetsuo ground his teeth, but stayed still, his muscles tense. She slapped him again for good measure, and he arched his back slightly, appeasing her by offering her yet more.

"My princeling," she chuckled warmly. She returned to sipping at the wine, watching him recover, his flesh pulsating with power and desire, and his body betraying nothing of the minor pain she had caused him.

Together, they breathed in the rich scent of power. When it began to dissipate, Ochina sighed and shook her head. "Unbraid my hair," she said, pouring more of the wine. Tetsuo crawled behind her and began to undo the practical windings of her hair with gentle and skilled fingers.

"My General," he ventured, as he reached for the second braid, "your miserable servant has...a concern."

"Yes?" There was just an edge of impatience in her voice.

"The Lady Echiko..." He faltered, despite having practiced a myriad of methods for approaching this delicate subject. "She is to be my wife..."

Ochina chuckled again. "Yes, my worm-prince, she shall. And therefore, we will have to remove your special ring so that you may present her with your royal bratlings. But it will return as soon as your princely duties are done."

Tetsuo sighed and brightened immediately. "Then...you shall meet me before and after each visit to the lady?"

"At first. Until Echiko learns herself how to remove and apply it."

Tetsuo's fingers fumbled and he drew them out of her hair in panic. "My General?"

81

"Finish what you are doing, you fool. That will cost you many stripes later." As his trembling fingers returned to working out the weaving of her tresses, she smiled, knowing that he couldn't see her face. How delightful it was to surprise him! Even the wise Prince could not possibly guess all of the twists and mysteries of her imagination. She hardened her voice, for her pleasure and his. "Were you so foolish to think that after capturing your manhood myself I would allow you to exercise it elsewhere? No, my prince, you are mine, from the moment I first held you down and opened you, to the day you leave this world and go to meet your ancestors."

"B-but...Echiko!"

"She will learn to keep you," Ochina stated. "I shall teach her myself. Echiko and I have...met before." She coughed out a laugh, a low sound like the growling of a caged hunting cat, and she could actually feel the trembling of Tetsuo's fingers as he realized the whole of this new chapter in his tale.

"I am sure she will be amenable to your situation," Ochina continued. "In sixteen days, when she arrives, you will send her at once to me, and I shall teach her how to properly train you, use you, and keep you obedient and pleasing."

"But what shall I tell my court? That is most irregular!" Tetsuo's panic had grown considerably.

"Bear yourself like a man, you excrement of turtles," Ochina snapped. "You will tell your royal bottom kissers that the Lady requires training in arms, as a good warlord's wife should have and that since you have the greatest female fighter in the world at your service, you shall use her to instruct your wife. Ten days from her arrival, you will set the date for your marriage...I have decided that the fifth day of the Month of the Falling Blossoms will be auspicious for the wedding."

Tetsuo's mouth fell open in amazement, and he buried his attention to his task, running his shaking fingers through her hair until it shone in waves of shimmering ink. Oddly, his mind fastened upon the word auspicious, and he wondered if his General had actually consulted the appropriate astrologers. Then, he remembered the astonishing revelation about his future bride, and scampered on his knees back in front of her, where he bowed deeply.

"Most honored General," he whispered, his forehead touching the surface of the mat. He held the position, his back muscles tense with the strain of the formal posture. "Your worthless slave begs for your attention!"

The Lady General gazed down on the bow that his back made. It was strong, bent like a cedar limb under great weight, an expanse of wheat blown over by a southern wind. She could see the faint lines she had once drawn with bamboo rods, broken across that expanse, tearing flesh and marking him the way everything she did marked him forever. Ah, but that had been magnificent! To indulge their drives so strongly that blood flew between them and the very earth rumbled with pleasure in their frenzy. But it had been some time since they had such freedom.

"You need to be taken," she said finally, her voice strangely soft. "You need to be held, like a girl child before pillowing, an old man before dying. It is not seeming that I, a descendant of peasants, be your Lady, so there must be another. And Echiko is suitable. She is amenable. And you will show her all the honor the wife of an Emperor deserves and she will be your taker, and your keeper."

The Lord of The Sunlit Isles shook as he raised his head to gaze at his beloved General. His lovely eyes were bright with devotion, but his face was composed properly, his lips parted only slightly. "This crawling one is overwhelmed by his General's forethought and generosity," he whispered. "But he fears for the loss of his one true master. He begs that the General reconsider. Please do not leave this broken one to the hands of a child!"

"You know the tones very well, my princeling," Ochina admitted, leaning forward. "And you flatter me with them. But do not fear; Echiko may be a child, but she is no novice to the use of a man such as you. Did you believe that I would cast you into the care of an incompetent? That I would abandon my ruler to the whims of a mere girl? Oh no, my Prince. Echiko and I have already planned what shall become of you. And there are many more years in these scarred limbs of mine, many more battles to your honor and power and glory before the gods (if they exist). Before I go to face my ancestors, I will be assured that you will be astride the Dragon Throne and surrounded by little grubs of royal birth to carry the swords when you have returned to me in the Other Kingdoms."

Tetsuo bowed his head again in mute acceptance, and shivered as she drew her fingers along his jaw.

"My princeling," she murmured, patting his cheek and smoothing her hand over his warrior's knot. "I will serve you unto death and beyond. Come to me, my worm, my dog, my soon-to-be Emperor, and please me. Perhaps if you do, I shall permit you to achieve clouds and rain tomorrow, or the day after. And perhaps I will not." She sighed and leaned back and parted the light robe she wore. "Come to me, my great Lord."

And like the princely worm he was, Tetsuo crawled forward, to the divided thighs of The Lady General, Asano Ochina, Mistress of the Four Provinces, Conqueror of the Battle of Kiyoshi and Special Retainer to him.

Note: I really like the name Tetsuo, OK?

One Drop

(Previously unpublished, first read for a FIST camping trip.)

Joyce stretched her arms up and clasped the chains in exasperation. Behind her, Rina continued her sweeping motions, trailing the soft tresses of the whip up and down Joyce's shoulders, back and forth in a slow-motion figure eight pattern. It was very nice, sensual, slightly teasing. It was a practiced move, one that several pillows on their couch had become familiar with.

It was boring as hell.

Joyce flexed her shoulders and back muscles and leaned slightly back, into the falling tresses. "Yesss," she hissed encouragingly. "Please, please, more…"

"What?" Rina immediately lowered the whip and stepped forward to hear better.

Dammit! Joyce bit her lip in an effort to keep from snapping. "Harder, Rina, please?"

"Oh! OK, baby - we'll turn up the heat a little." Rina obligingly did so, taking several careful aiming swipes before setting herself into another pattern. Now, the fall was more of a tender slapping that lightly tapped the skin instead of sliding over it.

It's very hard, Joyce thought bitterly, to have a top who's a bigger wus than you are. She set herself against the easy to undo bondage and tried to enjoy the sensations while fighting back the wave of guilt that swept right alongside them.

Back when the flavor of the day was vanilla, they never had this problem. They made love the way they felt best, wrestling playfully on Rina's big platform bed, swapping kisses on a lazy afternoon on the couch, grinding against each other on a crowded dance floor. They were pretty creative for a couple who did not own the *Joy of Lesbian Sex*, or even subscribe to *On Our Backs*, and their years together served to mellow them into a steady fondness for each other instead of sending them headlong into a case of lesbian bed death.

And then, Rina went to an SM workshop at Michigan - just out of curiosity, she said - and came back with a glint in her eye and a strip torn off her t-shirt. That night, she blindfolded Joyce and laid her down under the moonlight and whispered outrageous, dangerous, monstrous - and sinfully wonderful things to her. And made love to her, like that, naked on the grass, forceful and tender all at once.

It was love at first surrender for Joyce. Being held down and whispered to, being stroked but forbidden to come, having her lover close but being denied the right to touch her - it made her feel like she'd just discovered sex for the first time. She had moaned out loud, and made fists and pounded them against the ground, and every touch granted her was electrically charged. By the time Rina sat astride her, cunt to cunt, she was like an animal, dumb with passion and greed, with nothing but a primal hunger that made her buck and writhe until the two of them were covered with scents and tastes from both of their bodies. Until they both collapsed onto the ground, panting and sighing and holding each other until the hammering of their hearts settled.

And then, Rina started to buy the books.

Because unlike the sex they had worked out between them, this was now S&M - a complex style of interaction which had rules and regulations that must be followed, instructions to learn, codes to decipher. Together, they pored over the sexuality shelf at the local queer bookstore, and Rina selected one title after another for her newfound interest. And Joyce was in heaven - surely, this would open the door to a whole new way of having sex - and a very exciting one at that!

But as Rina studied, the actual practice became - different.

"We didn't negotiate that night," she said. "That was my fault, I didn't know enough. From now on, we have to be sure you want me to top you, and I need to know what you might like to do. Here, fill out these forms, that should be fun."

Fun was an odd word for filling out forms. But if Rina needed them, Joyce was willing to put her time in. She studied the long list of potential activities with curiosity, and noticed that several of their favorite activities seemed to be missing, so she added them at the bottom. Then, she went through the list, checking off things that turned her on, things that sounded strange, things that were out of the question. When she turned the sheets in, she grinned and winked suggestively. hoping that Rina would be up to trying some new stuff out that night. But instead, they had a discussion.

"When you say that you're not into humiliation but you do like dirty talk, does that mean we can use words like fuck and cunt, but you don't want to be called a cunt?" Rina asked, sliding her glasses up her nose. "I don't want to hurt your feelings, you know, I want you to enjoy this."

"Jeeze, Rina, I don't know! I mean, calling me a cunt might be OK, I guess, as long as you weren't pissed at me. It's just playing - call me whatever you want to!" Joyce grabbed the latest book and examined the pages suspiciously. "It's just a word."

"Yeah, but people can be funny about words," Rina said strongly, taking the book back. "I just want to be safe. And you want to be safe, too, don't you?"

"Yeah," Joyce sighed. "OK, Rina, you're the boss."

"Well actually," Rina said eagerly, swelling with newfound knowledge, "you're the boss. I'm not going to do anything to you that you don't want."

"OK! Let's screw. Right now."

Rina grinned and tossed the book over the side of the bed. "OK!" she giggled, hitting the light. And so they did - screw, that is. No one on top, and no dirty words either. It was very, very safe.

From there, things got even more complicated. Apparently, they couldn't just do this stuff, they had to connect with other women who did it too. And that was OK, at least it put them in contact with people who had made some pretty nifty toys, some of which found their way into the top dresser drawer nearest to the bed. The first item was a comfortable blindfold - the next was a pair of expensive but comfortable wrist cuffs, all in black leather. And the third was the whip.

It was made of nylon, lavender nylon, looped and fixed into a short rubber handle. Joyce privately thought it looked like a threadbare pom-pom, but she rarely got to see it anyway, so that didn't matter. What mattered was the way Rina was so painfully careful never to actually hurt Joyce with the dreadful little thing - which meant that Joyce tended to get bored real fast.

Discussions rarely served to do anything more than get Rina to be just a teensy bit more rough from session to session, after which she'd fall back to her softer, safer practices with relief. Joyce actually found herself watching two other women playing at a party and thinking about approaching the top. The pain of that internal wandering made her stick to Rina like glue for several days, but that was only a temporary measure. She had to do something - and soon. But she had no idea what. Please, she begged inwardly - harder, harder! Dammit, scare me, hurt me, I can take it! Make me cry, make me choke, make me beg you to stop and then keep going! What do I have to do to bring out the serious player in you??

Rina helped lift Joyce's arms up so that the cuffs and attached chains fell from the hooks they had driven into the bedroom doorway. Joyce really didn't need the help, she had practically fallen out of the cuffs on several occasions. It was a safety thing - the bottom had to be able to free herself in case the top suffered an instantly fatal heart attack. There had even been a book about such an occurrence.

Rina was humming as she put toys away. Joyce reached for the cuffs blind; she knew the buckles well enough to free them without taking the blindfold off. It was a little game she played with herself, keeping herself in the dark as long as possible, pretending she was a prisoner, a slave, a captive, anything but the lover who was supposed to turn around with a grin and kiss her beaming top and skip off to the kitchen for a snack - Damn!

Her fingers slipped, and the inside of her hand scraped against the edge of the buckle. She felt the sharp pain, and then a spreading warmth, and knew that she'd cut herself. "Shit!" she said out loud, raising her hand to her mouth. She was about to push the blindfold up, when Rina's touch on her shoulder made her jump.

Rina's fingers were very cold.

"What are you doing?" Rina whispered. Her voice was low, almost as though she was trying to make it sound mysterious. Joyce smiled and raised her wounded hand.

"Look what I did," she said, waving it. "Better check the book!"

There was silence for a moment, and Joyce wondered if Rina was shocked by the sight of blood. She brought her hand down again, reaching for the blindfold, and Rina caught it, held it in one tight fist.

"Yesss," Rina said, another harsh whisper. "I see what you have done. How evil of you to shed your own blood - blood which belongs to me."

Joyce stiffened and shivered. Rina's fingers were cold and hard against her wrist, and her mouth was hot behind her throat. How scary it seemed! She could feel the thundering of her heart, and listen to the way her own breath had become so shallow!

She's trying to scare me, Joyce thought with another shiver. How wonderful!

"Yes," she quickly said, falling into role. "Yes, I was bad."

"You will atone for this."

"Yes!" Joyce hung her head in mock shame.

"Yes, My Lady." The words came out flat, as though Rina was trying them out, and before Joyce could eagerly echo them, she felt a heavy blow against her back that sent her crashing into the doorjamb. She stumbled over the tangle of chains on the floor and landed hard on her knees, slightly dazed by both the force and the attack itself. That was certainly no technique recommended in a book!

"What-" she managed to get out before there was a tight fist in her hair.

"You will address me as My Lady, you slattern. Come and present your worthless body to me."

Joyce felt the pressure drag her away from the frame, and she cried out in pain as she was dragged into the bedroom. She tried to disengage the hand in her hair, but Rina's grip was like a steel bar, and every twisted movement caused streaks of stiletto sharp pain through her scalp. She was released, no, thrown forward, into the open space before the bed, and in an instant, Rina's hands had gripped hers again, and were busy affixing the cuffs together. They had never done that before - it would be too difficult for Joyce to free herself that way.

Deep inside her, Joyce felt a stab of powerful, indescribable, twisted pleasure. She wanted to scream, wanted to beg, wanted to shout out, what the fuck are you doing?! But she also knew that in the minute since she had cut her hand, she had gotten more wet and more painfully aroused than during the entire hour long beating and teasing Rina had bothered to do.

Better she should have started here, Joyce thought wickedly. But no - she meant this as a surprise! She moaned out loud.

"Slut." The word came out like a caress, but there was nothing soft behind it. Rina's fingers roughly pushed Joyce's legs apart, and thrust sharply into the cleft between them. The chuckle that escaped her lips was like nothing Joyce had ever heard from her gentle lover before. It was mockingly cruel.

"What a whore, to beg for pain, to beg for degradation," Rina's strange, new whisper continued. "Did you not think I would hear you? Did you not think someone would hear your pathetic pleas for suffering?"

"I'm sorry," Joyce gasped, unable to think of what else to say.

The fingers within her withdrew, and turned, and grasped the tender flesh of her labia and pulled, harshly. Joyce gasped in a new breath and made a whining sound that she could scarcely believe came from her throat.

"You are a sorry thing indeed," Rina hissed. "To forget how to address the one who came at your call."

Oh Jesus, right, Joyce thought. "My Lady!" she quickly amended. "I'm sorry, My Lady!"

"No, I think not. Not yet, as I breathe. But you shall be."

As the voice rose away from her, Joyce took another deep breath and ground her hips into the carpet. Damn, but Rina was good! And I like the style of language, too, she thought contentedly. All formal and everything. God, this is hot - I wonder why she waited so long...

And then, her thighs seemed to be splashed with a burning acid!

"Jesus Christ!" she screamed.

Rina's answer was a dry chuckle. "You do yourself no good to call upon a power to rival me, sorry creature. You only prolong your chastisement - and my entertainment. Pray, continue. Amuse me in your suffering, and I shall be merciful."

There was warning this time - something cool and snaky lay across Joyce's thighs and then rose away. When it came down again, it was that same sensation of being hit with a line of burning pain - a cutting, sizzling, sharp pain that drove sounds that had to be screams from Joyce's throat.

Steadily, these lines of agony worked their way up her body, covering the backs of her thighs and then finally landing on her ass. And staying there, over and over, until she was rocking on her belly, squirming, pulling her legs up, trying desperately to get away.

Safeword, she thought. I have a safe word. It's - red! No, yellow! She screamed again, and twisted as the weapon hit her high on one hip, and felt Rina kick her, sharply, rolling her over onto her back.

"Since you seem to wish it," Rina whispered. And chuckled again. Joyce panted, and worked her mouth to try to breathe normally, but the breath was knocked from her lungs by one of those awful strikes, right across her abdomen. And across her rib cage...and up, up...

The first one to cross her breasts didn't even get a scream. It drove Joyce into a silent mania, where not only did she lack the breath to react, but the shock shook her directly into panic. She tore at her cuffs - why the hell did she think they were easy to release? She threw her body to the side, squirming, crawling, anything to get away from that terrible pain!

And then Rina was on top of her, laughing, pinning her down. "You are mine," she snapped, and the sound of her voice was raw and triumphant. "You try to get away, but I know you too well, dear slut. Shall I show you?"

The chill fingers once again returned to that triangle between Joyce's legs, and what would have been a scream became a wail of despair as they sank into a flowing wetness that gave betraying testimony to Joyce's impossible arousal. They dipped and penetrated, two, then three, then four, and Joyce gasped as she felt herself stretching wide, welcoming those icy invaders.

"You would take all of me and all I commanded to use you, and still cry for more," Rina taunted. "I could bare you before a host and still you would yearn for my voice, my touch, the pain only I can give you!"

"Oh God, oh Jesus, yes, yes, My Lady, yes!" Joyce shook in tremors of shame and ecstasy, images called up from Rina's teasing making her buck her hips up, enveloping Rina's fingers, hungry for them. When they withdrew violently, scraping her, she wailed again, and when her wail was stopped by the forceful slamming of those wet, oozing fingers into her mouth, she came.

It was like being sucker punched - there was no warning, no preparation. It was just like her entire lower body compressed around her aching and wounded clit, and she bucked and gagged on the jabbing, punching fingers, and breathed in the scent and taste of her own essence. She moaned, and licked, and panted and clutched her legs together, aware of every muscle and joint in her body.

"You are a cat in season, a vixen to be mounted," Rina said, an amused edge to her voice. "There is no pain I can force upon you, no moment of anguish which will lessen your slavish devotion to your own destruction. And I shall destroy you, my sweet victim. In time."

Joyce blabbered, "Yes, yes, My Lady, yes," and fell back, shuddering as the cool fingers wiped themselves off on her breasts. Her nipples ached. Her wrists throbbed. Every line on her body seemed edged with fire.

And then, there was silence.

It took her about ten minutes to remember how to undo the clip which joined the cuffs. She sat up slowly, carefully, waiting to hear another word from Rina, a giggle, a growl, a tiny little, "was that what you wanted?" But nothing came. Finally, she pushed the blindfold up and off and saw that Rina was on the bed, face down and breathing as though she was asleep!

Wow, Joyce thought, trembling as she struggled to her feet. Must have knocked her out to do all that role-playing! Quietly, she made her way into the bathroom, where she stood in front of the mirror and examined her marks.

Now, this was something to boast about! Her legs and ass and even her chest and belly were all marked with angry red stripes, unlike anything she ever had before. Well - not that she'd been marked before. She looked like someone had ridden her hard - and she swelled with inner pride and contentment.

How do you like that? she thought, wiping herself down. I was ready to give up on her, and she was preparing all of this! God, I love that woman.

She went to bed and cuddled up close. Rina's hands were nice and warm now - she was probably so nervous while she was playing that she was driving herself bonkers, Joyce thought. That's OK - I'll assure her tomorrow that this was the BEST SM we ever did.

But the next day, the marks were gone, and Rina seemed surprised when Joyce got effusive over breakfast. At first, she was glad that Joyce had such a good time. But when Joyce mentioned how wonderful the "new attitude" was, and where did Rina hide the new whip, there was only puzzlement and a moment of confusion.

Rina insisted that she had done no role-playing at all.

And there was no new whip.

She's still playing, Joyce thought nervously. I can go along with it.

"Never mind," she said, buttering her last piece of toast. "I guess I was working up a really hot fantasy in my mind."

"That's great," Rina immediately said, nodding. "That's really healthy."

The next time they played, Joyce stood impatiently through the gentle warm-up and the teasing and the swishy feeling of the lavender whip, and then waited for My Lady to come out and play. But she didn't make even a token appearance - Rina worked her way up to where she felt comfortable, and let Joyce down from the cuffs as usual, and they went to bed, one satisfied and one thoroughly confused.

The next day, Rina once again insisted that she never, ever played any kind of role with Joyce, especially one that required a title. "We haven't negotiated that," she said petulantly.

My Lady didn't make another appearance for two months. And in that time, Joyce went back and forth wondering if she had in fact made up the whole thing, or if maybe Rina felt so bad about it that she had instantly forgotten the incident. But late at night, when Rina was asleep and Joyce awake and horny, the sound of Rina's harshly whispered voice, and the chilled feel of her slender fingers came back to her, and in the dark and the silence, Joyce touched herself and moaned in the memory.

Hurt me, she silently begged, spreading her legs carefully, pinching her own nipples. Frighten me, take me, please My Lady, please.

But there was no answer.

The answer came when Rina had Joyce spread out on their bed. Joyce tugged against the bonds and felt them give and relaxed back in her eternal frustration. Always the same...

"You're all mine tonight," Rina giggled. It was the closest she came to role-playing since the appearance of My Lady. "I can do whatever I want."

"Hurt me, Rina," Joyce said out loud. "Please, I need it so bad - I want it from you so much!"

The answer was a pinch of one nipple - sharp enough to make Joyce gasp, but not hard enough to make her cry out. "I'll do what I want to," Rina said happily. "And you can't do anything about it."

That's for sure, Joyce thought, enduring yet another hour of teasing and pleasure and gentle torments. The worst moment came when she found herself actually faking an orgasm - how embarrassing, and how sad! - just to end the scene. She went to the bathroom, leaving Rina to clean up, and stared at herself in the mirror. There were no marks, no bruises, no cuts...

It happened when I cut myself on the cuff, she thought crazily.

Now what made me think of that? was the very next thought. I'm bad, if I'm thinking up magical tops.

But the shaving razors were right there on the shelf. It would be so easy to make a tiny little cut...

She moved without thinking. The plastic handle turned in her fingers as she figured a way to expose more of the blade. If there was a rational voice in her, it was buried by the frustration and hurt and guilt that tumbled around her brain like dice in a cup. She turned her left hand around, and pressed the blade against the swell of flesh behind her thumb. At first, it didn't seem like she had managed to cut her skin. Then, as she twisted her hand to look, the flesh parted and a little thread of rosy moisture beaded up and out, to trail across her hand.

Hurt me, frighten me, take me, please, she thought, watching the blood move sluggishly out from between the skin. Please, My Lady, please.

She was struck the minute she walked out the door, blotting her hand and feeling foolish. Her head snapped once, hard, and connected with the wall, and then she was dragged back into cold arms, against a cold body, and she relaxed, and sighed even as she whimpered and fell into the embrace of My Lady.

"Idiot wench, to keep me waiting so long," the voice that was Rina's and not-Rina's said. "You will beg me to end your pain before I have yet begun to show you your errors. You will crawl on your belly and wash my feet with your tears before I leave you to your pathetic existence."

"Thank you," Joyce cried, looking up into Rina's eyes. That was a mistake.

Because they were not Rina's eyes. Rina's eyes were soft and hazel and round and they needed glasses. These eyes, the eyes of My Lady, were hard and cold, like green fire, with dark slivers of pupil that were elongated like a cat's, and when they locked onto Joyce's eyes, they hit her with the force of whip and threw her down, hard, onto her knees.

Joyce felt something give way inside of her, and barely knew that she was pissing down her own thighs. All she knew was that Rina was not there - and someone - something - else was.

"Thank me for attending to your hungers, my naked, yearning toy. Thank me for not tearing you apart for forcing me to wait upon your pleasure. And thank me for the pains you will beg for, and the ones you will beg freedom from. You will utter nothing save thanks to me tonight."

And trembling, shaking, Joyce inched forward and kissed the top of a cold, cold foot, and let her tears of terror drop onto it. When the hand came down again, she cried out in what might have been a protest, but soon turned into a sound much closer to ecstasy.

Joyce woke at noon, and wondered why she had not gotten up for work. She moved, and knew. And lay still, afraid to move again, until she was sure she was alone. Then, she carefully made her way from the bedroom to the bathroom, and looked into the mirror.

A horrifying sight gazed back. Her hair was a twisted mass of tangles, and she knew that it had been wet with blood and cum and piss when she finally collapsed into her fitful sleep. One of her eyes was blackened and swollen - and she recalled the moments of kissing and licking the hand that struck her, another series of desperate expressions of gratitude that forced her lower and lower, until she could do nothing but whine and squirm.

Terribly, she felt her cunt respond to the memory. Her nipples were tight in their twin erections, despite being covered with scabs and bruises - one line of bite marks went entirely up her right shoulder. Several red lines were still on her thighs - feeling behind her, she could feel the cuts on her ass as well.

This time, My Lady had left lasting souvenirs.

What am I going to do? Joyce asked herself, sitting on the toilet seat in shock. I can't let Rina see me like this, she'll wonder what the hell happened!

But what the hell did happen?

I thought that cutting myself would make her come - and it did. And I don't think for one minute that was Rina - it was something else.

Something inhuman.

She groaned out loud. Inhuman in many, many ways. Not only in the way she took over the sweet young woman who was Joyce's lover, but in what she did, and how she did it. Inhuman in the casual way she wielded pain and terror, inhuman in the way she laughed at agony and flicked ecstasy into being without a moment of attention. Inhuman in the way she always knew when to stop one particular pain and begin with another - like when she finally stopped whipping Joyce and attacked her with long fingernails instead, or stopped biting long enough to bury Joyce's face in her icy loins, laughing again as Joyce struggled to breathe, struggled to please.

Joyce groaned again, and resisted the urge to touch herself, She turned the shower on full blast, and as she stepped under the needle spray, had a physical memory of My Lady leaning over her, cold fingers locked around Joyce's throat, whispering, "Your life is mine, sweet slut, mine to take, mine to give" She sank to her knees in erotic agony and under the pounding water, she touched herself and came, screaming herself hoarse, giving herself to My Lady once again.

She told Rina that she hit herself in the eye with a door, and undressed in the bathroom, and tried not to think. Tried to work, to eat, to go through the motions of living. But every time her mind wandered, her body would recall another cold touch, another harsh blow, another soft breath - and she would tremble with need and ache with desire and freeze in terror. She shook her head the next time Rina offered to play, and Rina nodded in her understanding way.

I could control her, Joyce thought one day. I can call her up once in a while, maybe once a month. No, every other month. And then, I could have - that - and still have what I always had before. It doesn't hurt Rina, at least it doesn't seem to.

Jesus Christ, what am I thinking! It's a fucking monster, and I want it to inhabit my girlfriend, because it gets me off!

I don't know whether I'm the monster or My Lady is, she thought miserably.

No solution suggested itself. Rina was slightly confused by Joyce's continued resistance to SM play, but they went to bed and held each other and loved each other the way they used to, and that was more than enough. If Rina didn't realize that Joyce was thinking of a much colder embrace, or a much harsher way of pleasure, then so much the better. Joyce jerked off almost compulsively, fighting off the powerful urges to shed her own blood that came upon her like waves that could easily sweep her away. But the images never went away. In her dreams, she tasted the musky sweat of My Lady, so much sharper than Ria's sweet saltiness. In moments of reverie, she felt the scratch of My Lady's long, sharp talons along her back, so unreal next to Rina's carefully trimmed fingernails. She found herself shivering and sensing the warmth of piss when rain splattered the roof, and tensing with the thought of another blow across her back when she leaned against a wall.

I have to do something, she thought.

Hurt me, fuck me, take me, scare me. She gave herself to her pleas, and drew the edge of the blade against the inside of her arm. Come to me, My Lady, and take what is yours.

"You do not learn quickly, my wicked slut - or is it that you desire my wrath as much as you have begged for my whims of pain and pleasure?"

Joyce didn't look, couldn't bear to see those eyes again. "I am unworthy, My Lady," she said, already terrified. There was a chill in the very air that night, as though the creature inhabiting Rina's body was bringing a rising mist with it. Joyce's heart felt like it was beating against her ribs. She clutched at her bleeding arm, sliding her hand across the blood. "Please - help me."

"I shall," My Lady whispered. "Crawl to me, pitiful little baggage, and make your reverence."

It didn't matter what Joyce had planned to do. She dropped the knife and let it clatter to the floor and she dropped beside it, aching, dripping blood and arousal. It was useless to try to fight My Lady. She had to surrender, had to give herself to her.

She kissed the black length of ice and flame that appeared with My Lady and kissed the hand that held it. She opened her mouth to the butt of the thing, allowing it to plunder her lips and throat until she choked and gagged and was slammed to her belly to atone for her shameful display of incompetence. She writhed in pain, and rolled for caresses both profound and profane, and lifted her breasts, her hips, her loins for pain and sharp pleasures.

And when finally, My Lady pinned her and rode her, Joyce took all of her strength and used it to please, to satisfy, to work at pleasure until she couldn't breathe, couldn't think - and she knew when My Lady moved to caress her throat again, that there was truly death in those cold hands, those once gentle hands that belonged to the oh-so-serious intellectual who still loved to giggle and drink chocolate milk and snuggle under flannel sheets on winter nights. And Joyce opened her eyes again to those terrible fire-green eyes, and cried out a long, despairing cry that My Lady drank like she drank tears and terrors and exhalations of agony. The sight, the sensation of being so taken and devastated, worked on Joyce like the magic it was, and her body exploded yet again in a terrible orgasm that wrenched her like a doll, tearing at her joints and muscles in spasm after spasm.

Then, unbound for once, since she had so completely surrendered to My Lady, Joyce reached up and pulled that cold flesh closer. My Lady grinned a feral grin and licked her lips and exposed those evil, triangular teeth, eager to savage, eager to tear - but Joyce bit her first.

It was difficult, fixing her teeth into the throat of her lover - which was why she had to look into My Lady's eyes once again. Exhausted, wrung out, aching, Joyce caught a fold of flesh and bit down, hard - and twisted her neck.

My Lady growled and spat, and heaved backward, pulling Joyce up with her. But Joyce locked her arms around her body and held on, even though she was wracked with agony from the second her teeth met My Lady's flesh. Twice more, My Lady pulled back, and each time, her hands dug into Joyce's body, slashing and tearing ragged wounds that bled and burned.

But Joyce held on - and broke through. She tasted the sweetness and the heat of blood in her mouth and sucked it in, feeling it run over her teeth.

"Mine!" she shouted, over the roaring and crashing of the creature above her. "I sent for you; I send you away!"

My Lady broke away, her eyes wide with surprise. She lifted an elegant hand to the dripping blood from the wound and her lips curled back in distaste. "Fool!" she spat. "I will always be with you!"

And then, those terrifying eyes rolled back, and Rina's entire body became limp and fell across Joyce's. They two of them lay there for quite some time, both of them bleeding. It took almost an hour before Joyce felt like she could move again.

Joyce blindfolded Rina one night, and frightened her and hurt her and pleasured her, and Rina at last admitted that she really wanted to be a bottom, and at last they started having good SM-sex. And if Joyce chose not to use a single lash, or to do cuttings, why no one thought it odd - she was, after all, a highly respected top in all other areas.

But there are nights when she goes out alone, and even her lovely slave Rina can't tell you where she goes. But it is true that in the darkened clubs and alleys where the polite leatherfolk never go, there is a new Lady on the prowl, an expert at cutting you down with her whip or her tongue. They say she has a taste for blood - but no one can really say, because no one speaks of her who has actually met her.

The Little Urban-maid

(Originally printed in *Once Upon a Time*, edited by Michael Ford.)

Far, far from the skylines of Manhattan, where the roads stretch dark and twisted like squid ink fettuchini, there, where no public transportation enables you to go, there, in the chain of towns all ending in -bay, or -port, live the sub-urban people. So far from the towers and spires of the City, you would have to lay many Long Island Railroad trains, one after another, before you could even reach their carpooling parking lots.

Now, you must not think that the neighborhoods so far from the center of the City are desolate and barren. No, there are the sprawling green lawns of those who don't know how to start a lawn mower and will never have to learn. There are many beautiful and well-groomed plants and trees, all grown to satisfy the purest of landscape technical designers. Big cars and small tour through the twists and turns of the roads, eagerly seeking out the immense, glamorous acres of pure capitalism known as Malls. And here, in this sub-urban area, the Fish King has built his castle. Or rather, his six bedroom split-level ranch, with a two car garage, finished basement, and guaranteed genuine redwood deck.

Sol Goldman, the Fish King, (for so his trucks read, on the side - Smoked Fish to Crown Every Table!) had been a widower for many years. His mother kept the house for him, a proud, intelligent woman whose only fault was an over fondness for pearls, which everyone forgave her for. She took excellent care for the six - count 'em! - six daughters that the estimable Mrs. Goldman, (deceased) had borne, and raised them to be good little girls and fine young women, and cast them out into the world one at a time, to seek their fortunes.

The youngest of these daughters was the most different. She was the boldest, whose journeys took her farthest away from the lovely house and gardens that were perfectly acceptable for her older sisters. She alone sulked and protested when given new and pretty clothes to wear, and was the one most often found in the middle of scrapes and messes and complex arrangements of neighbor children that had all the local parents wondering if therapy might be an option. But she was still a good girl - she was neither disobedient nor willfully cruel. And she was very, very smart.

All of the little princesses loved to hear their Grandmama tell tales of the lives elsewhere - in Big Cities, and in Other Countries, where there were many other people doing jobs the princesses couldn't imagine, and having adventures which seemed dubious at best. But alone among them, the littlest princess loved the stories from her Tante Ester, who visited rarely and cackled and laughed and made cryptic comments which made Grandmama blush and the Fish King bluster, but left the little princesses confused. Tante Ester lived alone - or so they said - and far away, in the reaches of Brooklyn, a place Grandmama was very firm about. It was Not Safe. It was Not a Place for Princesses.

But when Tante Ester came, she brought stories not of someone else's life, but of her own. Stories of late night shopping and dancing until dawn. Stories of exotic foods and strange places, all full of new words that the littlest princess gobbled up like sweets. The little princess knew that she would be going to these places, eating these things, dancing until dawn. And she knew something else, too.

She wouldn't be doing those things with any damn fool boy, either.

For that was what was expected of her and her older sisters. One at a time, as they turned the magical age of eighteen, they were decked in their finest new designer garments and given the freedom to seek out the companionship of young men, princes, to be sure, who would then squire them around, providing transportation and meals and entertainment in the hopes of a cuddle and a peck on the cheek. (Not to mention a nice job working in the Fish King empire and a very fancy wedding and a brand new split-level ranch house should the proper princess pronounce them acceptable.)

Each princess went forth and returned, bearing tales of her adventures and making her younger sisters turn positively green with envy. And of them all, the youngest most wanted to venture beyond the sub-urban world. Of course, she was also the one who waited the longest before she could go. She could watch it all on TV - but the lure of the night lights of the City called to her, and she knew that her older sisters, with their whispered secrets and bold lies, never came near to the places she would have to go and the things she wanted to do. They went out just a little way, and came right back to where they felt most at home, prince in tow or not.

So, she bided her time, and when finally the age came upon her, she had a plan. She took her father's birthday present, a diamond tennis bracelet - a strange gift, since she loathed the game - back to Fortunoffs and got a refund. And then, she used that refund to purchase a nice Honda motorcycle. She finally had wheels. She could escape. And she knew where she was going, too.

"Brooklyn!" the Fish King thundered, shaking his castle to the very aluminum siding.

"Tsk," said Grandmama, adding things up in her head. It was clear where the little princess had gotten her brains. "I think I'll ask Ester to keep an eye on her."

"Ester? That perverted hag?!" Sol thundered again. "My beautiful little girl depending on that crazy old witch?"

Grandmama ignored him and dialed the phone.

She saw which way the tide was coming in, after all.

As it turned out, Tante Ester's was the first place the little princess turned up after that long, harrowing ride west on the Long Island Expressway. And in no time at all, one visit turned into a tiny studio apartment and a job in a pet shop, a subway map and two rolls of tokens, and guaranteed dinner every Friday night. The littlest princess had found and settled in a new world.

She learned how to pinch her pennies until they dripped copper. She learned how to buy cheap, funky clothing at the used clothing stores and thrift shops, and how many ways Ramen noodles can be made interesting. She found her way into the company of woman who were like her, yet so unlike her, and she followed their movements and soon started to dish with the best and dance with the drunkest. She cut her hair and threw away all her makeup and all her pumps and nearly all her dresses. She went to the movies late and ate dinner early, and learned country western dancing and Melissa Etheridge songs. She found herself a girlfriend, and then another one, and then decided to experiment with non-monogamy. Single again, she learned to cruise the bars, the personal ads, and even borrowed a computer to cruise all the brainy girls online.

Then, one night, after the sun had just set, when the clouds were the color of pale roses set against the bleeding scarlet haze of the horizon, she looked up from her perch along the piers in the West Village and saw that a star had actually peeked through the clouds and the smog to sparkle against the deepening evening sky. The air was warm, and the river quiet, and not nearly as smelly as it sometimes was. The streetlights were coming on in shifts. Feeling refreshed and bold, she strolled through the streets not knowing where she was going to go, and ended up outside one of the biggest, roughest, toughest bars in the neighborhood. It had two pool tables, and two bouncers and a rainbow colored flag hanging out the front window. The evening was early, but the place was filled with gay-ly dressed people, so she want in, thinking a beer would be nice.

Once inside, she glanced around at the happy gathering of people and realized that she had walked into a party. And the most handsome person there was the guest of honor. She looked no older than thirty, and that was, in truth, her age; that very day was her birthday. All the festivities were for her.

She was a tall woman, and broad, in a well broken in leather jacket. Her dark hair was cut brutally short, even shorter than the little princess'. In fact, it looked just like an old-fashioned boy's haircut, a crewcut. But on her, it looked stunning, revealing her powerful jaw and cheekbones, leaving her strong, slender neck exposed. Her body was hard, and not very womanly - she barely seemed to have breasts at all. Of course, if she did, they might have been camouflaged by the men's shirt and tie she wore. She gestured broadly and stabbed her fingers when she spoke. She had a wide stance and a wide smile and a quick anger. She smoked and drank with a blunt hunger, sucking in the smoke and gulping down the beers, and the little princess had never seen anyone so beautiful in her entire life.

She watched this fascinating person, noticed how the other women who were dressed in man-clothing seemed to defer to her and how the women in dresses and high heeled shoes giggled and vied for her attention. And suddenly, the little princess wanted very much to light this woman's cigarettes, to fetch her a drink, and to cuddle up to that soft leather jacket and nibble on those noble looking earlobes and find out what was under that starched white shirt. It grew late, and still she couldn't take her eyes off of her. As the bar shut down and people filed out, the little princess found herself quietly wheeling her bike in the direction the leather jacketed one had walked off in. But in trying to keep back enough to not be seen, she soon lost the woman and her flouncy, lace bedecked chosen partner.

I must be in love, the princess thought deliriously. I've certainly never felt so dizzy before. I must see her again!

An ominous rumble sounded below her feet - it was a subway car tearing through the tunnels, echoing against the walls of the buildings she was passing. In the distance, she heard what sounded like a shout of joy - and then brakes screeching. There was a feeling in the air like a storm brewing. Nervous and panicked, she hopped onto the bike, pressed her helmet onto her head and pressed the starter, not caring about stealth any more. One, two blocks away, she saw something terrible was happening.

A large, old car had pulled up onto the sidewalk, and it was clear that it had run into someone! The little princess gunned her engine and pulled up onto the sidewalk and gasped in horror. For the car had struck her leather-jacketed idol! The woman was laying on the sidewalk, on her back, one powerful arm thrown back as if in defiance - and one look at the hysterical young woman in the beaded party dress and the little princess knew that the last gesture this bold and handsome woman had made was to push her attractive little date out of the way.

Her heart swelled for such a noble, brave, and altruistic gesture. But now was not the time for emotion. Snapping the kickstand down, she parked her bike and was off it in a second. The jabbering of the drunken driver was just noise, like seabirds squawking. She knelt beside the stricken woman and touched her throat, and temple. She was still alive! And there was a hospital just four blocks away!

The little princess didn't remember snapping "Stay!" at the two sobbing people who were at the scene. Nor did she remember riding her bike to the emergency room, or pounding her fist against the desk for attention. But when she returned to the scene, she did remember that the woman opened her eyes when she was lifted into the wheeled stretcher, and that they looked at each other. The woman's eyes were gray, like warm steel. The little princess felt like she could lose herself in them forever.

"Thanks," the woman croaked out. And then, the emergency workers wheeled her away.

The little princess was left alone on the street. Feeling somewhat in shock, she mounted her bike and slowly headed for home, where she fell into a deep sleep and was subsequently late for work the next day. But she couldn't get that handsome woman out of her mind. All day, she wondered about her - where did she live? What did she do? What was her name? Fantasies rose like bubbles through a clean filter - fantasies of feeling those long, powerful arms sweeping her into hugs, those sensitive, blunt fingered hands exploring her body. Slowly, she realized that this was her prince - this was the kind of woman who would make her feel like her Grandmama insisted a good prince should make a princess feel.

She wanted to put her newfound prince on the back of her bike and take her riding off into the sunset.

But how does one even approach such perfection?

First, she had to make sure that the prince was OK. She dashed back to the hospital after work, and was dismayed to find that there was no way for her to find out anything about an accident victim whose name she didn't even know. So, she started going back to that same bar every other night, anxious for a glimpse of one of the women who had been there celebrating the birthday party. It was a painstaking and annoying task that kept her awake at night, which led to activities personal and lustful and terribly sad, considering she didn't even know which name to cry out at the opportune moments. She began instead to cry out, "my prince, my prince!" - which worked just as well as any proper name.

In time, she had a name, and an address, and a history - and by the time the prince showed up back at the bar, one arm in a sling and a chorus of well-wishers fighting for the privilege of bringing her drinks, the little princess was well prepared for her campaign of seduction. In no time at all, her prince would be in her futon, and they would find nirvana together and live happily ever after.

It didn't work.

It was as though they lived in separate worlds! When the princess tried to buy the prince a drink, she got a growl of warning and a cool stare instead of that warm smile. It was clear that the prince did not recognize her biker rescuer - and no wonder, because the little princess had been wearing a full helmet at the time. Not sure whether to identify herself, she kept quiet. After all, she didn't want to be tolerated just because she saved the woman's life! Or whatever she did with her quick action that night.

But when she tried to slide up and start a conversation, topics rapidly became bikes, babes, or bitches - bikes, being things that purred and carried you around, babes being things that purred and giggled, and bitches being the last things that purred and giggled but stopped doing that before the prince was ready for them to stop. Any attempt at discussing anything personal was rebuffed or redirected or utterly ignored.

Many a night, the little princess heard the other women talking to each other about how wonderful and tough the prince was, and she was glad that the woman was no wimp. But she remembered those warm steel eyes, and that look of dignity under the pain and sighed when she remembered the fleeting touch she had placed on the prince's body to make sure she was all right.

More and more, she grew to love the distant prince, and she wished she could find a way - any way - to be with her and love her properly. It seemed to her that the prince was larger than life - exaggerated to the point of absolutes, a thrilling figure or power and danger, and yes - pure, raw sexuality.

"What am I doing wrong?" she wailed to Tante Ester one Friday night, her fork making patterns in the sweet potatoes. "Why is this woman different? She's a dyke like me, right? So why can't I get through to her?"

"Because," Ester said with all the wisdom that was her the greatest quality of her branch of the family, "It looks like you've fallen for a stone butch, baby. And you are neither butch nor femme, fowl, or, you should excuse the expression, fish."

"Well, why aren't I?" the princess asked earnestly. "I'd give anything to be what she wants, if that would get me by her side!"

"So you say. But you don't know what you'd have to change," Ester sighed. "You shouldn't even think about things like that. You should thank your lucky starfish that you don't have to! In my day, you were one or the other, and that was that! Now, you can wear a nice blouse and your jeans. You can put on a little makeup and walk proud in your engineer boots. You can lead the dance one night, and follow the next, if that turns you on! Oh, no, you have it much better, baby. Eat, and find a nice girl like yourself. You don't want to mess with a stone butch."

"Oh yes I do!" the princess insisted. (She wasn't a princess for nothing!) "And you have to help me, too! Tell me what I have to do! Tell me what I need to change. I'll take care of the rest! Do I have to be butcher, is that it? I can do that!"

"No, honey, sweetie. To catch a stone butch, you need to be a high femme. Do you know what that means? No more jeans and boots. Grow your hair. Wear makeup, and perfume, and nice shoes. And no more job at the pet store - get something nice and ladylike, so you don't smell like beagles when you see her." Ester ticked items off on her long, slender fingers and sighed. "It's silly, sweetie. Trust me."

The little princess sighed and looked down at her sensibly trimmed nails, and pulled at her shoulder length hair.

"Be happy the way you are," Ester said firmly, ending the conversation. "You can do anything you want.

That should have ended the situation right there, but of course it didn't. The little princess realized that she would have to be focused on this and take things one at a time. As days and weeks and months passed, she started growing her hair, letting it fall down her back again the way it did when she was back at the castle. And stubbornly, despite a number of accidents at work, she grew her nails, too, and started going to manicures every week. Searching the want ads, she found a new job, sitting at a desk and answering phones. She wore her three skirts over and over, and realized that there was going to be a lot more to this high femme business than she thought. She just couldn't do it alone - and the other women at work were all too alien for her to learn from. She would have to go back to her Tante and beg for help again. But this time, she was sure to get it. This time, Tante Ester would see that she was determined!

And so, on another Friday night, she sat at the table and picked at her food until her Tante sighed and leaned back and said, "You are going after that butch, that prince of yours."

The little princess nodded.

"You're a fool," Tante Ester said. "But you're a fool in love, and god only knows why I'm going to do this for you except that you're in love. But I'm telling you - this is not an easy task. You'll have to give up a lot of things for this woman - and that's just to get her attention!"

"I'm willing," whispered the little princess, and she thought of her prince and winning that brave, handsome soul for her very own.

"And remember - once you're a proper high femme, there's no turning back! If you slip, it's all over for you and this butch. This woman has to fall in love with you and keep you - and you have to be able to fight to keep her. She got to give up the hanging girls, the ones who are waiting for you to fall, and join with you so that you're two sides of the same coin, or else there's nothing but tragedy and pain in store for you. And did I mention the pain? The clothes, the hair - the shoes? It won't be easy, baby, it won't be one bit easy!"

"I still want to try," said the little princess.

"OK," Tante Ester sighed again. "Let's make a list of some stuff you'll need. First - some nice dresses, and shoes, and then some stockings. We'll get you some makeup, and an appointment at that place on Flatbush, where they do the nice hairstyling. And you're going to have to learn how to walk, and talk, and flirt. And everything else about how to act! Girl - you're going to wonder how anyone does the things I'm going to teach you. But you're going to do them the way I say, or else you're going to fail. Do you understand?"

"But - but - if I learn new ways to walk, and talk, and act, and look - what will be left of me?" the little princess asked.

"Your beautiful body," her Tante Ester said honestly. "You have some natural grace, and lovely, lovely eyes. And you will have the strength and wisdom of your family inside you, and these will make her love you, if nothing else. But first, you have to walk in her world - and that, I can teach you."

"Let's do it," the little princess said. "I'm ready!"

In the days to pass, she often wondered why there couldn't have been a potion for her to swallow instead of the painstaking changes she had to make in her lifestyle. First of all, and hardest to begin with, was when she looked over her shopping list and her bank account and realized that she would have to sell her motorcycle in order to buy the wardrobe her Tante described. She thought of going back home and asking the Fish King to buy her some of these items, but she realized that he would love to do that only if her prince was the proper type to bring home. And besides - this was something she was going to do for herself, wasn't it?

So, she lost her wheels. It was a loss like a sword piercing her body, and each time she walked out of her apartment she looked at the space where it used to be and she ached for it and cried just a little. But she went to her Tante's house and put on the new clothing and then gasped as her Tante pulled a pair of beautiful shoes from out of a colorful box.

They were white leather, not pumps, but high, slender heeled shoes of an impossible arch and height, and they buckled with the most exquisite little buckles of gold. The slipped onto her feet like softened butter, and locked on with grips like crab claws. She looked nervously down at them and set her feet on the floor and stood.

Knives! Razor sharp knives drove into her feet! She gasped and sat back down, with leftover tears from the loss of her wheels dotting the corners of her eyes.

"Holy shit, I can't walk in those!" she cried out.

"Oh, you can and you will," Tante Ester said. "They are the traditional shoes of a high femme. You'll have several pairs, in different colors, and you will learn to wear them and walk gracefully, and your butch prince will love them. And mind your language, missy! There'll be no cursing in front of your prince; she won't like it. Learn to say evasions like children do, or better yet, learn to suffer silently. And here's something else for you, too." She opened another box and pulled out a strange garment that was unlike anything the little princess had ever seen before. She was amazed when her Tante pulled it around her midsection and positioned it over her hips and under her breasts. As it began to tighten, she asked, "What is this, Tante?"

"A corset," the woman answered, pulling the strings sharply. She grunted with satisfaction when the little princess gasped and then pulled the strings tighter still. "You really should have played more tennis, my dear! This will give you a nice, womanly shape, with a slender waist and nice, rounded hips. I also got you a wonderbra - those little tits of yours could use a lift."

The little princess blushed and fell silent - not because she didn't know what to say, but because she could barely breathe with the corset drawn so tightly. Silently, she stood, little knife-edged spasms of pain shooting up her legs, as her Tante slipped one of the expensive dresses over her head. She turned to look in the mirror and gasped.

A beautiful young woman looked back at her - svelte, shapely, elegant and tall - with lovely legs and long, shining hair! Was this the same girl who rode her motorcycle through the streets whooping and hollering? The woman who carried cages of budgies and cleaned fish tanks? The woman who went line dancing and arm wrestling and then talked about cyberpunk at a coffee bar all night?

Well, yes, sort of. But she was also a major, major babe. No matter how much it all hurt, her Tante was right. She was turning into the kind of woman her prince paid attention to.

She turned to her Tante and beamed. "More," she tried to say. But her usual way of breathing was restricted - the corset made it hard to be firm and loud. Instead, she whispered, "More, please."

Tante Ester nodded. Well, that was love for you. "OK, back to talking. Remember - don't be too sharp, and don't be critical. Giggle whenever she says something funny. Be patient and don't fidget - and never look bored. She's the center of your universe, got that?"

The little princess nodded and felt very calm. That was one lesson she didn't need to learn at all.

In due time, she was ready to see if her sacrifices and training had paid off. She showed up at the bar in her new regalia, every step still sharp as knife blades, every breath an effort. Her entire body seemed a very symphony of pain and discomfort - yet she walked into the bar with a grace that turned many heads, and slid into a seat with a set of moves that had every butch's heart pumping and quite a few of the femmes, too. She could barely move her torso - and her breathing made her wonderbra'd tits rise and fall in a rhythm that hypnotized at least half a dozen women at once, and made their girlfriends slap them. She didn't even have to raise a finger before the bartender came over to personally take her drink order.

Hey, this is not bad, she thought, trying not to move too much.

But every attention paid to her was nothing, until the prince ambled in. The little princess' heart leapt - she had nearly forgotten how handsome and dashing her prince was. And the sling was gone, apparently the injury had healed. How wonderful! Elegantly, as she had been taught, she angled her throat and looked over toward the prince, and batted her long, artificial eyelashes.

It was like tugging a leash.

It was that easy.

"Hey, sweet thing, where have you been all my life?" said the prince, bowing slightly over the table. Eyes watched them from all corners of the bar, some smiling, some bitter. "And more importantly - care to dance?"

Ohmigod, I've wanted to for weeks! the little princess thought. But instead of speaking, she smiled gently and gave a squeak of a giggle and extended one very manicured hand and rose to dance. Every step made her believe that she was leaving bloody footprints in the sawdust, but she turned and rocked and swayed exactly as her prince led her, and for the rest of the night, the prince had eyes for no other. And as she sighed and smiled and nodded and giggled, she felt that the sacrifice of any deeper conversation was worth the warmth of the woman's arms and the charm of her smile, and the gentle touch of her hands.

"Come home with me," the prince murmured, while nuzzling the princess' ear.

"Yes," she sighed in response. It was a word, her Tante informed her, that butches loved to hear. The prince was no exception.

In the moonlit night, she accompanied the prince home, carefully allowing herself to be led the entire way. And once inside, she waited until she was touched to respond, and kept her responses silky, smooth, and only in reaction. In this too, she had been well coached.

"These nails are just too inconvenient," she had snapped at her Tante one night. "What if I - I mean, when we're close - won't they, um, hurt?"

"The only place those nails are going to do damage is on your butch's back, when you scratch and claw her in passion," Tante Ester said calmly. "Don't be thinking you'll be doing a dance on her privates. You'll be lucky if you see them."

"What??"

"Butch and femme isn't just clothes, sweetie. The butch does, the femme gets done to. The butch leads, the femme follows. You stretch yourself back, and your butch pleasures you."

"Doesn't sound very equal to me."

"If you're lucky, you'll get a butch who opens up and lets you in some," Ester said dreamily. "That's very special. But don't take me literally, sweetie. Leave that rubber thingamajig at home, and don't ever mention that you have it."

The little princess had blushed at that, but remembered every word. And now, in the arms of her prince, she was glad that the searching hands found the sweet satin and lace undergarments instead of a leather and chrome harness, because the prince made such a wonderful sound of appreciation when she pulled the skirt up high and touched so boldly and sweetly! It was clear that these were the right garments to wear.

"You're so hot," the prince whispered. "God, you're perfect. Every move you make, every breath - I could hold you forever!"

"Oh, yes," the little princess sighed. And when she was finally laid down onto the bed, she forgot the pain of her feet and the pain in her chest and the unforgiving bones of the corset - all she knew was the heat, the passion, and the touch of her prince. As every sensation written and spoken about reached her, she rocked on the soft bed in wave after wave of pure ecstasy, saying nothing but "yes." over and over again.

She rapidly became the prince's favorite, eclipsing all the others. Her gentleness, demure attitude, and her silent allure gave nothing to compete against. Any other girl was too bold, too direct, too mouthy. The prince loved her completely, and spoke to her for hours, holding her and wanting nothing but a murmur, a sigh, a giggle, or a sweet touch for responses. And she never realized that this was the same woman who had ridden to the scene of her accident on a motorcycle, never realized that this was the same woman who had tried so often to buy her a drink.

It was true that they never had in-depth conversations about the future, or politics, or anything else. There was little to talk about when your chest was so constricted that deep breathing made you dizzy, and every word had to be watched anyway. But there's more to life than talking, the little princess scolded herself. "I've never been so happy!"

For quite some time, this went on to their mutual satisfaction. It was true that the prince never offered the princess a ring, nor took her to be registered as domestic partners, but according to Tante Ester, commitment was a major issue with butches, and came slowly to them. But that was OK. It was clear that the prince only had eyes for the little princess.

Until *another* princess came into the bar one night.

She is smaller than I am, the little princess thought, some new feeling rising in her that she couldn't name. Why, I'm sure she isn't wearing a corset at all! And look - her feet are so small, and she moves so quickly - can it be that her shoes don't feel like razor sharp knives to her? For in fact, the new princess moves even more gracefully than the little one did, and her hair was a long train of shimmering gold, instead of waves of glistening copper tinted brown.

"Holy Hannah," said the prince as she walked into the bar. Everyone turned to see the new femme, and the little princess felt another stab of that unfamiliar emotion. That was the way they once looked at me, she thought. She touched the prince lightly, and the prince turned back to her and grinned. "Can't blame me for looking!" she said with a laugh, and then kissed the little princess on the mouth and patted her on the hip.

But it was much more than looking a week later.

"And then - then - the prince danced with her! In front of everybody! And I was standing there - and - and these other women came over to ask me to dance, and the prince never even noticed!" The little princess had taken her troubles to her expert, and was wailing them out over a nice beef stew that was getting very cold without having ever been near her mouth.

"You've got to fight for your butch," Tante Ester said, looking down. "It's the only way. If you stand by, she'll take up with the new girl and never say boo to you again. You've got to take action this time, sweetie. Ruin the new girl. You're stronger, faster, smarter. Scare her away, and while she's gone, threaten to leave the prince. She'll be cut to the quick - it isn't her fault that she doesn't see your pain, but now, she needs reminding. While she's in pain, you'll have the upper hand. Demand commitment. You've waited long enough. And when the new girl comes back, as she will, you just cut her dead with a nice ring on your finger and your clothes hanging in your prince's closet. That's the way to do it, sweetie."

"It sounds so cruel," the little princess said softly.

"It's a cruel world out there," Tante Ester said wisely. "This time, you have an edge. Use it. Now! Before you lose your prince and everything you've struggled for."

It was midnight when she found the two of them, still talking and dancing in the bar. Her pains were sharp, especially the one in her stomach, where she realized that the new emotion was pure jealousy, burning through her like a heated garrote cutting her to the spine. She knew that if the prince took this new woman home, that would be the end of it - all these sacrifices and struggles for nothing, all cast away like refuse of the end of a pier. She pulled open the door of the bar and felt another twinge of pain as she realized that no one saw her - they only saw the loveliness of the new princess and the charm the prince was working on her.

The prince's warm steel eyes were happy, and it was clear that no thought had been given to the missing princess she had been squiring about for so long. It was a bitter hate that filled the little princess as she worked her way through the bar, thinking of how she would cut this interloper down, and how she would grasp the prince's arm and make her remember who brought her so much pleasure, who saved her, and yes, who had so long desired her! And then, she blinked and saw the ripple of her shoulders against the man's shirt she was wearing, and the sway of her strong hips as she danced, and she knew - the prince loved this new girl as instantly and honestly as she loved me.

Fighting back the tears, the little princess turned and left the bar.

Stumbling, she walked on those damn shoes until she felt like she had nothing but open wounds for feet. As it began to rain, she cursed, and kicked the shoes off, one after the other. Not caring about the showering drops, she tore through her own fancy, lacy dress until she found the strings of the corset and pulled and twisted until they unbound or snapped free. People passing were astonished to see this woman contort and pull a boned lace structure from under a now torn and disarrayed dress and throw it violently into the gutter.

Taking a deep breath for once, she screamed out her pain, and then sank down onto the curb and folded her arms around her knees and sobbed out keening cries of anguish and sorrow, until she coughed and sputtered and realized that a river was running over her feet. She lifted them one at a time, sniffling, and realized that her expensive stockings were all twisted and run up and shredded around her ankles. But at least her feet didn't hurt so much.

Someone heaved down next to her. She looked over and saw a man! A young man, very closer to her age, it seemed. And amazingly, he was wearing makeup - which made her realize that sitting in the rain had probably made her own mascara run until she looked like a raccoon. He was also wearing a gauze top that was soaked through, exposing a ring through one of his nipples, and long, soft colored pants made of a similar material. On his feet were army boots. A strange combination.

"Are these yours?" he asked politely, as though they were not sitting on a curb in the rain, bubbles rising around their feet. He was holding her discarded shoes.

"I threw them away," she said, astonished that an entire sentence could come out.

"Can I have them? I think they might fit," he said.

She blinked away the rain, and nodded, wondering what a boy would want with those shoes. Her astonishment didn't let up as he pulled his boots off and tried the shoes on. And sure enough, they fit!

"Awesome," he said, standing in them. "I could never afford shoes like these! Take mine, you'll catch your death of cold sitting there with wet feet!"

The thought made her giggle - army boots with a party dress! But she did have a long way home, so she pulled them on, and found them warm and supportive, especially when she wrapped the laces around her ankles. The boy helped her up, and she sighed in pleasure as her feet no longer felt the stabbing pains of the cursed shoes.

"I'm glad you're happy with them," she said, realizing that she could speak as much a she liked now. "They brought me nothing but pain."

"I can see that. Wanna come out and forget your troubles for a while? We're going to a new club on the east side."

She looked at his group - for he wasn't alone. And there was the oddest collection of people she had ever seen! Two girls holding hands had purple hair and matching nose rings - and another young man had a tattoo over one eye and an arrow shooting through one eyebrow. There was a woman in black leather from head to toe, and her date, who was wearing what looked like a latex miniskirt and a lace top scavenged from the trash. In fact - it was the little princess' own torn corset! There was another boy, in a long sarong and a plaid shirt, holding onto a woman in a pink party dress - and army boots.

The little princess looked down at herself, at the bedraggled lace dress and the shredded stockings and knew that she belonged with these wet, wild people. She took the hand of the sweet queerboy who was wearing her shoes and followed them all to a lit up club with high, high ceilings and a soaring sound system, and she heard music that no one could just rock and sway to, music that made you want to scream and throw yourself around! And she let herself be wild, moving in ways that would have shocked the prince to her royal core, and feeling the beat and the tones run through her body like gusts of wind. Hands pushed and pulled at her, and she struggled and followed, pushing back and laughing and allowing herself to actually reach the stage.

There, she looked into the eyes of the lead singer, a lean and hungry looking woman with scars and rings and a smile like an angel, and she stretched her arms wide and stood at the edge of the stage. Falling forward, she felt a sea of hands rise up to meet her, to carry her, aloft and rising, until her tears faded at last and only her laughter remained. She was flying, soaring - and would never have to be bound to the razor sharp prison of who she was not meant to be.

GenderFucks
Stories About Boyz and Men

Anti-venom for the Soul
(plus conversations I never really had)

(First published in PomoSexuals, edited by Lawrence Schimel and Carol Queen.)

There would come a moment, when the silences punctuating the discussion would stretch to two, three, five, ten seconds. When the postures would relax and tense up - one leaning back, the other arching forward. I'd know when it was time, and I'd excuse myself to the bathroom, ostensibly for its mundane use. There, I'd take off my bra, adjust the harness tight between my legs. There, I'd struggle to shed my body, my self-image, my entire gender identity, so that I could walk out, my cock hard against my thigh, my nuts aching, ready.

It rarely worked. I'm no slender androgyne, with tits small enough to bind or even leave free. My tits and hips and ass are wide and soft, my belly full - no washboard abs or long legs. My face is soft and rounded, eyes large and framed by ridiculously thick lashes. No human being on the planet would mistake that form for male.

No, I'm not a guy. That piece of silicone between my legs will never feel piss or cum shooting through it. I will never actually feel the tenderness and ecstasy of a hand on its shaft, at its base, the sensuous flicking of a tongue at its tip. I do not believe in my own prick.

Until his hand was upon it.

Then, I believed. Close enough, so they say, for jazz.

"That's my daughter who wants to be a boy," the man who married my mother said more than once. I repeat it these days to knowledgeable friends, understanding strangers, my voice heavy with the irony of his prescience. How little he knew, I laugh. I can laugh now. I grew up and indeed, I became a boy. And it was every bit as interesting and liberating as I thought it would be. It was also more challenging than I could have ever imagined. It has left me with a burden of tales untold. Until now.

I had been living and traveling in a world full of dykes, almost every one of them butch as can be. I was a little awed in this company, because it was so unlike the way I thought I lived at home. They were so bold and direct, swaggering and strong and tough and all so handsomely clothed in tight jeans and leather boots. I aspired to be one of them. I didn't yet realize I already was. In our moments of honesty and courage, we exposed ourselves and our wounds to each other and found that a remarkable percentage of us had suffered at the hands of adult men in our lives and families.

We said:
"If I had been a boy, he would have
been proud of me
not noticed me
left me alone

loved me
just yelled at me
just hit me."

Someone said: All women are really looking for father figures.

Of course I was disturbed by the neo-Freudian implications of what we (I) were (was) doing, who we (I) were (was) pretending to be. My fuzzy Psych One theorizing left me with images of women seeking to reenact episodes of abuse and injustice, pain and humiliation. Even as I spiraled deep into a competitive drive for experiences that were more intense, more shattering, more damaging, every shift came with the struggle to get beyond what seemed so obvious. In order to achieve the sense of danger and intimacy I was driven to, I needed to find a paradigm to adopt, a role that would make it safe for me. Safe to say the words. Safe under a hand.

One night, I was brave enough to say it. "I want to be a boy," I said. "Actually, I think I am one."

This story would be almost commonplace, if it happened on the West Coast, and the person I said it to was another dyke, and everyone reading this was into leather and knew what a Daddy/boy relationship was.

Naturally, I live on the East Coast, and the person I said it to was a bisexual man, and most of the people we knew were into D/S and SM, not "leather," and if they could be made to understand the "Daddy" part, there was simply no explaining the "boy" part.

"And you're his little girl," one thoroughly heterosexual man said brightly and kindly, after hearing that my chosen top was my Daddy. He was so pleased with his reasoning skills. He didn't know why I never liked him, couldn't give him the time of day.

Fact was, what he suggested disgusted me. I'm no man's little girl. I never was.

Becoming a boy felt like the right thing to do, to me. It was a way for me to enact the fantasy life I dreamed about, to engage in a relationship with a man that had limits and boundaries, yet went so much deeper than a friendly, casual fuck buddy arrangement. It gave me a chance to cocreate a relationship that was both nurturing and authority laden, forward thinking and traditional. It gave me a chance to try again, to have that special kind of relationship that we imagine could/should exist between a parent-like adult mentor and their junior partner, a person learning through emulation and reward and punishment scenarios. But consider the ample contradictions inherent in the situation - a dyke, woman-identified abuse survivor with an older, not purely gay identified man - doing SM in an intimate and publicly acknowledged relationship.

It cost me dearly. Not only in the various ways I was made to feel unwelcome in parts of the lesbian leather community, and just odd in the mixed/hetero SM scene, but by being in one of those places that defied conventional use of language.

As a writer, I am very concerned with language. When I say I'm a dyke, I mean dyke, not lesbian, not female homosexual, not gay woman. I was never one of those people who say, "I don't believe in labels, they're so limiting," as though not believing in something makes it go away. Labels are vital in our culture; they provide instant identification, associative reasoning fodder, and a base from which to move on. Adopting the paradigm title of boy meant taking on all the gay male cultural implications of the role, plus examining the identity of the masculine, period. It also meant examining my deepest fears and my terrible self-image. It took me to the core of my identity, dyke/woman, and shook it repeatedly as I wondered what it all meant.

Someone said, *How can you call yourself a dyke? Dykes are like super lesbians. If you have sex with men, you're not a lesbian at all. You're bisexual.*

I once identified as a bisexual woman. I took that to mean that I had a more or less equal chance of establishing a relationship with a man or a woman. That almost all of my male partners were queer themselves didn't really sink in until years later, when I discovered that every other lesbian on the planet had not grown up fantasizing about and having sex only with girls. I dropped it when I realized that really, I would never want to actually share all of my life with a man. That no matter how fine they looked, how well they played or fucked, or how friendly I was with them, they would never feel right in my bed, night after night. I dreamed of women. I was a dyke.

To settle into feeling, breathing, living as a dyke, and then find that I was drawn to a man - a big, hairy, masculine man, who was not the safe, sexy, but ultimately untouchable gay leather daddy who I could flirt with, act with, and never actually do anything sexual with - was a surprise, to say the least.

To be drawn to him at the same time that my mind was entertaining such complicated puzzles as my core identity and the meaning behind my fantasies, was pure luck. When we were flirting and getting to know each other, neither one of us could have seen what was ahead. Perhaps we both would have shied away if we had. How glorious that we didn't.

Someone said, This is a lesbian woman's event. Bisexuals only bring male energy to this space, and taint it. We need a space to be safe among our own kind.

"Then you're saying," I repeated, a moment away from tears of betrayal, staying strong, staying calm, keeping myself proud and composed, "that I am not welcome to return."

To my face, she said, "Yes."

I went back anyway, and never hid my past, my tastes, my relationships, my fantasies and life choices. I *would* hide my tangled feelings of exposure and hurt and yes, shame, and I never let them know how I felt in reaction to what they said, what they suggested. Each time, I walked across new thresholds and felt the sickening terror that comes with being uncloseted and accessible. Each time, I waited for the next confrontation, the next time a woman used the power of womanspace to attempt to segregate me, to negate me. Perhaps I should have let them know. Perhaps I should have cried a woman's tears of frustration and pain and anger and made them see how their defense of turf was actually hurting another woman. But I was too proud. I went back and let them see my calm strength and occasionally my anger. After a while, it wasn't considered as important. Or perhaps my increasing notoriety as an author and editor gave me the added weight as a desirable personality that could overcome the distaste some women felt for my sexual (and emotional) proclivities. Or, maybe it was because more women began to admit that they, too, had SM relationships with men. But I knew I was still different. My particular man was known to be bisexual. By extension and logic, so, therefore, was I.

Someone said, *If two queers are having sex with each other, it's still queer sex.*

People ask me now, were we fags together? In other words, did I pretend to be a gay man, while he pretended to be a gay man, and then we could both play happily in a world of make-believe?

Yes, it was like that exactly, and no, it wasn't like that at all.

I wore a dick, but it never shot cum. I took my bra off, but never hid my big tits. I never changed my name, never adopted a "boy name," like I hear others did, and there was never the slightest attempt to alter pronoun usage with me. "She's my boy," was always a conversation grenade, guaranteed to cause an immediate reaction. Tossed into a circle of people, it would hurl semantic shrapnel into the dialogue as people grappled with what it meant.

The struggle with my core identity never even approached the level of suspension of disbelief necessary for the sort of method acting that I would have to do to pretend I was a young man, pretend that I was raised as a boy, that my body was built on a masculine frame. For me, gender role was only a part of the attraction, and eventually not even of central importance. It was the definition of the role beyond gender or orientation. A boy was potential and glory, a bearer of pride and attention and strict, loving affection. A romantic ideal with real-world models in every corner of literature, myth and folklore, modern culture.

A boy was expected to grow up.

And it was so necessary that I had the room to grow the fuck up.

How I needed that structure, that framework for survival! Years of playing at doing SM had provided me with some measure of skill, some level of expertise, but my passion for order and stability was never sated for long. Having found a pattern to lay down and follow, I needed to complete that leg of the journey, to go from start to finish in an honorable way, to experience the pain and joy with all the energy my long closeted fantasies could generate. I needed to sink myself into it. So yes, we were fags together, a sexual transgressive kind of thing, and no, we were a man and a woman acting out a complex, deeply seated romantic fantasy which neither one of us could have predicted or entirely controlled.

Someone said, *It's OK as long as you never have sex with him. That would be unhealthy, dangerous, sick.*

Entering into this relationship created a whole new way for sex to become complicated. Was it sexual to be beaten, or disciplined? Sexual to endure pain, or teasing, or bondage for its own sake? Or is it what people really wanted to know - did I suck his cock? Did we screw? If he fucked me, exactly how did it occur? What combinations of genitalia and bodily fluids were encountered, and how often?

And the complications weren't only in the direct and personally demanding way these things were asked of me, (and yes, people did ask me) but in the knee-jerk way I almost felt compelled to answer them. Fighting off defensiveness was always a part of my struggle, striving to balance the righteousness of my own passion with the enduring discomfort I seemed to cause in others. Why even now, years later, I wonder if it is necessary to say something, if it's part of this story or not. After all, I don't ask other people about the details of their sexual lives; I take their word that they are what they say they are, and leave any theories about how exactly they act on their identity to idle and private musings. And then, only if I really care to wonder.

But how could it not be about sex, and sexual acts? I don't do these things strictly for mental jollies, my body is as hungry as any one else's. When a voice or an action or a touch turns me on, it's my cunt that responds and gets wet, it's my large and very unmasculine nipples that get hard. Sure, my metaphoric dick gets hard, but when I come, it's going to be via my clit, no matter what the circumstances were that made me ready for it. So hell yes, it was a sexual thing.

But what did you do? I still hear the voices asking. Insisting. Did he ever fuck you? *Was* it the queer sex that we imagine? *Was* it a reenactment of your past abuse? *Was* it just another example of patriarchal violence against women, perpetrated with the woman's pseudo-consent? Was it good, did you come? Did he? Where? How?

None of your fucking business.

He was my Daddy.

I was his boy.

The rest is personal.

Someone said, *I seen you've gone back to being a lesbian now.*

I never left. I didn't even take a vacation. I never stopped loving women, lusting after women, wanting women. I never doubted that my primary partner would once again be a woman. Just as I never really became a boy-child, so I never really became authentically bisexual, let alone straight. Yet still, I find it difficult to talk about that time, nearly impossible to write about it. Who can I tell this story to, the tale of a soul which was injected with the poison of a toxic childhood and adolescence, but which found solace in the melodramatic mimicking of a parent child relationship? Where could there be a place to talk about the challenges and rewards of not-being-het? I could pour it out into a novel maybe, but every time I try, it comes out raw, and rough, as though I was discovering a new form of storytelling. I need to wrestle with the language, almost physically wring meaning from the words one at a time, stopping to define and redefine at every step. It's torturous, and clumsy. It doesn't suffice. It doesn't do that time, that place, or those two people, any justice.

But it's a story that has to be told.

Isn't it?

Succession of Honor

(Published in *Looking for Mr. Preston*, edited by Laura Antoniou.)

It had been a long time since I'd seen the old man. I figured, hell, it had to be at least ten years since I moved west, maybe more. Although we still kept in touch now and again, my travels hadn't taken me back home for ages. I was real busy, yessir. What with a house, my work, my community service, my own kids, and a former slave turned spousal equivalent, I had every spare moment parceled out.

But I can't complain. Shit, I should boast. In the time I had lived out here, I had amassed everything I ever wanted in life. Sure, I wasn't the young, arrogant piss-and-vinegar youth who used to look back at me in the mirror. And the scars have all but faded from everywhere on my body, except for that one special place. But I had become, with all due kicking and screaming, a mature human being. I try to set an example to those who serve me; I try to be fair and honest, to see them through the tough spots and guide them to their own maturity with a firm, loving hand.

After all, I had been taught by the best.

Even though my own western family had never met him, I taught them to revere my old man, to think of him as highly as I do. And when I took my first sash, under those bright lights, my body glistening with oil and sweat, I thanked him before the audience, wishing that he was there to see his boy triumph. I knew that he would have come, even though he hated the damn things, just to see me compete. He always said that I didn't need any studded cow skins to prove to him that I was OK. But I wanted them for me; external validation that other people could recognize.

Well, I kept winning. And each stop on my way to the top meant that my old man got another public thank you from me. It was the least, the very least that I could do.

I remember the first time I played with the old man. We were out at his place, after the longest courtship I had ever planned and executed with a top. I couldn't tell you what attracted me to him. It sure as hell wasn't his leather; the man didn't even have a vest. And it wasn't that someone pointed him out to me at some contest or bar, either; in fact, we met at a restaurant. But something about him, his classical manners, the little sparkle in his hard eyes, the way he looked at you when he was listening to what you were saying, all these cues told me that he was worth pursuing. I found out early that he was into SM. Not leather, he reminded me. SM. Sadomasochism. He liked to deal out pain, to train eager bottoms. And he wanted his bottoms to like that.

I liked it a lot. And let me tell you, that night, when he first stood back and had me strip down for him, when he pulled his worn belt through the loops of his jeans and pushed me easily over the edge of a table, I flashed on every other scene I'd ever done with a top. Every basement dungeon decorated in early naugahide, every spare bedroom with extra strong bolts sunk into the studs, every rigged bed frame and every stroke of a paddle, belt, whip or rod. I remembered them all, in seconds of intensity that made my eyeballs hurt, and then watched as they burst into flames and crisped into ashes. All those memories were wiped away by the simple, powerful beating this old man gave me, and by the way he held me afterwards and told me that I would have to take it much better than that if I wanted to be his boy.

Naturally, I thought he meant I had to be stronger, so the next time, I gritted my teeth, and grunted when I couldn't take it any more. Then, suddenly, he stopped, and pulled up right behind me. He laid the whip he was using across my lower back and asked me how I felt about what was happening. No other top had asked a question like that of me while they were beating me.

"I feel… good, sir," I answered. And there was a silence so heavy I swear I could hear myself sweat. I suddenly realized that I should have probably said something like "Well beaten," or maybe, "Eager to please you," or something like that. In an instant, I thought of about a hundred things I could have said that might have sounded better than "I feel good." What was I, James Brown? I cringed and waited for him to tell me to get dressed and get the fuck out.

Instead, he said, "Then why aren't I hearing how good it feels?"

I couldn't believe my ears. "What?" I even forgot the sir!

"I expect, when I put so much effort into using your body the way you like it, that you should express your happiness and gratitude on a regular basis," he continued. "Otherwise, I might think that you are not enjoying this, and therefore I'll switch to something else, and you will have missed out on a good thing."

"But... aren't you punishing me, sir?" I asked, my manners coming back even though the fog that was settling through my brain.

"What the hell could I be punishing you for?" he demanded. "I barely know you!"

That's when I learned that my old man never makes up stupid excuses to punish his bottoms. He likes to make 'em hurt, and so he does it. Over the years, through the various times that I actually was punished, he never once hit me with something I liked. Nossir, he would haul out the meanest, nastiest, most unpleasant things when I was rude, or sloppy, or when I forgot stuff. Or, he would simply send me away.

And you know that hurt the most.

On the plane east, I went through my itinerary, making sure I had enough time to see him for a nice long visit. I had three speaking engagements and about two other appearances, not counting the night of the contest. I also had a big surprise for him. I used the phone on the plane to call the almost frantically eager young man who was picking me up at the airport. It's nice to be a celebrity sometimes.

Of course, when I met my old man, I wasn't what you'd call a celebrity. Oh, I had done my time in the local clubs, wore some MC colors for a while. I was known enough in what passed for a scene, had a couple of brief relationships and had done my share of workshops and committee meetings. But not more than most other folks. I admit that I was disappointed that the man I was chasing didn't seem interested in the leather scene; but I was arrogant enough to figure that when he took up with me, he'd become a part of it, come out to the clubs and bars, go to the shows and conferences. I guess he did, a little. It took me a couple of years to realize that almost every time he did come out, it was to please me. He would stand out in his shirt and tie and shoes, alone in enough black leather to make an entire herd of Angus. But he would come out for my sake.

I guess he was about one of the most generous tops you could get, really. I mean, he was tough with me, demanding in certain things and unwavering in his rules. But he was also patient and always interested in what I was doing. He never let me stay comfortable in one place, always pushed me to do better, to rise higher, to excel. "Your success," he told me one night, "honors me."

Well, it was time for me to do him some honor. By the time the plane landed and the neatly dressed young leatherman heaved my bags into his car and whisked me into the city, I was feeling pretty good about what I had in mind for my old man.

I remember the feel of his collar, the smooth leather that had no lock on it. "It needs none," he said. By that time, I knew what he meant. I swore, with all my strength, to come and to go, to do and leave undone, to speak and be silent according to his will and whim. He swore to protect me, to teach me, to improve me.

It took him about three years before he announced me improved. They passed like dances after midnight.

I remember that I begged him to take me on again, swearing that there was still plenty of room for improvement. But at the same time, deep inside, I also knew that I was already starting to cruise the bottoms I socialized with, and that I hungered for my regular haunts and activities which my old man had never really denied me, but had encouraged me away from. I wanted to feel the power of a vest with colors on it, wear run pins and go to conferences and wild weekends. I wanted to show off my new manners, and teach them to others. It took almost another year to pull myself away from my old man, and even then, I cried into his shoulder one night that I would always, always be his boy.

And he nodded. "Yes, you will," he said. "I don't see how I could hardly forget you, either."

It was only a few months later that I got the job offer out west.

I was smoothing out my chaps on the hotel bed when there came a knock on my door. I figured it was one of the organizers, so I opened it a crack and turned my back to continue what I was doing.

"Shouldn't do that," his familiar voice cracked. "Y'never know what kind of riff raff is skulking around these places."

My heart stopped, and the enthusiastic greeting I had planned for my old man got caught in my throat. Barely realizing what I was doing, I turned and sank down to my knees, and damn if I didn't blush the way I used to when I was with him so many years ago!

He took the gesture as honestly as I gave it, and then came over and brought me up into one of his great old bear hugs. It was just like him not to make a fuss over it, just to accept it and go on. And then we commenced to fill each other in on our lives. Or, rather, I filled him in. He seemed duly impressed by the photos of my kids and mate, and grunted good-naturedly at my silver encrusted sash. I asked him if he wanted to come to the contest, and he declined, which I expected. That was all right. The real surprise would come at the bar, afterwards. We were able to have about two hours to ourselves before the calls started coming in, and I had to start getting ready for my appearances. My old man left, promising to come by the bar on contest night to see what I had for him.

I shouldn't have been surprised at the deep reaction seeing him gave me. My visit with him made me realize that it had been longer then ten years. He seemed a lot older now, still the same old man but a little out of shape, a little slower. I loved him with a fierce intensity, and I knew that what I would do at the bar later on that weekend would be a peak moment for me. And for him.

All during the weekend, as I sat on panels and addressed groups, I kept flashing back to scenes from a previous life. Standing rigid against a wall, suffering in silence for an act of forgetfulness. Kneeling contentedly at his feet, keeping my need for further abasement in check because he wanted it that way, and feeling the pride of being able to control my emotions, allowing him to see them without making them into demands for his attention. Little tasks done at his command, each one thrilling because I was allowed to be useful.

I was so proud to have served him. He truly made me what I am today.

The contest was over before I knew it. I made my speech to roaring applause and cheers, thanking my old man, and promising that he would be making an appearance after the show was over, over at the bar. I could see that many people were visibly touched by my declaration of love for him, and it made my heart seem close to exploding. This was my community, and my old man. At last, I was going to bring them together. And, the surprise that I had kept so well, was that my kids were gonna join me up on stage, both of them, and they were about to meet the man who made their own old man. They'd be on their knees, of course, and me, I'd uncover and give my old man a bow.

It was gonna be enough to make you cry.

We poured into taxis and private cars and shuttle buses, and marched into the bar in a raging sea of leather and chrome. We literally had to push our way through, and I asked at the bar if my old man had come by. None of the bartenders had been approached by any man answering his description. I should have seen it, right then; my old man was never late. But I was riding the wave of my own pleasure that night, my own fucking fantasy that everything would go as I planned. As time began to pass, I started to make rounds through the crowds, scanning, watching, trying to figure out where my old man could be.

I began to panic when it came time for the short speeches; this was the time I wanted to gather my family on stage, and show how the lessons I learned are being passed down to my own, how our traditions continue through the years. Soon, they had to start, and I waved the new winner onto the small stage and dived out the front door. But there was no sign of my old man on the street. I grabbed one of the bouncers and described him, shouting over the noise from inside the bar. The man seemed to understand what I was saying. But his own answer was partially drowned out, not by the ambient noise, but from a strange, heated roar that rose in my ears, accompanying the pounding of my heart.

"...shoes!" He was shouting back at me. Then, "Not even, (something) jacket!"

I stared at him, comprehension flooding me with chill throughout my leather clad body. Figuring that I didn't understand, he pointed to the door, where the weathered sign hung. "Dress code!" He bellowed.

I almost walked away; I didn't know what to do. But no, my kids were still inside. I walked back in, and at the mike, the new sash queen grinned and waved me over. I was waved over to the stage with an enthusiastic move that made the sash glitter under the overhead spotlights. "And here's the one we all owe so much to," I heard. I looked back at the stage like there was a lunatic shouting at me. At once, my kids came up to me, and they knew something was wrong. The older one, a man of the sash himself, took my arm, that's how bad I must have looked. I stumbled once as I made my way to the raised platform, and I looked out into the mass of my siblings in skin. I tried to say something, but the words couldn't come. I loved them, loved my place in this world.

My beautiful, heavy sash fell with such a thud that it hit the mike and caused a single screech of feedback. I shrugged the vest off, heavy with pins and ribbons and bars, and it actually made clinking sounds as it fell. My cap sailed over inky puddles of similar covers, and the snaps on my chaps exploded open even as I made my way off the stage. I turned away, stripping them from my legs, and started making my path back to the door as a new roar of confusion rose.

And my kids? Well, they made me proud. The little one came and pushed the way ahead of me, making it easier for me to leave. And elder brother took his sash off too, and left it in the damn bar, probably seeing his dream of wearing the bigger, fancier one go up in smoke. But they trusted me to act on what I did without questioning.

After all, I trained them.

And I had been trained by the best.

I only hoped my old man would have the decency to send 'em out for ice-cream while him and me had our little talk.

Dedicated, with respect, to those unrighteously turned away at the door. And of course, for John.

Everything Under Control

Frank DeCarlo is a man with a mission. Tonight's goal: getting laid. Preferably with some good-looking blond kid from the suburbs who would do just about anything and be tearfully grateful afterward. Yeah, Frank knew what he was doing. Cruising these college dances was always a winner. He was trim and good-looking, with a mustache that younger men envied, and his body looked good in the tight t-shirt and jeans that was the uniform of the day. He was everything a young faggot should be looking for, Frank admitted to himself. Older, but not too old. In good shape, but not all buffed out of proportion. An experienced man, but not to threatening. Just the kind of guy you'd want to pop your cherry and welcome you to the world of manly sexual encounters. It always worked before.

So why was tonight any different? Because the fish weren't fucking biting, that's why. He caught a few glances from guys who might have been former graduates of the DeCarlo School of Sex, but no repeat timers tonight. He had to have cherry! Fresh, young meat, ready for action, that's what Frank wanted. And he was going to get it, yes sir. Any minute now. Yep, any second, some kid is going to slide up and say something like "Hot party, huh?", and it would be home free. Or the next guy Frank decided to ask for a light would catch his eyes, and bang, they'd be off! Real soon. The next one, for sure.

People began to leave. Frank edged away from the main doors, debating about whether he should split before the exiting kids made a tide that would just carry him out. What a fuck-up of a night. You'd think these kids weren't even fucking queer, for crying out loud. Serves him right for coming to such a fucked-up dance to begin with; it's not as if it was a queer college or something. He might as well cross this place off his cruising grounds, find some new spot to choose the new meat from. Yes, sir, even as the DeCarlo strikes out, he's planning some new conquests. As for tonight, he'd just go to one of those clubs that catered to the out-of-city kids and pick up some new thing there. No problemo.

Ducking out of the gym, he almost ran into a few guys obviously returning from some kind of dipshit football thing. Was there a game? Shit, did this geeky school even have a fucking team? They must have been practicing; they looked tired and annoyed. Maybe they were losers just like the kids at the dance, Frank thought uncharitably. He snickered but avoided confrontation. You never knew when one of those steroid-induced rages might come on, and the DeCarlo was not in the mood to be bashed. He went wide, pleased that he remembered the phrase, and delivered the cruise of death to this cute number in cutoffs and a pink triangle t-shirt, who promptly dropped the quarter he was trying to get into the phone.

Bingo! The DeCarlo charm works again, Frank thought as he sauntered over. Ignoring the passing of gay dancers and tired footballers, he leaned over the phone and prepared his classic never-fail lines.

The kid was obviously too dense to get with the program, Frank thought as he watched those sexy cutoffs swish their way down the hall. Have to get home, my ass, that piece of meat was just too goddamn dumb to realize an opportunity when he saw one. Pity, too. It would have no doubt cleared up that last dotting of zits on his stupid face. Too stung to even toss him the finger, Frank turned back toward the exit again and started to walk. Man, when you're down, you're really down. Maybe that new rave thing downtown might pan out...

A low whistle entered his thoughts, and Frank jerked around to see who was being so blatant. To his surprise, it was one of the footballers, his jersey still on, leaning out of one of the blue steel doors that led to the other areas of the gym building. He was not as young as Frank liked them, and he wasn't blond, but he was hitting Frank with a gaze that would stop a lesser man in his tracks.

The DeCarlo was being heavily cruised. Well, that was a change! And not an unwelcome one, seeing how much the evening had turned out to be fucked-up.

Well, of course he's got the hots, Frank noted smugly to himself. He's probably the only queer on the fucking team, and he's gotta shower with those animals. Probably as horny as hell; probably aching for some guy to pay attention to his body. Well, OK, I can show him a good time. He swaggered over, confident in his ability, and thinking of how tight a football player's butt was, considering all the running around they do.

"Looking for a good time?" Frank asked boldly, feeling like the direct approach was probably going to be best.

"Shit yeah," the guy answered. Frank brightened and looked quickly over his shoulders. No one was looking, so he slipped into the room with

126

the athlete and ran a hand up under the jersey. Fuck, this was no kid, this was a big, grown man, hard and heavy with muscle, his brown hair damp with sweat.

Hm. Not the usual fare for the DeCarlo-meister. Frank was about to say something else, when the guy slipped one long arm around Frank's scrawny shoulders and almost lifted him off his feet. Frank felt the intrusion of a wet, slightly bitter tasting tongue between his teeth, and with a muffled cry of nothing, surrendered to a mouth rape that made him tingle to the toes in his designer knock-off cowboy boots.

Wow, this was one hell of a kiss from some college jock! Frank struggled to disengage himself, but it was a losing proposition. For one, the so-called "kid" was taller than he was. And two, well - it wasn't really that bad. Damn fucking good, actually. When the player eased back to breathe, Frank felt his heels connect with the tile floor and his head seemed a little woozier than the two lite beers he had consumed would have made it.

Whoa. Time to regain some control here! He started to say something, but it got caught in his throat, and he had to cough to clear things up. As he did, he glanced down at the player's waist and found that below the belt, the only thing he was wearing was a well-filled jockstrap.

Well, that was better! Nothing like a jockstrap to frame a man's butt and keep his jewels out of the way while he was being fucked. Frank patted the bulge affectionately. "You're ready for some action, kid," he said warmly, knowing that a few compliments always worked like fresh grease in a hot hole. He'd say some nice things before burying his bone.

"Yeah, and you look like you're up to it," the guy replied, turning his back. "Come on in, the other guys are gone."

Nice fucking view! The DeCarlo gets a football hero, film at eleven! It took all his control not to swagger some more. Instead, Frank slipped the packets of lube out of his pocket and into his hand, and started to unbutton his jeans. Yeah, he was gonna ram this big guy but good, give him a slice of Italian salami, make his butt ache with the pounding need of a good fuck, and then bring him off, splattering these lockers with something nicer than gater-fucking-ade.

But the football player returned to the locker area and started to strip off the heavy padding that still adorned his shoulders, and every move of his looked as though he was entirely unconcerned with flashing Frank with another peek at that muscled butt, and his attitude was definitely very cool about the whole thing. Frank's lips twisted into a grin. OK, so the guy was trying to fake him out by acting cool. That was OK - he'd be whimpering soon enough. Frank wrapped a fist around his love muscle and squeezed it, hard. A drop of precum was already at the tip. "Like what you see?" he asked, lifting it for the player's vision.

"Gimme a break, pal," the taller man said. "And come on over here, I want a little more tongue action from you."

"Fuck you, man! I'm outa here," Frank shot back. Shit, the fucking kid thought he was in charge of the fuck. Imagine that! Well, no one made DeCarlo roll over, that's for fucking sure. But the guy only smiled and gripped a handful of what was in the jock, and Frank's brain shifted into overload. That was some basket being carried there. Meat-filled, stuffed to the brim with a fistful of fucker. Jeeze, it would feel so good, so solid in his mou - er, hand!

Yeah! Maybe they could do a little mutual J/O, that was always good. Yeah, maybe a little guy/guy shit would work for now, until the kid was ready for the old DeCarlo meat. It's OK, he assured himself. The DeCarlo-meister has got everything under control.

There were still faint sounds of dance music discernible from the main gym. Frank found himself comfortably up against his target's body, one hand on those wrapped up tools between his legs, and the other sweeping across the broad, rippled back. Man, but this guy had a hot body! They kissed again, this time even longer, and the electric chills that ran through Frank's body were like trickles of sweet water, making him grind his exposed cock against the mesh of the jockstrap.

"You're kinda cute," the player said as he drew back for air. "Let me see your butt. I wanna hold onto it."

Hey, hey, that's the ticket, Frank thought, quickly shucking his jeans. Get a good feel of the old buns, and you'll be down on your knees sucking up the old tube steak in no time! He wondered if the weird juice that the guy drank while working out would tingle on his dick. He hoped so.

But the player showed no signs of going anywhere. He just reached down and cupped Frank's soft asscheeks in his two huge, rough hands, and practically lifted Frank off the floor! Their crotches ground together, and Frank could hear the pounding of his heart echoed in the chest he was being pressed against.

This was not going as he planned! But that new dick was so close, and so good-looking, so long and easy to grab! He reached for it with one hand and felt along the entire length and moaned out loud. It was a beauty, all right. Perfect for - perfect for...

Suddenly, he was pushed back again. "Strip to skin," came the terse command, and before he knew it, Frank was ripping the fucking t-shirt off his own body. Yeah, feel that flesh man to man, he thought, watching as the player scooped his nuts and dick out of the jock. Oh shit, that dick was a hot piece, nice and meaty, and so hard!

"Yeah. Come here, buddy, and get a whiff." Frank's nose took a dive and the rest of him followed. The jock smelled of old bleach and fabric softener and old piss and new cum. And the dick, rising from out of the white cotton nest, gleamed with sweat and precum. Frank dimly felt the hand at the back of his head. But he really felt it when that perfect dickhead slammed into his mouth, filling him with the tastes of everything he had just sniffed up!

Without even thinking, Frank reached up to caress the firm asscheeks of the man whose cock was stuffing his face. Oh yeah, just right, so hard, so hot under his hands! And the cock strained and jerked in his mouth, with every swipe of his tongue, until it felt like there was no other place for a cock to be, except for Franks slutty cocksucking mouth.

"That's it, baby, slurp that down! I'll take those!"

Frank moaned as the player leaned over, pushing him down to his knees. For a moment, Frank couldn't figure out what was happening until he heard a slight growl and a spit. That was a sound that DeCarlo often made, the sound of a man ripping open a little pack of lube with his teeth and spitting the top portion away.

That's a fucking hot sound, Frank thought for a second. But that was all the time he had, because the player jerked him off that delicious cock and up into the air to plant another soul burning kiss on him. "I'm gonna ream you out, baby," the player said, grinning. "I need it bad!"

And before Frank could say "What the fuck?" he was spinning around again, and bending over, his hands braced on the bench in front of the lockers, scattered bits of uniform and padding all around him. The jockstrap landed on the narrow bench in front of his face.

"Something for you to chew on," came the voice of his target. Frank moaned and took another strong sniff. It would help, he reasoned, to have something to sniff, 'cause it had been some time since he'd been...

"Shit! Goddamn, shitfaced, motherfucker!" Frank screamed as the athlete's cock slid into him, riding a wave of cool lube. "Oh, holy Madonna, goddamn!"

"Oh yeah!" cried the player, gripping Frank's hips in hands like steel. "Oh, baby, you're so fucking tight! Yeah, pull me in!"

Frank practically sucked that jock into his mouth. It was so uncool to scream like that! But that log being shoved into his rear was like a poker at first, reaming him good and true until his body kinda got used to it, and then he was able to relax and start pushing back. Steady, now - try to keep cool, even though your entire fucking body feels like it's gonna explode! Don't show how goddamn fucking good it feels to have that pole shoving in and drawing out -

"That's it, that's it," the player chanted. "Oh yeah, you fucking whore, fuck my stiff pole, oh, yeah, come back and take it all!"

Frank gave no argument. The stench of the soiled undergarment in his teeth was making him dizzy, and the steady pounding in his ass was making the blood rush to his dick. He looked down between his legs and saw his boner bouncing with every thrust, his balls swinging back and forth as the player happily banged away. It was too much! It was too much! He grabbed at his dick and gave it one, two, three tugs, and then the sperm rushed upwards through his nuts and shot out like cannon fire, exploding all over the bench, splattering exactly the way Frank had pictured cum splattering just a few minutes earlier!

The pulsing and clutching of his ass drew the player's cock in even further and massaged it until the guy couldn't hold onto his hard-on anymore. Frank was still grunting over the cloth in his mouth when the player reared back and then slammed forward one more time, thrusting deep inside his grasping channel until his own cum started to foam up around his plunging cock.

For a moment, they both kind of stood there, stuck together by a softening dick and a lot of mingled sweat. Then, with sighs, they pulled apart, and Frank eased himself down onto the bench. He felt like someone had just banged his butt for an hour.

The whole thing took barely fifteen minutes.

"Not bad, kid," Frank managed to croak. Funny how his throat seemed a little sore. He spat off to one side, cleared his mouth, and pullied a white cotton string from between his teeth.

"Yeah, you liked it," the guy said.

"So did you." Frank licked his lips and grabbed his t-shirt, trying to salvage the situation. "What do you say you give some of that back to me, huh? My turn now."

"Nah, I'm not into being screwed. But, you know, call me." The guy scratched his crotch absently and stalked over in the direction of the showers, leaving Frank there, clutching his t-shirt to his chest.

When he came back, the t-shirt was still there, but his jersey and jock were gone.

DeCarlo strikes again, Frank thought, feeling the night air through the mesh of the jersey. Yeah, this shirt was going to be a lucky charm for sure. Flash it around, let a guy take a whiff, and Frank would be balls deep in some stud's gullet by the time you could say "halfback." Hell yes, he was in fine form tonight. Couldn't miss! Everything was perfectly under control!

Looking for Bubba

(First published in *Southern Comfort*, edited by David Lawrence.)

"Seems lahk ya found yerself one sorry-ass fuckin' faggot, Charlie!"

"His ass is sure gonna be sorry when we finish up, ain't it, Hank?" This was accompanied by a jerky, tortured spasm between a giggle and a snort, an almost spastic growling, snurfing sound that might have been a death rattle or someone laughing so hard they had forgotten to breathe.

"You bet, Charlie." Hank fingered the fly of his ancient, dirt-encrusted no-name denims and scratched the thickening bulge while expertly ejaculating a thin stream of shit-brown spit into the dust. "Less see if his purty mouth is any good first, OK? That's what faggots like to do, right? Suckin' a real man's fat cock? You want my big fat cock, don't ya, faggot? Tell me ya want my dick in yer cocksucking faggot mouth, and maybe me an' Charlie'll be nice ta ya. Like maybe we'll let ya keep a few teeth!"

Suddenly, coming South for my summer vacation didn't seem like the brightest idea I'd ever had.

There's a certain mystery in whatever you don't have at home - isn't that always the truth? The allure of the strange, of the unpredictable, of anything that's just damn different.

But I never counted on the killing summer heat.

City born and bred, the product of three generations of college-going proper upper middle class accountants and civil engineers and car salesmen, Catholic and Democrat - my existence was nothing but comfortable and educated and, well, civilized. I didn't turn out bad, coming from all that. At twenty-four years old, my master's in hand, I was capable of doing just about anything I wanted. My family was supportive, encouraging, even enthusiastic when I told them I was going to do a little traveling before settling into some nice, comfortable, predictable job. They might have been a little perplexed at my stated destinations, but still they saw me off with all due fanfare for my summer of adventures.

No one warned me about the 'skeeters.

But then, I never told them exactly where I was going - only gave them a rough idea. When I said Georgia, they assumed Atlanta. When I said Tennessee, they might have thought Memphis. (I'm sure my sister did, because she asked for a souvenir of Graceland.) I don't know what they made of Alabama. Maybe they assumed it was a package tour, take two states and you get the third one free.

So, all their warnings were of the typical worried family type; don't flash your money, lock your valuables up in the hotel safe, take your vitamins.

Maybe if I'd said more, someone might have mentioned that I should probably travel with a companion. Someone who was bigger, stronger, and much more willing to fight than I was.

In the final analysis, I should have done more research. After all, it was my bliss I was following. It might have made sense to know a little more about it! But I was obsessed with my goal, my treasure of the South. I was looking for Bubba.

Not a specific Bubba, mind you. But not just any Bubba, either. First of all, he'd have to be queer, like me. I knew that wasn't going to be very easy. But then, I didn't want him *too* queer. After all, I can get a dozen fairy cowboys with weird accents on any night down at the Roundup.

No, I wanted a *real* Bubba. A born and bred Son of the South, a backroads, white-trash, drawl speakin', coon eatin', huntin' and fishin' Bubba, complete with beer can and pickup truck. And I was confident I'd find one, too. My experiences out west, at college, had taught me that we were, in fact, everywhere - even in Hicks-town, USA. And the eye contacts, subtle signs and blatant cruising that worked in Chicago worked twice as well in rest stops in the middle of nowhere, Nebraska. In fact, the men who lusted after dick and lived in the sticks seemed even more willing to duck into a stall, or behind some bushes, or rarely and wonderfully, in the "coffins" of their 18-wheelers, for a blowjob or even a quick screw.

I will never forget that big-bellied trucker from Iowa, whose body was as hard as it was huge, and whose dick was an uncut masterpiece of manflesh. He spent six blissful hours fucking my mouth and ass, snoring between bouts, keeping his meaty hands on my body at all times. I staggered from his truck, dizzy and exhausted, and didn't even mind having to wait until the following morning to catch a ride back to school. Hell, would you?

But my one idol, the kind of man I lusted after since I first realized it was men who turned my crank, was not the Midwestern blue-collar worker, the Eastern sophisticate (or his California/Seattle counterpart), or even the Western cowboy. I wanted Bubba. A tobacco-chewin', whisky-drinkin', old-car-on-cinder blocks in the front yard, thumbs in the overalls, cap-wearin' Rebel Howler, whose Daddy taught him how to shoot, and whose Mama taught him how to treat a lady.

I dreamed of him at night, alone in my bed, my hand busy on my cock. How he'd appear, scruffy and arrogant, the hole in his jeans put there while 'rasslin', or even by just plain workin', not by some sissified city-bred designer. I dreamed of his voice, rough and teasing and slow, and the smell of his breath, tainted by old smoke, barbeque and beer. I saw his thick, heavily-veined cock, never deprived of its foreskin, and his low-hanging, fat balls. I felt his hard, calloused hands grasping my head or my butt, as he speared that dick into me, cursing and spitting, and slamming into my faggot holes until he was finished.

OK, so my fantasies are a bit on the self-hating side. But just as I hear some women get off on rape stories, so did I. Over and over again. Except that really, I didn't want to actually be raped. I just wanted to find me a queer Bubba.

It turned out harder than I thought.

I started out in Atlanta because it was cheaper to fly there first. And of course, I ran into nothing but the biggest queens I ever saw in my life. You'd think they learned all about how to behave by watching *Gone With the Wind!* And every one of them had their lovely accents dulled by years of watching television, or a conscious effort not to appear as though they came from the Bible Belt. One young piece of manflesh, who had attracted me with his cut-off sleeveless shirt - the one that exposed the proudly waving stars-and-bars tattooed on one rippling bicep - turned into a genuine Southern Belle after I admitted I'd recently gotten my degree.

"Oh honey," he exclaimed, running one finger down my arm, "I love a thinking kind of man. Want to show me your thesis?"

I left Atlanta as soon as I got hold of some maps.

My first forays took me to the scenes of my best hunting, roadside rest stops. Once on the road, I hitched rides and took local busses from town to town, slipping out at likely places whenever there appeared to be a preponderance of pickups and old Chevys in sight. It was a brutal summer - daytime highs made me dizzy, and the bugs were so numerous, I thought I'd stumbled onto a section of the Amazon by accident. I doused myself with sunblock and Off, and suffered through it all, looking for my knight in overalls. At one genuine truck stop, I took up my place at the urinal as soon as I saw this one guy saunter through the door.

Oh, here was my Bubba! Six feet of pure-bred, pork-fed back-country gristle, sweatin' like a pig and stinkin' of the road. His long, dirty-blond hair was caught up in a red bandanna that was oil-spotted and threadbare, and there were cracks in his heavy shit-kickin' work boots. I slid my eyes over to his meat, and was rewarded by a heavy, long dick that curved down in a perfect angle for my very hungry throat. He pissed a thick, yellow stream that splashed noisily against the back of the porcelain, and sighed as he let it go.

"Ain't nothin' like a good piss," I said, sighing myself.

"Uh-huh," he grunted. He shook himself, once twice - and oh yes, there was that telltale third and fourth shake. I trembled as I put my own equipment away. I dared to look into his eyes.

They were blue, of course. He looked me over and gave a shake of his head, toward the door. At that point, I would have followed him to a KKK rally. I eagerly trailed him between the rows of tiny crash rooms, and when he unlocked one door, I almost came in pure excitement.

I was on the thinly carpeted floor as soon as he closed the door behind us. There was barely room to move around - the bed took up most of the floor space. But I didn't care - I needed that dick socketed tightly in my throat! He whipped it out and presented it to me and I swallowed it whole, in one long, loud slurp - that's how starved I was.

This was my dream come true, my Bubba, in the flesh! Sure, he was cut, but he had a big ol' dangly dick that slid down my faggot, cocksucking throat like butter over cornpone - whatever that was! My own cock was pressed so hard against my fly, I thought it would rip right through. But I didn't want to offend this good ol' boy by taking my dick out - if he wanted to see it, that was fine. But I was prepared for hostility at the possibility that we might get so "queer" together.

No, I had what I wanted - a big cock down my throat, slipping back and forth over my tongue. I worked it as well as I could, and was delighted that he didn't at once take hold of my head and just fuck my face. How nice of him! When I backed away and licked at the head, he even moaned a little, and sighed heavily when I sucked my way back down the shaft.

Then, suddenly, I did feel his hands on my head. "Slow down," he said, gently. I was so startled, I left off sucking and looked up at him.

"Man, you're good!" he said, stepping over me and plopping down on the bed. "But you're getting all the action! Come on up here and let me see that nice chunk of meat you've got on you. Let's sixty-nine!"

His voice was pure city - his accent, well - missing! I gaped for a moment, and then blinked, and he chuckled. "Well, come on up, kid, I haven't got all day! Got to get back to Detroit the day after tomorrow. Let's get it on!"

Great. I'd come to nowhere Georgia to meet a trucker from Detroit. But he did have a nice cock, and it had been a while...I climbed into bed and we did indeed suck each other's wangs until we both had a respectable orgasm, after which I made my farewells and spent five dollars on a shower and a burger and hit the road again.

And that was the first scene in my summer vacation comedy of errors.

In Calhoun, I found a former Professor of English Literature at a country/western bar, arm wrestling for beers. We had a lovely chat about post-enlightenment novels, and whether Gatsby was a repressed homosexual.

Outside of Chattanooga, I was picked up by a redneck auto mechanic who, after shooting down my chest within moments of my first slobbering on his dick. He sat down next to me under a big tree and sobbed about how his wife caught him looking at Playgirl once, and threatened to tell the minister, and how he couldn't leave her, ever, and my God, wasn't he a big sinner? I swatted mosquitoes and tried to comfort him as best as I could.

On my way to Shelbyville, I thought I was going to get it bad when the cowboy type I eyed in the roadhouse bar stood up and growled at me. But his friends calmed him down, and I figured I'd escaped a bashing. But later on, as I walked toward the motel that the highway sign promised was "just down the road a ways", that same cowboy pulled up in a red pickup and I stared up at the guy when he popped open the passenger door.

"Come on, pal," he said, in a perfectly clear and educated Atlanta accent. "Don't you know some of these boys can be dangerous to your health? Sorry to scare you, but I had to stop you from makin' eyes at every good ol' boy back there - they'd stomp on you until there was nothin' left! Want a ride somewhere? I know a place where you can get some iced cappuccino that's just to die for!"

Steve - even his name wasn't Southern! - gave me a lift to Shelbyville, and I gave him some very good head, and he also tucked a list of gay bars into my pocket before he roared off, his radio blaring songs of heterosexual frustration.

I was beginning to wonder if the gay gene also made men into urbanites. Because I sure as hell wasn't finding any tough, backwoods country bears. Two more times, I struck out in Tennessee, and for each time, I got a lecture about not cruising the straight men. It was no good trying to explain that I wanted a gay man who just acted like a redneck. I mean, yeah, I wanted a guy who would appreciate me opening my mouth and butt for him - but I didn't want him to be "gay," per se. Apparently, there was no such thing.

I wandered into a revival meeting tent in Scottsboro, Alabama, after deciding that the mountain boys of Tennessee weren't quite working out. It was a steaming day, and I was aching from the road. Normally, you couldn't even get me to go to our nice, air conditioned church back home. At least the tent was shade, and these sweet old ladies were handing out plastic cups of icy lemonade. I decided to stay for the show.

And it was a show, all right! A rocking choir, swinging and swaying to gospel music, a thunderous, handsome preacher whose voice carried throughout the area without a mike, and people leaping up and dancing, shrieking, and shouting lively answers whenever the preacher asked them a rhetorical question. I would have gotten into it if I hadn't been so damn tired. And then, I noticed the guy standing off to one side, obviously a latecomer.

He was wearing an old pair of working pants, frayed around his boot-tops, but clean. He wore no belt, but a pair of suspenders held the pants up around his hips, and provided an excellent frame for his broad chest. The light blue chambray shirt was stiff, but so thin that I could see the entire outline of his arms and shoulders under it. A dark colored tie was knotted and loosened around his throat, but not enough to look sloppy. His hair was an assortment of darker colors bleached by the sun on the top.

Here, surely, was Bubba, in his Sunday best. I was drawn to him, and why him out of the hundreds of men who eventually came to the meeting, I don't know. There were certainly prettier men there, and a few men who better fit my picture of white trash heaven. Maybe it was the way he kept thumbing his suspenders, running his digits up and down the straps in a mesmerizing pattern that I knew was putting pressure on his groin.

I know it was putting pressure on mine!

I tried to move closer to him, but we were separated by a sudden rush of folks getting up to be touched by the preacher man, who had just finished a rhapsody about the healing touch of Our Lord and Savior. I had a different kind of touch on my mind, and groaned out loud when I realized that my golden Bubba was gone, vanished into the crowd.

I declined the chance to get slapped or pushed by the preacher and instead made my panting and dripping way outside of the tent. I was a wreck, sweat soaked, exhausted, frustrated - but I knew that if I hitched a ride from one of these folks, they'd happily see me to the next air conditioned motel, with the blessings of Jesus ringing out around my head. So, I staggered over to a row of tables where more drinks were available. I doused my head with a handful of ice cubes and gulped down more lemonade while I pretended to be interested in little plastic Jesus babies and glow in the dark crosses. I bought a fan that read "Make a joyous noise unto the Lord," and put it to good use, while scanning the area for the best place to hitch a ride.

136

And that's when I saw him again! He was standing outside the main tent, looking around the area. My heartbeat quickened, and I worked my way through the crowds to put myself into his line of vision. When his eyes fell on me, I grinned.

To my amazement, he grinned right back! And cocked his head in the direction of the side of the tent that lead off toward the dirt road. Then, he began idly strolling that way, his thumbs locked onto his suspenders.

The grin was too friendly for my faggot-snarling Bubba, but what the hell! He was damn cute, and I was used to settling for Southern queerboys. I casually followed him, getting through the crowd and sliding alongside the big tent. The dirt road led over a little hill, and then down into a wooded depression. Perfect for a brief erotic encounter! I looked for him, and then almost jumped right out of my sneakers when I felt a tap on my shoulder.

"Hey there, purty boy," said a gruff voice from behind me. I whirled around, and was faced with an enormous, filthy specimen of manhood - if he was indeed homo sapiens. Maybe six and a half feet of hairy muscle, topped with dank, greasy black hair and a few days worth of growth on the face. His tobacco stained teeth showed when he spoke, and every word sent billows of heavy, beer laden stench into my face. He spat. "Lookin' fer someone?"

"Lookin' fer me, I betcha," came another voice. This one was my Bubba, now divested of his shirt. His chest looked every bit as fine as I would have expected, streaked with sweat and glistening. But his friendly grin had transformed itself into a feral, sadistic leer, as he came up from the side and giggled. "Whut did I tell ya, Hank? Ain't he whut I said?"

"Seems lahk ya found yerself one sorry-ass fuckin' faggot, Charlie!"

And this is where you came in.

"Sorry," I said, trying to back away. "I just thought you were someone I knew - my mistake -"

Charlie made another of those choking laughs, and I wondered how the hell I'd ever found him attractive. "Y'sure did, motherfucker! You done made a mistake you ain't nevah gonna ferget!"

Hank was still clutching at the bulge in his jeans, and he spat again. "Y'can suck my cock good and gentle," he growled, popping the button open, "or y'can take my big dick down yer cocksuckin' throat like a fifty dollar whore, until you fuckin' die, you got that, faggot? Now, I want you gobblin' my meat like a good faggot, before I get real angry."

"Mine, too!" Charlie exclaimed. "Yer gonna get all the dick y'can handle, you fuckin' fairy! Man, I ain't screwed me a butthole in ages - I bet you want that too!"

Erection or no erection, this was not working out right. I had no illusions about these two; they were going to fuck the shit out of me and probably leave me a pounded red mess on this dirt road. I started to run.

With a whooping noise that must be an abbreviated rebel yell, they took off after me. I wanted to head toward the tents again, but they had blocked that way, so I ran off the side of the road, hoping to at least come around in a circle to where there were more people. But it was hot, and I was tired, and they were strong and, well, determined. It was Charlie who tackled me and brought me down, and with one powerful head butt, knocked me flat. At once, his mass slammed into me, driving what little air I had out, and in the next minute, I found myself turned over onto my belly, as powerful hands grabbed at my jeans waistband and started to pull. I screamed, and felt something slam into the side of my head, once, twice.

"You be a good lil' faggot," Hank snarled, lifting my head by the hair. "And we'll show ya whut real men do to fairies like you!" His hand passed in front of my eyes for a second, and then I saw his dick, wet and hard, and aiming right at me, his fist tight in my hair. Meanwhile, Charlie had managed to strip off enough clothing to get at what he wanted, and I was dragged up onto my hands and knees, and I ground my teeth in despair.

"Well, look a'dis, boys - I din' knows Hank an' Charlie wuz faggots!"

I was dropped quicker than a worm po'boy, and Hank and Charlie both scrambled up. I gasped and struggled to pull myself together.

"Wha'thefuck y'all doin' here?" Hank demanded. "Get yer butts back ta niggerland, this ain't none o'yer business!"

"We ain't faggots!" Charlie screamed. "This faggot's the faggot!"

I looked up, and saw two black men, neatly dressed - they must have come from the meeting. The one who had spoken was nearly as big as Hank - bigger, in fact, in the chest and shoulders. He was wearing a lightweight tan jacket over a tightly fitting white shirt. To me, he looked like a god. I tried to roll away, and caught a kick from Charlie.

"We're jus' teachin' this faggot a lesson, ain't none o'yer affair," Hank growled. "Now, git!"

"I reckon it's our business, Hank," the tall one said. "I reckon it's our business whenever you gets it into yo' head to beat some po' city boy into the groun'. Now, I figure it's all done, you had your fun. Why don't you leave this boy be, and git yo'self back t'yo own business?"

"Yeah," added the shorter black man. "You don't want us tellin' folks we foun' you, wit' yo' dicks hangin' out fo' some man, do you?"

"Two o' us, two o' you," Charlie sniggered. "We gonna pound you into the fuckin' dirt, nigger, and then mess up this faggot, too!"

"No, I don' think so," said the first man. "I think you's gonna put yo' dicks away an' go on home. 'Cause there ain't but two of us here - my

138

other bro's 'r' right down th'hill. An' you don' wanna make me call 'em up, do you?"

Hank glared at them and spat at me again. But he did shove his dick back into his jeans. "Whut are ya doin', Hank?" Charlie complained.

"Too many niggers aroun' here," Hank sneered. "Seems like they want a lil' butt action, to. Everyone knows niggers is all faggots, anyway. But you watch yer butts, boys - one day, you ain't gonna be all t'gether!"

And with two more kicks solidly landed on me, the two men stomped off down the road. Within moments, I could hear Charlie's strangled laugh. I wondered dimly what Hank could possibly say that could be funny.

"Y'all right?" I heard from over my shoulder. I grunted and spat out some dusty blood and then groaned as I tried to push myself up. "C'mon, bro', we gotta git you ta mama," said the man with the deep voice. I nodded and felt myself lifted easily up, and thanked my stars, God, and the luck that follows fools that I had been saved from my own fantasies.

When I awoke, I found myself in a large, soft bed, sunlight streaming in between blue speckled curtains. I was aching, especially around my head, but felt clean and cool. I was in a small room, made smaller by the presence of the bed. Across from me was an old dresser, the top crowded with pictures of black people in various arrangements. I remembered my saviors and tried to get up. I was almost naked - only my jockey shorts remained. I looked at the colorful bruises on my chest and across my stomach, and stretched. And that's when the tall, deep voiced man came in the bedroom door.

He wasn't in his good clothes any more. Today he wore overalls over a faded gas station T-shirt. His powerful arms were dotted with a little sweat, and there was a faint odor of gasoline or motor oil around him. He grinned when he saw me up.

"Hey there," he said amiably. "I brung you somethin' cold t'drink. Mama says you c'n eat later, after you gets some liquids in yo' belly. I figgered I'd bring 'em over, since I got some time."

"Thanks," I croaked, gratefully accepting the tall glass of water. It went down like an icy beer after softball, sweet and filling. It also eased some of my pounding headache. "Listen," I said, when I put it down, "I didn't get a chance to thank you last night. You saved my life!"

"Well, I figger we at leas' saved your butt," he said, his deep brown eyes dancing.

"Yeah," I admitted, blushing.

"An' it's a mighty fine butt, if'n I say so," he continued.

"Um," was the best I could manage. I stared at him as he popped open the buttons holding the flap of his overalls up.

"I don' know whut y'all did t'Hank an' Charle, makin' 'em think you was a faggot, but I sure know 'bout some of them places y'all had on a note in your pocket." He pulled a folded piece of paper out of his own pocket and showed it to me. It was the list of Tennessee gay bars that whatshisname gave me back when I was up there! "An' I figger y'all might want to, well, thank me proper, if you're feelin' a mite better now." With that, he stripped the shirt off of his powerful, dark chest, and then drew the heavy zipper down the front of the overalls. There was a light smattering of short, black hairs down the center of his chest and belly, leading directly to the thatch of curled strands of ink which covered the base of a mighty pillar of, well, what I could only think of as dark meat. A long, thick tube of a cock, foreskin already peeling back over a burgundy colored head.

I untangled my legs from the sheets and scooted over to that magnificent specimen of manmeat. That cool drink of water seemed ages ago - my mouth was thirsty for more. I opened wide and sucked in the head, feeling it fill my mouth. It seemed to pulse, to expand, as my tongue did its little dance around the crown. And I moaned as I probed the tight crevasse created by the wrinkled foreskin, and I tenderly licked out the sweaty essence this hot man was carrying with him.

Eagerly, I licked up and down that thick shaft, getting a feel for its heft and weight. He sighed as I swallowed him down, and out one huge hand on my head to encourage me to take him all the way to the root! Oh, yes, that's it, I thought, make me take your big horsecock right down my white, faggot throat! Give me this load of flesh until I choke! He took my throaty smacking noises as encouragement and held onto me, drawing me in tighter, until at last my lips slammed into his pubic hairs, and I could barely breathe!

I let him lead, my muffled sounds of pleasure spurring him on. Soon, he just jerked me around onto my back, pulled my head off the bed and just slammed his dick down my outstretched throat like he was fucking the ass he saved the night before! I was in heaven! Above me, I was surrounded by his powerful legs, and the musky scent of his balls. When he pulled out and let me lick the head of his cock again, I whimpered like a whipped pup. But he wasn't denying me anything - he was just reaching into his fly to tug out the most godawful huge balls I'd ever seen.

"See if y'can get these in that faggot mouth," he growled, cupping and pulling on them. "Suck my nuts, you purty whiteboy, suck on my goddamn nuts!"

It turned out that I could not. The twin sacs were just too huge to fit in my mouth. But it wasn't for lack of trying! I drooled and choked and sucked and licked for what seemed like ages, until he couldn't stand it any more and socketed his dick right back into my sucking throat.

140

"Suck me off, suck me off," he grunted as he pumped. I barely had the room or strength to really suck, but I kept myself open for him, and when he grabbed my hair and ground into me, I found my own stiff dick and jerked it out of my jockeys just in time to shoot a stream of cum so hard that I almost blacked out! My cries of pleasure and the panting I did around his rod hit the right combination for him - all of a sudden, he started to convulse, and growl, and then he pulled out and covered my own splatterings of cum with his gigantic load, splashing ropy streams of cum all over my chest and belly.

"Oh, yeah," he sighed, milking the last drops out and shaking them over me. "Now, that was some nice cocksuckin', boy. Ain't nothin' like bein' sucked off by a real fag."

I was still breathing heavily, so I just dragged myself back onto the bed and concentrated on recovering while he tucked his beautiful cock and balls away.

"I guess I gotta get back t'work," he sighed, picking up his shirt. "But I'll be back aroun' dinner, maybe y'can do it again."

"Anytime," I croaked.

"That's nice t'hear," he said. "I guess it'd be nice ta be introduced. I saw your driver's license, so I knows your name is Gregory. I'm Robert, Robert Keller."

"Greg," I said with a slight cough. "My friends call me Greg."

"Well, Greg, 'round here, folks call me Bubba."

Finally!

Brian on the Farm

(First printed in *Switch Hitters*, edited by Carol Queen and Lawrence Schimel.)

There was a certain symmetry to the it all, the eternal rhythm that poets attach to work they've never done, that historians pass off as the fate of the invisible masses who built pyramids, raised cities, spread over the world like a blanket that was torn and mended by forces larger and more relevant than the fabric itself.

On the other hand, Brian thought, shouldering the fertilizer bag and grunting as he unbent his knees, it could be that this is the most boring, repetitious life a human being can live, and you gotta dress it up to make it sound like it's something worth doing.

"Keep moving, shithead, there's a ton of that shit's gotta move before lunch!" The station manager laughed at his misfire toward humor, but his fingers snapped and Brian moved. To anger Ross, or worse, to make Ross think you were shirking, was to invite the flat, heavy blade of the odd tool used to keep the farmboys in line. Brian never imagined that he would miss Chris' old strap, but this device made him positively lust for the comfort of the old, oiled leather, so warm in a man's hand, so comforting on his ass.

What Ross, and every other manager on the Farm had, was a stick that propelled a single thickness of cut and looped strap leather. It flew sideways, a failure at aerodynamics, and then hit the body with a thud, sometimes wrapping around a thigh or arm, or even slapping against the back of a head held too high. Used heavily, it could knock you down. Used lightly, it hit like a knotted rope. It didn't excite. It didn't thud, or leave a warm impression of personal attention. It smacked hard, and went away, and made you feel achy and foolish.

Amazing how they always found things that don't make me hot, Brian sighed. But it works, doesn't it? I picked up the damn shit and moved the damn shit, and I didn't get hit - this time. And when another man did get a smack from Ross, Brian moved even faster, heaving the bag over the side of the cart and running back for another one. He was a good worker, according to his charts. Much better than he had been in the first few months. But then, the owner had said, after personally whipping the bejesus out of Brian for not fulfilling his quota of tasks that week, he was only a city boy. Probably thought he'd be sucking cock on some carpeted floor somewhere, perfumed and pretty in some leather harness or some such. In fact, the owner continued, maybe he misses those fancy duds. Put him in a harness, fellas, he had said on his way out of the barn. Brian fell backward into the arms of the managers, who laughed as they put him to bed that night. He didn't understand the laughter then, but when he was harnessed to the cart the next day, the straps padded so they wouldn't cut into his aching shoulders. He hated the laughter. He hated California, his training, his owner, his sale, and most of all, he loathed his stupid self, for ever thinking he wanted a life like this.

There were two other men in the harness today, and when the last bag was loaded, Brian whistled, and they put their backs against the straps and the cart lurched along the treads in the dirt road. Brian was just not a very good cart man, he didn't have the back or leg muscles. Yet. But the way he was building, he was certainly at his physical peak. He'd always been health conscious before, never carrying too much weight, never being too soft. But now, he was in better shape than any of his gym buddies back home would ever believe. His chest had deepened, and his arms bulked up. His waist was narrow, his stomach flat, and the curves of his ass were hard and round. He could scarcely believe it was the same man who looked back at him in the mirror. But there was no doubt. With a ring in each of his nipples, one through his cock head and one behind his balls, he was still every inch the Brian who left New York awaiting a life of sexual servitude.

"Brian! Stop loafing and get your sorry ass over to southwest four. The irrigation system is down!"

"Yessir!" Brian snapped, and instantly went off at a run. Slaves did not walk here, unless they were indoor slaves. Outside workers wore thick boots with running treads and heavy socks, brief shorts and no shirts, unless they needed padding for carrying or harness work. The chain collar around his neck didn't bounce like it used to, because he used their one permitted decoration, a bandanna with the name of the vineyard on it, to wrap the chain.

He had learned to do this in his first week, by watching the senior slaves. That night, they took him down in the bunkhouse and made him pay for using their technique without asking permission. It had been a wet dream made into a strange kind of nightmare, to be held down by a bunch of hunky, hot cowboy types who spread his ass cheeks and rammed their hard cocks into him like some kind of anonymous fuckhole. They had condoms, and piled them in front of his face as they finished, and he cried when he saw them accumulate.

"They learned ya good," one of the managers said the next morning, as Brian staggered along the breakfast line. "We're gonna keep that video, ya snot nose city boy."

That evening, Brian looked up, and to be sure, there were video cameras in every corner of the room. Not only had his after-hours gang rape been acceptable, it was obviously part of his service to the owner he had rarely seen. It was a terrible thing to know, although in a way it was also reassuring. He had survived the incident and the men did not place him in any danger. And somewhere, men were watching it, holding their cocks, laughing, or groaning, and blowing their hot loads at the picture of Brian's butt being mercilessly plowed by his fellow farmboys.

And that was OK.

He caught one of the trucks heading over to the section he was being sent to, and swung onto it, helped by the two men who were already hitching rides. This was permitted, as long as you took responsibility for hopping on and off without getting yourself injured. An injury cost time at work, and cost you ride privileges. You learned how to run at a speed to match the truck and make sure you could make the final jump. And you learned which men were likely to help, and which ones might pull their hands away at the last minute to watch you fall. The politics of the farmboys were as intricate as those in the real world. You had to know where you stood, not only to the senior slaves and managers, but with every other man on the place. All forty of them. On the Farm, all menial labor was done by a man with a collar around his neck. It was like a world out of a fantasy novel, except that fantasy novels don't mention heatstroke and raw wounds on your hands and insects and blisters and…well, everything else wasn't so bad.

"Barbecue for dinner tonight," one of the other men said, eyeing his jumping off point. "Chicken. Looks good. Gonna be at the swim?"

"I'm there, dude," Brian laughed. As the cook's helper jumped off, Brian shifted over to the corner and fought back the slight feeling of hunger. He was hungry a lot, although not truly. It was the hard work that did it.

Two hours after a good meal, the very thought of food would make him salivate. He missed snacking, a lot. He missed soda, and beer. They told him that they got beer once a year, after the harvest was done, at a big party, where the slaves competed in games and were rewarded or demoted for their year's work. This would be his first harvest. He was looking forward to it the way he used to think about summer vacation. He was so entranced by the thought, he almost missed his jump off point, but the truck hit a bump and he was startled out of his reverie. He ran the rest of the way to his next job and put food and beer out of his mind.

It had not been easy to learn how to do that. Ignoring discomforts and inconveniences was one of his first lessons back when he was being trained. His trainer, a short, stocky man named Chris Parker, had no patience with the slightest evidence of Brian's displeasure. Every grimace, every twitch of the body, every hint that Brian was not devoted to the task at hand, was punished. Here on the farm, that level of control wasn't necessary all the time. The managers understood about reactions to pain, about the groans that accompanied the announcements about which task needed redoing, and how much later they were going to be working. But if any of them took a disliking to you, those little reactions were ample reason to pull you aside and use that damn linked strap, or just plant a kick into your ribs or butt.

I like my punishments more on the formal side, Brian admitted. He always had. The feeling of a man's hand against his butt, the tightening in his gut when he bent for the lash, the way his body relaxed into the floor when the bondage was tightened - those were the things that called to him in his dreams. They were in no short supply here - but they were to be earned by good behavior, not fucking up. There were no fools managing the Farm.

The irrigation systems were vital, and constantly needed tending, especially in a season of drought. Leak or stoppage was equally dangerous, and when you were called on to help the water team, you went at light speed. He showed up and they put him to work immediately. He went where they pointed, held what they gave him, and did what he was told until they all grunted with satisfaction and sent him away again. Once, he had asked how it all worked. One man looked at him suspiciously. Another man laughed and told him to get lost.

When you had a good job on the Farm, you wanted to keep it.

On the way back to the main buildings, he jogged along the side of the road, stopping and bowing as one of the house vehicles passed him. It slowed, and pulled over. Obeying standard instructions, he jogged over to it and collapsed to his knees at the side of the road, bowing his head and spreading his legs wide. He was a mess. His shoulders and arms were still streaked with the dark smudges of the bags of fertilizer, and his shorts were muddy and soaked through. He was dirty and smelly. But likely, they thought he was someone else. He wanted to brush his nose, for a fly came to annoy him, but held the position as two sets of boots came to stop in front of him.

"Name."

"Sir, Brian, Number 139, sir.

"From?"

"New York, sir."

"Oh yes, last year's sale. You were from Elliot."

Brian's head twitched, and he couldn't stop from glancing up. It was the Master himself! He gasped and almost lost his position. He hadn't seen the man much since his sale - and then, just a glance, as he was pulled away from his table and shackled and hooded and hustled away by two other men. And then the one time he'd been personally beaten by the man, hehadn't been able to get more than a glimpse. All he had seen was an older man with dark, honey-brown skin and iron-gray hair and a thick mustache. He had seen pictures of his Master from time to time, especially in the wine magazines and papers that were available for the slaves to read on Sundays. He knew that his owner was born in America of a Mexican mother, and had risen from a vineyard manager to the owner of an entire wine making industry, married to a woman who brought old California family names into the arrangement. He was a multi-millionaire, somewhat of a recluse, and the vineyards where immaculately dressed young men guided tourists through an orgy of grape products were far from the ones where half naked slaves toiled for the owner's pleasure.

"You make the strangest buys," the other man was saying. "This is no farm hand. Leatherboy, right?"

"On the nose. Raw, absolutely raw. But he seems to have worked out. Haven't you, boy?"

"Yes, Master, thank you, sir," Brian answered immediately.

"I like the novices. It astounds them so - all of this. Is that not true, Brian? Eyes up."

Brian swallowed and looked up into the face of his owner. The man's eyes seemed kind, which was somehow more frightening than if they had been hard and predatory.

"Yes, Master," he answered quickly. And then, he took a glance at the other man. He was unfamiliar, a pale faced man in a stylish suit with soft, draped trousers. The crossed throat of his silk shirt was dark with a ridge of sweat, and his eyes were hidden behind cobalt blue sunglasses. His jaw was long and hard, and his body slender. He looked like a record producer, or a coke dealer. He had a hard-on that made a tube of silk down his right leg.

He didn't seem very concerned with it.

"All right," Cobalt Blue said with a sigh. "I'll give him a try. But you will have him bathed first - I'm not into raunch."

"Of course! Not everyone is like Dane!" They laughed, and Cobalt Blue headed back to the air conditioned comfort of the car. Brian shook uncontrollably as his owner tapped him lightly on the head.

"Report to the main house, and tell them you are for Harrison tonight. Do you understand?"

"Yes, Master," Brian choked out. He bowed his head all the way, touching his forehead to the ground, his legs aching, and stayed there until the car pulled away. When he got up, he was trembling.

He had never seen the main house before.

He reported to Ross first, as he was supposed to do. Ross shook his head in disbelief, and had Brian strip down and shower first. The slave's shower was outside, and the soap they used was plain. In a fresh pair of shorts and a pair of sandals, Brian hitched onto another truck and took four miles off of the trip to the main house. When he got there, he reported to Gregor, the butler, and was immediately sent to the kitchen for a light meal. He ate like he was starving, relishing the taste of food prepared for the house instead of for the field. Then, after he licked his lips and drank down almost a full quart of milk, he was taken to an indoor bathroom for yet another cleansing, under the supervision of the house slave manager. This time, he was cleansed inside and out, and the soaps and shampoos were scented and commercial and luxurious. He was inspected for any traces of hair on his body, and his buzz cut was pronounced acceptable.

He had a sudden memory of the scene in *The Wizard of Oz*, when Dorothy was propelled through a series of makeover parlors on her way to finally see the Wizard. He wanted to start singing, and struggled with the impulse.

It was clearly panic.

"He's for Harrison," the manager said, passing him off to yet another man, who took him upstairs and into the guest wing. Finally, he ended up in one of the western exposure rooms. There, with no vocal warning at all, he felt for the first time since those earliest days, the stiff embrace of leather around his wrists and ankles. They pulled a hood over his head, and he breathed in the scent of it, of the sweat of other men, of oils and traces of musk. His eyes were blocked by a padded blindfold. His mouth was left open, but he knew that there would be a mouthpiece nearby. It could be a bar, a ball, or shaped like a cock. Or, it could be a ring, or a tube. He found that he was shaking again.

"Poor thing, fresh from the fields. Don't worry, Harrison won't hurt you," came a whisper, hard against the side of the hood. Brian almost felt like crying - acts of such spontaneous kindness were rare and treasured. He felt his hands being cuffed out to his sides, his legs brought under him and clipped together. There was something for him to rest his butt against - he settled back as comfortably as he could.

Then, it occurred to him that his "benefactor" could have been lying through his teeth.

I was insane for doing this, he thought bitterly. They should have kicked me out the first day. I'm out of my fucking mind.

But his cock was hard.

"Hello, Farmboy Brian, number whatever-you-are," said Cobalt Blue. (Harrison, thought Brian, Harrison. Sir.)

"Good evening, sir."

"Farmboy Brian, do you suck cock?"

"Yes, sir!"

"I mean really suck cock, Brian, like dragging a bus down the road by the pipe, like a drowning man sucking in a last breath of air?"

"Yes, sir," Brian almost purred. It had been a long time since he actually got to suck a cock. Cocks were far too often just shoved into his mouth, or down his throat. The last time he had actually sucked one, lovingly and with all the skills he possessed, had been several months earlier, when one of the managers took him home to try him out in private, turning oddly gentle once they were away from the bunkhouse.

"Too bad," Harrison sighed. "You all fucking suck cock like a dream. I was hoping you'd be an exception."

The sounds seemed to indicate that Harrison was seating himself opposite Brian, in a comfortable wing-backed chair that would leave his crotch at perfect cocksucking level for someone on his knees. But Brian was stunned by the strange comment that the man had made, and he tried to figure out some way to answer it.

"Would - would you like me to - to be bad at it, sir?" he asked hesitantly.

"No, not especially. I'd just like you to be different. Every god-damned one of you Farmboys is the fucking same. Caesar gets you and turns you into clones. I bet you clench your butt muscles real good too. Give a nice hand job? I bet if I wanted to rub my dick on top of your head there, you'd purr and stroke me until I came all over your neck."

As a matter of fact, Brian had done just that, at least twice before. He decided not to mention that. "Sir, I am here to please you, sir," he said instead.

"Oh yeah? Well, what else can you do, then? What if I don't like blowjobs? What if fucking another hard butt bores me limp? What if just putting my dick in you isn't what I have in mind?"

Well, what indeed? Brian knew that the house had the services of a perfectly good masseur, and there were also two female pleasure slaves for men who got out here and actually happened to like that sort of thing. You just didn't bring a field slave up for anything else but pretty straight fucking and abuse. He hadn't been trained - and, more importantly, assigned - to do anything else.

But to be sent away without pleasing - would they think he was unacceptable? Brian swallowed and choked, trying to think of something to say.

"Forget it, Farmboy Brian. I'm not going to turn you in. In fact - I'm going to turn you loose."

Harrison's touch was a surprise, but Brian controlled the little jump in reaction to it. The cuffs dropped free, and Brian carefully pulled his arms together and worked out the stretched muscles. He shifted slightly, and this time did jerk when Harrison's hands touched his throat.

"Shit, calm down, I'm not going to strangle you. I just need to figure out how to get this thing off." Brian knew, but couldn't bring himself to volunteer. Luckily, it was fairly simple, and Harrison loosened it and left it for Brian to tug the rest of the way.

"There, that's better. You were starting to remind me of some kind of cheap and sleazy murder of the week movie." Harrison had opened the collar of his shirt, and looked more relaxed without those bold sunglasses. His eyes were a light blue, and Brian blinked in the late afternoon sun and avoided those pretty eyes.

"What is your pleasure, sir?" he asked stupidly, hoping this strange man had made up his mind.

"What indeed. Come here and help me figure it out," Harrison drawled. "Let's get on with it, spectacular cocksucker number whatever you are."

Brian crawled, and tried to shake the feeling that he was doing something wrong. When he got to the chair, he slid his body up, careful not to lean against Harrison's legs, and breathed out warm air over the thick bulge in the man's trousers. At least he was turned on, Brian thought. He glanced up, asking permission, and Harrison waved him back and unbuttoned his trousers himself. Thank goodness. Unbuttoning Levi's was one thing - soft pants that would be spotted and wrinkled by a wet, sucking mouth was another matter entirely.

His cock was every bit as big as advertised. It was pale, circumcised and meaty, good for sucking on. Harrison flipped a green wrapped condom down into his lap, and Brian retrieved it among the light brown pubic hair. He unwrapped it gently, and placed it over the crown of the cock, and then licked and pursed his lips and took the head gently into his mouth. Swiping it with his tongue, he lovingly pulled at it, lifting it free of the folds of the wispy cloth, and settling his lips just behind the head. His fingers gently rolled the rest of the condom down the shaft, nestling it at the base.

It was a favorite technique. Porn was full of men who just slurped the entire rod into their throat like it was an ice cream cone or something. But some men like to have the ultra-sensitive head played with, nibbled, sucked all by itself. It was a wild guess, but you had to start somewhere. And by the way Harrison was just passively accepting the attention, it didn't seem likely that Brian was going to get skull fucked.

There was something pretty wonderful about sucking the cock of such an inactive man. It meant that the sucking mouth was free to roam, up and down, twisting around the shaft, licking, searching, probing - until every aspect of what got the guy hot was researched and mapped out. Brian sent the tip of his tongue probing against the pee-hole, and almost purred when the response was a slight rise in the cock, a twitch that brought it deeper into his mouth. Again, he swirled his tongue around, soothing, swishing, sucking. Soon, he could start working his way down the shaft. He wondered whether Harrison's balls would like similar treatment. Damn it, he was going to show this man a good time, or die trying!

The condom was slick with his spit, and the cock stretched it properly thin. Brian went to work in earnest, sucking the way he was taught, the way he knew men liked. And it seemed to be working - Harrison was enjoying it, or at least his cock was. Then, suddenly, a hand pushed Brian away. The cock popped out of his mouth with an audible slurp, and Brian sat back on his feet, hard.

Automatic. He shuffled backward, and bent his head down to the carpeted floor. "Forgive me, sir," he whispered. "Please correct me, sir!"

"Aww, fuck you. Get your ass out of here, you're just like the others. Go on, back to your kennels, or wherever you clones sleep."

Brian lifted his head and ducked it again as Harrison rose and buttoned his trousers over his still stiff erection. The condom floated onto Brian's shoulder, and he shuddered to make it fall. He watched Harrison run a hand through his hair and then tug his shirt open. He walked across the room and shrugged it off, allowing it to fall. Bare chested, he threw himself down on the bed.

"Well, what are you waiting for? Should I kick you? Get out, your sucking sucks, to coin a phrase."

Brian straightened up, although protocol would have been to crawl from the room. Then, carefully, he rose to his feet. His own cock was hard again, and jutting out from his body, seemingly large because of the lack of dark, curly hair at the base. He grasped it in one hand, and worked it, boldly, cocking one leg back.

"I suck damn well," he said, slowly, fisting a drop of white precum out of his cock. "How do you?"

"Well, shit, I thought you would never ask," Harrison sighed. "Come on over here, and I'll show you, Farmboy."

Brian climbed onto the bed and knelt up, making Harrison slither over on his hands and knees. The condom had to go around the ring, because Brian was forbidden to take it out, but there was a strong one in the basket by the side of the bed. It seemed to make no difference to Harrison, who moaned the minute his mouth covered Brian's shaft and his tongue discovered the cool touch of metal under the thin sheath of latex. He murmured and sucked and just breathed Brian's cock into his mouth, cupping Brian's shaved balls and tugging lightly on the ring set behind them.

Brian let the man suck for a while, and then dropped one hand on Harrison's head. The response was an immediate stepping up of the action - the suction got harder, and the motions faster. Sighing, Brian fisted his hand in Harrison's hair and set the pace.

The man who looked so cool in those cobalt sunglasses accepted that like cream in his coffee. Soon, he was sucking on Brian's cock like a man who has been too long without it. Much like, Brian thought, sucking a bus down the street by the tailpipe, or sucking in a breath before drowning. In order to keep from coming, Brian directed Harrison's attention to his balls, and found that Harrison liked that just fine. He wondered if he would have to fuck the guest, but Harrison just squirmed and sucked wherever Brian led him. In fact, he came while sucking on Brian's nipples, one after the other, his hands wet with his own spit, his mouth working those hard, ringed nipples with a passion that matched the attention he had paid to Brian's cock. He made loud, smacking noises, and then shuddered and grabbed his cock and shot all over Brian's crotch, one nipple in his mouth and the other under his left hand.

"Yeah, that was good," Harrison sighed, the first articulate sounds he had made in over an hour. Brian nodded and scooted off the bed, quickly. He stripped the condom off his aching cock, and gathered the old one from the floor. He knew what would come next.

"OK, get the fuck out, Farmboy. And if you ever say a fucking word, I'll come back and personally rip those rings from you, OK?"

"Thank you, sir," was what came absurdly out of Brian's mouth. But Harrison didn't seem to notice - he was stretched out on the bed, one arm thrown back, the other over his eyes. "Tell them to wake me for dessert," he snapped, raising his voice.

Brian crawled out of the room, shutting the door firmly behind him. He gave Harrison's message to the butler, threw the used condoms away, and was allowed to have more food with the late shift of house slaves before going back to the bunkhouse. It was barbecue - but veal, stuffed and juicy. He even got to drink a whole can of Pepsi. No one spoke to him, but that was OK. They were house slaves. He was only a farmboy. He got a ride back to the Farm, because it was after dark, and checked in with Ross.

"Guest plow you good?" Ross asked absently. He had one of the other farmboys under his boot, while another one busily polished it.

Brian shrugged. It was acceptable not to gossip about guests. He passed into the room where he slept and shook his blankets out. Two men were engaged in what looked like the tail end of a long session of mutual cocksucking. He watched for a while, and then settled down as they disentangled and cuddled. The lights went out, and they all went to their blankets and settled for the night. Randy, the man who slept next to Brian, and who was Brian's first choice for sex when they both had the energy, tapped his shoulder.

"Top or bottom?" he whispered.

There was silence as they all waited for Brian's answer.

"Bottom," he sighed. The men stifled giggles and rude sounds, muffled them against their forearms and blankets.

"Jeez, what does that make? Twenty-six out of forty?"

"At least."

"Faggots! Why don't they just admit it?"

"Let them sleep one night in here, they'll change their fairy ass minds!"

"Hey! Quiet in there, or I'll fuckin' hose you down!"

They settled down, snickers and grunts fading. Brian laid on his back, and took his cock in his hand. He gave it a light tug, and the motion drew Randy over. Carefully, they nestled together and reached for each other, each holding the other's cock. Quietly, they worked, and played, and when they came, it was with a release of pleasure that almost made Brian cry. He hugged his buddy warmly, and amid the dampness, they slept like the hardworking men they were.

Steamgauge

The little needle on the gauge kept dipping into the red area over and over, but Taylor pushed the battered Ford from one truck stop to the next with a sweaty determination. There was just no money to fix the radiator, not yet. He kept the fluids high and took long breaks at noon, and cursed fluently when he saw the thin line of steam rising from under the hood.

His boots hit the dust so hard that clouds followed him as he stomped to the back of the truck to get the water can. His jeans were damp along the seams, and at the backs of his knees, and his thin cotton shirt was plastered across his body, even though it was open all the way down his chest. The bandanna wrapped around his neck was soaked, and he wasn't sure whether that was helping or hurting - but he wasn't that interested in taking it off, either.

He popped the hood and cursed again as the steam billowed up and out. As he waited for the radiator to cool down so he could pop the cap and refill it, he walked along the shoulder and stretched out. There was not another car in sight. But he was used to that - it had been two days since he'd been in a town large enough to have two bars. Weeks since he'd been in a town large enough to have a bar where he could get the kind of relief that all the air conditioning and swimming pools and cold beers couldn't rival

But that was part of the curse of the job. When you wander through the big ranches, taking on seasonal jobs and doing a little breaking on the side, you don't often end up in Dallas. Hell, it's a good year if you can hire on somewhere near San Antonio, and drive sixty or seventy miles to that little dark place where all the cowboys are looking for something a little different to ride…

Taylor scratched his groin comfortably - the heavy rod that lay coiled against his right thigh had been neglected lately; a little too much solo two-stepping for his tastes. The last one had been in the men's room at a nearly deserted gas station where the pump boy gave him a longing look and Taylor didn't end up paying for his gas. That was always nice. But that had been…a long time ago. Still, Taylor's hand caressed his dick, coaxing it gently through the soft denim, thinking about that boy's sandy colored hair, his snub nose, and the way he gasped when he saw the cock that was shortly going to fill his world. Hot damn, but that fella was good, sucking it down like a slurpee through a straw, holding onto Taylor's legs like he wasn't ever going to let them go.

Just as the thoughts became a full-fledged reverie, Taylor heard the engine and dropped his hand. Way off in the distance, another truck was approaching. No good to be caught jacking off the old crank when Pastor BigBelly and the whole BigBelly clan came rumbling down. He stuck his thumbs into his belt instead and tipped his hat back to see it as it passed. It wasn't likely anyone would stop.

But this one was clearly pulling over. Taylor coughed the dust out of his throat as the fancy vehicle pulled to a stop along the shoulder, crunching the gravely dust between its fat tires. Taylor snorted out something to express half derision and half longing. It was one of those four wheel drive modern jeep things, black and tan. It probably had A/C. Nice rig, if you can afford it. And in the next instant, he felt the same way about the driver.

His boots were old and comfortable but shiny, protected from the eternal dust by the soft carpeting and no-doubt cushy interior of his Wrangler. His jeans were tight around his ass, and there was just that faint hint of fading around the crotch. A silver roping trophy buckle hit him dead center, as his body rose up tall and strong and broad shouldered. This city cowboy had short hair, too, black as night, a good contrast to the weather-beaten tan colored working hat.

He was a big man, six-four at least, but he walked like he was used to running, and smiled like he was used to pleasing people. Taylor swallowed hard and held out his hand, allowing a smile to break through his usually stern exterior. "Thanks for stopping, buddy," he said. "Can't see how you can help much, but it's awful nice of you." Shit, he thought, kicking himself mentally. That's goddamn talkative!

"Hey, you never know," drawled the newcomer. He shook Taylor's hand firmly and looked at the steaming Ford. "Busted radiator, huh? Bad luck. Want a lift to the next station? I passed one about five miles thataway."

He pointed down the road. "There's a real stop about nine, maybe ten miles further. You can get a truck out here, and catch some sleep, too."

"Well," Taylor almost used his standard excuse, that he had a buddy who would be coming by. After all, ain't no need to take charity, that's for weaker folks. But something in the stranger poked at him, and he tipped his hat forward and brushed one toe against the sand, tossing a little storm against his tire. "Damn. I ain't got the money to fix the damn thing. I guess it's a goner anyway. Yeah, I reckon I'll take that ride. I better figure out what I'm gonna do now."

"I'll help you load up your things," the big man offered.

He made no further comments, except to admire Taylor's rig, and he did treat it gently when they laid it in the cool, dark interior of the Wrangler's storage space. Taylor spotted a custom case for a saddle and tack pushed up against the side. That confirmed this guy as a little more than just a done-up dude, and made him feel better about taking the ride.

As they hit the road, Taylor coughed again and sucked in frigid air that chilled his flesh instantly. "I didn't get your name, pal," he said, wondering at the comfort of the bucket seat that caressed his body.

"Oh, shit, sorry! I'm Ken, Ken Lurie. Pleased to meet you!"

"Ken Lurie? Hell, I heard of you!" Taylor said, so surprised he grinned again. "You got that spread out over the other side of the res, don't you?"

"Yep, guilty as charged."

Nice living, Taylor thought. No wonder the guy can afford these wheels and the custom case and nice boots. Shit, his critters are spread out for miles, and his boys do some nice circuit work, too. Damn. You never figure rich guys would be nice, though.

"Don't suppose you're hiring," he said, trying not to sound too hopeful.

"Sorry, Taylor, but we're full up for the season. That's a nice rig you got though - cuttin' and ropin'?"

"Yeah. General ranch work, too. And I do a little breaking when I can find it."

"Now, that's a lost art," Lurie said fondly. "These days, it's all psychology. Plus, you're raisin' the working horses from foals, they're already gentled when you get them in the ring. Shit, I remember when I was a kid, we'd fetch us some mustangs and then you'd really see some breaking!"

Taylor nodded. "Yeah, I've done the scrub ponies. Tried a little bronc showing, but it never sat right with me."

Lurie turned to him and nodded again. "Me too. Doesn't seem right, putting that strap on, does it?"

155

"Nosir, no way. I want an animal that's fighting me, not fighting a strap around its nuts. Beats the hell out of me how they can call that a sport. It ain't winning when the horse is just dyin' from the pain. I mean, I'd be pretty docile if you put a bundle of tacks around my nuts, too!"

Lurie chuckled. "Oh, I don't know about that," he offered. "You seem like a tough guy. Doesn't seem like much would make you docile, nuts or not."

You could, Taylor thought. But he grinned like an idiot again and turned his eyes to the road, hoping that Lurie couldn't see the very noticeable boner that was pressing him so hard it felt like he'd jammed a rope down his pants. He was grateful for the A/C. It kept down the flush that was building around his face and throat.

They passed the gas station and drove on to the truck stop, where Lurie pulled up besides the register. "Let me float you a loan," he said, looking out the window as he took on that difficult topic. "I'll put you up for a few days, OK? You can come out to the ranch, say, in two months, and work it off or pay me back."

"That's right nice of you," Taylor said, also not looking at the other man. "But I can't take charity, and you and me know that's what that would be. You won't have work when the season's over, and I can't find work without m'wheels. I'll sell the rig and get myself back to my kin, and start over next year. But I thank you."

"Well, if you want to work some of it off now, there's a way," Lurie said. "Can't help noticing you're in a situation there."

Taylor looked down and agreed that it was, at last, a situation. But he coughed and kept his gaze away. He could deny it, take umbrage and bristle, or he could just ignore the comment and thank the man for the lift.

"Well, can't say I ever done that before," he lied.

"Yeah, but you'll do it for me, cowboy, won't you?"

Taylor's heart quickened at the ranch owner's tone. Hell, this was a man here! Not some pimply faced, cowboy worshipping city brat with a hunger for denim dick, but a fellow rider, and champion roper, and a man whose self-made riches were the envy for miles around. Hell yes, this was a real man.

Taylor turned his head at last and nodded. "Yessir, I'll do it for you."

"Then stow your rig, and I'll get us a room."

It was that easy. Taylor took the money, feeling ashamed and excited, and paid a storage fee for his saddle, and then mutely joined Lurie as they stomped down the row of identical doors. The view from behind the rancher was every bit as good as the one from the front. Taylor figured that Lurie had about two inches and thirty pounds on him - and a lifetime of being top dog. It showed in the way he walked.

"Strip down to your boots and keep the bandanna on," were Lurie's first words when they got inside.

Taylor pulled the shirt off first, baring his damp chest, with the streaked mat of light brown hairs that ran between his nipples and down his body. He had to kick off his boots to get the jeans off, but he kept his black hip hugging briefs on in order to keep them for last. It seemed the right thing to do. Lurie was seated on the bed, watching with a gleam in his eye.

"You got a nice body, cowboy," he said. "Real nice. Now show me the rest of it."

I'm a whore, Taylor thought, hooking his thumbs into the sides of his briefs. A fuckin' five dollar whore, taking down my shorts for this man who's got the power, the money, the looks - hell he's got everything I ain't got. The cotton moved slowly down his legs, and the thick slab of dick meat nearly slapped as it fell from across his thigh to covering his balls. He let the briefs fall and kicked them off.

"Now, there's a piece of tube steak that ain't never had a strap around it," Lurie said appreciatively. "Bring that fucker over here."

Taylor walked stiffly forward and gasped as Lurie took his cock firmly in hand. "This belongs to me right now," Lurie said, with a slight grin. "It needs to shoot off, but that ain't in my plan. So -" He reached into his pocket and pulled out what looked like a wide strip of soft leather, coiled into a ball. He let if fall free, and it spilled into a rust-colored ribbon. Two twists, and there was a loop in the end of it. Taylor gasped again as the loop settled around his cock and balls and pulled tight. His hands flew to protect himself and Lurie slapped them down.

"Mine," he said firmly. Then, unimpeded, he continued wrapping, turning the leather ribbon so that it divided the cock and balls, and then pulled them all up tight together. When he tied the package up, Taylor could barely stand to look at it. His family jewels were wrapped tighter than a calf at a 4-H meet. If he ever felt sympathy for a bronc under a bucking strap before, he felt it more keenly now.

"That'll come off when you're finished showing me a good time, cowboy," Lurie said. "So you might as well get to work. I ain't felt a mustache on my nuts in days - might as well start with my low hangers. And don't let me feel teeth, you hear? If I do, you'll think this little bundle is a cool drink of water under a sweet shade tree. Got that?"

"Yessir," Taylor said. He dropped to his knees and unbuckled the man's belt. Lurie stood to he could shuck his jeans and shorts, and Taylor sighed as the big man's cock and balls came into sight.

Just as Ken Lurie was big, so was his equipment. Easily as thick as Taylor's meat, Lurie's cock was longer, too. And his balls! Hell, they were huge, matted with sweat and hanging so low, they'd clank if they were chrome. Some stud on Lurie's ranch was surely missing his filly-maker, because God had done a job and mixed two cocks up.

Balls first, Taylor reminded himself. So, carefully, he lowered his face to those twin orbs and began licking, spreading them up and across with the flat of his tongue.

He had a flash, recalling this kid from Denver who was doing the rodeo circuit, who had spent two hours doing nothing but licking and sucking on Taylor's balls while Taylor watched some queer porno on the motel's in-house system. Man, that had been nice, jacking himself off, drinking beer, and pissing it down the kid's back while that licking never stopped.

He imagined Lurie doing the same to him, and shuddered.

"That's right, you bastard, lick my nuts. You're playing with the boss man here, and you better make me happy."

Taylor decided that he didn't really need to answer that, so he kept mouthing the balls, trying to get them both into his mouth. It was an impossibility - the best he could do was one at a time. But he worked on them steadily, feeling a pounding ache in his own nuts that made him dizzy. He was almost ready to groan out loud when Lurie's hand in his hair pulled him up.

"Nice work, cowboy. I reckon it's time you got plowed, though. Get your ass on this bed."

Taylor had expected to take Lurie's cock while he was on his knees - that's mostly how men had sucked him off, after all. But he followed the boss' directions, and ended up on his back on the lumpy bed, with his head hanging over the edge. He gulped, seeing what was going to come next.

"Oh yeah, you're gonna take all of me, cowboy," Lurie promised, jacking his cock off over Taylor's face. "Right down your throat. I'm gonna screw your throat like an old whore's pussy, cowboy. And you're gonna take it, aren't you? 'Cause you want it."

Taylor wanted to plead for mercy, wanted to say, no, please, it's been a while, I ain't ever done that! But instead, he said, "Yessir. I do want it."

"Tell me, cowboy."

"Sir, I do want your big, fat dick down my throat!"

"Then take it!" Lurie pointed the head down, bent his knees, and slammed the entire length so deep into Taylor's throat that Taylor almost leapt up on the bed. It hurt, bashing into the tightness of Taylor's spasming throat muscles, jerking his head back and stretching him out further. And then Lurie pulled back.

"Just a few more times," he said softly.

Each time was like getting burned. Taylor tried to relax, tried to anticipate it, but the huge length and width of the fucking machine spread him open and raped him, and he cursed in frustration as involuntary tears dripped from his eyes. Then, finally, Lurie sighed and slowed down, and said only one word: "Suck."

Thank God, Taylor thought, swiping his tongue around the battering cock that had plundered his throat. He sucked, pulling in the velvety flesh, feeling every ridge of every vein as he worked on that cock like a giant titty. And when Lurie reached down and pulled one of Taylor's nipples, he groaned around the thick cock in his mouth, but didn't pause in his action. Lurie liked that. And showed it by yanking even harder on that mantit.

"Cocksucker," he growled. "Suck my big dick. You've been wantin' it since you laid eyes on me, now suck it down!"

Taylor followed instructions, and let out an involuntary moan as Lurie switched nipples and began working on the other one. It was a distraction, but not nearly enough to take his mind away from the succulent slab of meat that he was adoring, his head thrown back. Lurie's fat, heavy balls slapped into his forehead and eyes, and he could see the edges of the man's asscrack, and wondered if the boss man would have him suck there, as well. The thought shamed him, thrilled him. He shuddered again.

"That's enough for now, cowboy," Lurie said, withdrawing his dick. "Time for a little ride. Get up and show me your hot fuckin' hole, cowboy. I know you don't need no hobbles to hold you down - show me where my horse cock's gonna shoot."

Taylor flipped himself over, and drew his body up onto the bed. Dizzy, he turned and presented, and the thought of mares, their sex parts inflamed and eager, and the stallions, their screams cutting through the mornings, heavy cocks sliding out of the sheaths - the primal, monstrous act of mating, watched by giggling hands and critical breeders - and again, he felt the flush of shame. When Lurie's hands spread him wide, he gasped.

"I do believe it's been some time since you were serviced," Lurie said. "Too bad your first had to be me. I'm gonna rip you open, cowboy."

"Rip me, sir," Taylor said, grinding his teeth. "Do it!"

It was only right.

Fingers first, slopping something greasy into that hot, twitching hole, spreading it wide for the blunt head of that heavy cock. Taylor groaned and bit his own tongue to keep from yowling like a baby, but he stayed in position, arching his back to make the entry easier, and when Lurie slammed in, Taylor pounded the mattress with his fist and collapsed onto his elbows.

"Slut," Lurie chuckled. "Hot fuckin' cowboy, puttin' your butt in the air for me. Cocksucker, butt-whore, I'm gonna slam you so hard my jism is gonna leak outa your mouth."

"Yeah," Taylor grunted, the words making him ache. His dick throbbed and his nuts felt hot enough to give off steam. "Do me, boss. Do me like a fuckin' stud!"

"I am your stud, cowboy. Ain't nothing you can do but take my cock." With that, Lurie commenced seriously fucking, just like the way he had plowed down Taylor's throat. With a deliberate cruelty, he pulled almost all the way out, and then plunged back, ball deep, and sighed with every sinking motion.

"Should have whupped you first," he panted. "Should have made you beg. But there's always time for that, right cowboy? You'll beg me, won't you?"

"Yessir - whatever you want, sir!"

"And you won't mind if I do hobble you, will you? You'll even hold still like a good mare, just so you can get a taste of my dick."

"Yessir!" Taylor groaned as one particularly slow thrust teased him, and then sighed as Lurie kind of squirmed against him.

"Yeah, I like this hole," Lurie said. This time, his words sounded harsher, and Taylor know what was coming. "You wanna work off that debt, you just come on back with me, cowboy. I'll make you my personal brood mare."

"Oh, Jesus!" Taylor cried. "Oh, Jesus, God, my nuts, please, Mr. Lurie, please boss, fuckin' God, I'm gonna explode!"

"Not before I do, cowboy!"

And suddenly, that body-splitting load of cock vanished from Taylor's aching rear passage. He yowled at last, both from the pain of the exit and the sudden feeling of loss. But he didn't have time to think - two hard hands flipped him over onto his back, and the wrappings around his nuts started to come off. He gasped at the sight of Lurie, one hand on that massive cock, the other hand busily unbinding the cock and ball sculpture he had made.

"You'll put your cum right on top of mine, cowboy," Lurie said. "Right over - mine!" And with a practiced ease, he jacked his thick cock over Taylor's body, and shot out long, thick, strands of man-juice, a heavy, wet load that slapped against Taylor's chest and belly. Taylor cried out again at the unfairness of it all - that load should have been in him, in his mouth, or up his aching butthole! But even that disappointment couldn't halt the straining in his own dick. And when Lurie pushed his legs up and tilted him backwards, he knew what to do. He grabbed his cock and jacked it, once, twice, and then that explosion he threatened went off, and his nuts almost contracted with the speed and force of his shoot. He watched as his own jism arched through the air and landed on his chest, come of it splattering his chin. And when Lurie let him down, he just lay there, weak and wasted.

"You're gonna learn to shoot into your own mouth, cowboy - that's if you're fixing to follow me."

Taylor looked up, but didn't say anything. He couldn't say anything yet.

Lurie walked into the bathroom and came out wiping his dick off. He tossed the harsh little towel onto Taylor's stomach and bent down to retrieve his jeans. "That was fun, cowboy. I liked giving you a good ride. If you come down to my place, I'll do it again. And again."

He pulled his wallet from his pocket and unfolded a few bills. Taylor blushed and turned away.

"You can always mail 'em back to me if you don't want the loan," Lurie said with another chuckle. "You decide. But if you come over to my place, ready to work this off as my little mare, you better be wearing this."

The rust colored leather strap slipped around Taylor's throat. Lurie tied it off, and pulled the old bandanna away. And then, he left, closing the door firmly behind him.

Taylor took a long time in recovering, laying on the lumpy bed and fingering the smooth leather around his neck.

Bandanna Hanky code

Top	Color	Bottom
Cowboy	Rust	His Horse

Musclebound, first chapter

(by "Christopher Morgan"
Musclebound and Other Stories is currently available through Alyson.)

EARLY AUTUMN

The man on the weight machine could only be described as darkly beautiful. Many men (and more than a few women) had told Will Rodriguez that he was handsome, masculine and almost feral in his attractiveness, but it went deeper than that. His sculpted, deeply tanned body was truly a work of art, a type of classic Latin beauty that attracted attention and sexual hunger.

It was no accident that he was like this. As he went into his last series of reps, sweat trickled down his body in rivulets that spilled into the towel he had laid down to catch them, a towel already nearly soaked. His curly black hair was plastered around his head and face, and his muscles strained with the effort he was putting forth. He was clad only in his workout boots, the weight gloves, and a pair of hip hugging shorts. The tank top was crumpled under his neck to catch the sweat there.

Each time he pressed the bar and raised it, his stomach muscles contracted and rippled, and his chest rose and fell with the rhythm. He was so engrossed in his workout that he didn't notice the door to the private room opening and shutting, admitting a spectator. All of his concentration was on finishing this set, putting the finishing touches on this workout, getting really pumped up.

Some called it obsession, that behavior of those men who sought perfection in their bodies. But it was far more than that. For an obsession is a useless thing, a compulsion to do something because it filled some emotional void. The sculpting of one's body, however, filled many purposes. It kept you healthy, and strong. It made you attractive and desirable. And in Will's case, it made your prices much, much higher. For services that were very much in demand.

The bar rose and fell. His breath came in harsh whistles between clenched teeth. A much lesser man would have given up before the series was finished, but Will stuck to his regimen, and got in his last dozen with a passion that was almost furious. He cried out at the last one, a sound of angry triumph, and relaxed back against the bench, allowing his arms to come to rest at last. A tremble ran through his shoulders and upper arms, and he forced himself to lay still until it washed through him.

The sound of his spectator's voice was not as surprising as it might have been. "Good workout, Willie."

Will cringed at the diminutive and grunted a response. With his right hand, he reached for the squeeze bottle next to the machine and brought it up, just holding it. He took several deep breaths, not responding to the voice.

"I'm glad to see you're sticking to the plan I outlined. I promised you results if you did everything I said, didn't I?" The voice was insistent and thick with sarcasm. Something in it demanded a response, and tension began to curl in the space between the two men, one lying back, the other standing.

The beautiful young man drew himself up to a sitting position and nodded, bringing the straw from the squeeze bottle to his lips. He avoided looking at his visitor in a way that suggested that the squeeze bottle held his attention as much as the workout had.

"Stand up, Willie. Let's see that new body." The attitude was pure authority, no cajoling, no joking. Will put the bottle down and stood up, drops of sweat falling off his arms and trickling down his face. He wiped some of it away with his crumpled tank top, and then stood free of the weight machine.

Will stood five foot eight in his workout boots, but his compact muscular frame compensated for the two inches he felt would have been better for him to have. He finally had the washboard stomach so admired by other men, and there was a fluid grace in the way he moved his body. He knew he was hot. But his posture before the spectator was almost designed to minimize his attractiveness. He stood with his head hung, his arms limp at his sides.

The other man laughed out loud and allowed that laugh to drain into a sneer. "Don't give me this shit, Willie boy. When I want to see your body, I want to see it, sweetie. Get those arms up! Show me some hip! Flex! Now!" He snapped his fingers and moved closer. "Show me what kind of a man I made out of you, you cheap greaser punk!"

"Mr. Marcus, I'm not really in the mood....I had a real tough workout today, and I gotta get home." Will said this in a dispassionate voice, continuing to avoid the eyes of the spectator. His teeth were clenched as he said it, his shoulders slightly tensed, but he made no move in response to the demands or the insults.

"I don't give a rat's ass what mood you're in, Willie boy. Moods are for girls, aren't they? Now, are you going to do what I said, or am I going to have to teach you a lesson?"

There was a long moment as the two men stood in silence. The room was thick with the smells of masculine labor, old and new sweat and the musky odor sexual release. Will imagined that he could see the smells, mingling with the bleach and disinfectants. He stood until the silence grew to be oppressive, and just as Mr. Marcus was about to walk toward him again, he lifted his arms and struck a pose.

If his body was a classic, so was his training. He mutely went through a series of bodybuilder poses that showed him off to his best advantage, holding each pose for about ten seconds before curling into another one.

"Good boy," Mr. Marcus said, coming even closer. "That's it, keep your head up. Round those shoulders a little more, show off those nice tits. They look better now we've got that dipshit hair off, don't they?" And when Will refused to respond, Marcus lifted one hand warningly. "Answer me, you scumbag!"

"Yeah!" Will spat, coming out of his pose. "Yeah, they look better."

Marcus laughed. "Get those fucking shorts off."

Will released the cord in the waistband and dropped the soft, damp garment to the floor, where he stepped out of them. He had no tan line, the same caramel color that covered his chest extended down around his cock. Even his dick was a creamy brown, uncut and curved down over his balls, cradled in a wiry nest of damp black pubic hair.

"Good." Marcus snapped his fingers again. "Do it again. This time, make me hard." He cupped one massive hand over his crotch and nodded for Will to start posing.

This time, Will's efforts were more concentrated. It was a different set of poses too, more sexually charged, slower. His tan skin barely hid the flushes of embarrassment he felt as he turned and bent over, sliding his hands down one muscular leg, and then the other, exposing his rounded cheeks to the man who had compelled his obedience. Finally, as he reached for his cock and balls, to hold them and display them as though they too were part of his bodybuilding development, Marcus opened the fly of his jeans and brought his machine out.

Because that was how Will saw it and thought of it. It wasn't a dick, or a prick, or a cock. It was no dong, no tool. It was a machine, capable of doing things no other man-meat could match, and even as he gripped his own manhood in his hands, he was stunningly aware of how inadequate it was compared to the thing that Marcus was displaying.

"Get over here and do what you were born to, punk. Get your mouth on some real meat and take it down."

Will dropped to his knees and let his cock and balls go free. Slowly, he took hold of the cock before him and licked his lips, and then lowered his face over the tip. The head fit into his mouth, a fat, silken ball, and Marcus pressed into him relentlessly. Will closed his eyes.

"That's my boy, take it down. You know you want it, don't you, you fucking little spic...just like you did the first night, huh? Come on, let me feel your tongue, that's it, suck on it. Think that now you've got a real body that you're some kind of man, huh? Not with me, you fairy punk. You're still my fuckhole, aren't you?"

Marcus began to rock his hips back and forth, and when Will tried to pull away, he grabbed a handful of curly black hair and ground his crotch into Wills face ruthlessly, not pulling back until Will's body began to fight the lack of air. Then, Marcus pulled way back and slammed forcefully into Will's throat.

"Don't even think of trying to get away from me, Willie baby. You remember that you agreed to this? You're gonna be my good fuckhole, and I'm gonna make a man out of you, right? You remember that, don't you? Cheap ten dollar blowjob trick, you never even *saw* a real man until you met me. And, you'll never be man enough to take me on, fucker. Got that? Never!"

Will struggled, but not to get away. He struggled to get in a deep breath in between Marcus' deep thrusts. He made no more attempts to please the man, just to keep his mouth and throat open, and to keep his lips closed around the massive shaft.

Finally, Marcus pulled his machine out of Will's mouth. Using one hand, he milked the shaft, and growled instructions. "Arch your back! Spread those fucking legs! Pinch your tits! Hard! Harder! You want me to stop and do it?"

Will ground his teeth and did as he was told and sent sparks of pain shooting through his own chest. Above him, Marcus moved so he was standing right on top of him as Will bent backward. "Good boy...now grab your cock, boy, grab it and see why you'll never be a real man..."

Will reached for his cock as he was told and watched as Marcus worked the machine into a climax. Fat, thick gobs of white cum splattered across Will's chest, some hitting his neck, and some hitting his taut belly. Marcus continued to work his huge dick, shaking more of his cum all over the kneeling younger man. Then, he reached out, grabbed Will by the hair again, and pulled him forward.

And wiped his dick off in that curly black hair.

"Hey, bravo, boss!" A new voice in the room surprised both men, and Marcus turned away to look at him.

"I didn't even hear you come in, Frank," Marcus said, tucking the slightly depleted machine away.

"Yeah, well, you were busy." Frank Dobbs grinned, and it wasn't a pretty sight. All the workouts in the world couldn't change the fact that he was ugly to the bone, a big man with a face that could prevent trucks from starting, let alone stop them in action. He was wearing sweats and a loose tank top that showed off his built up chest and upper arms, and a weight lifter's belt was draped over one shoulder.

"What do you want, Frank?" Marcus asked.

"I just wanted to let you know that the Hong kid split town. You want I should send the tape?"

"Of course. No harm in letting people know I mean business. Yes, send it at once, by messenger. To the family, and to the business in Queens. And then, to the distributor. Anything else?"

"Nah. But we're gonna need a new helper. And you told me to remind you that you got a private session with that model today."

Marcus nodded. "Oh yes...well, that takes care of me for the afternoon. You want this piece of shit?" He pointed down at Will, who was still on his knees, the cum drying on his chest and belly, his head hung low.

"Sure thing, boss!"

"Well, I got his mouth, why don't you plug his butt? Take your time, I'll put out the 'help wanted' sign. And do me a favor - he was kind of slow to respond today. Teach him not to be."

Frank pulled the weight lifter's belt off his shoulder and doubled it in his hands. "You got it, boss. My fuckin' pleasure."

"Of course it is." Marcus left as Frank advanced.

Two hours later, Frank left the private workout room, swinging the belt around and whistling. An hour after that, Will Rodriguez left the gym, and grimly passed a bright sign in the window advertising that a job opening was available.

166

Grrrls, Women, and Goddesses

Some Women Do

(Introduction to *Some Women*, edited)

Women, in general and specifically, have been told about their sexuality and lives, told in simple terms and with shattering redundancy so that they could conform with the patterns which their dominant society demanded. The old cliché is that it all begins with the pink tag and blanket a girl gets in the hospital; it will determine how long she will be held and comforted, and how often brought to breast. By the time she gets home, adrift in a pink sea of clothing, toys and tchotchkeleh, she is forever labeled with familiar words like sweet, cute, dainty, pretty, soft, a good child, a nice girl.

And she's told: girls don't fight, don't run fast, don't climb, don't talk back. Girls shouldn't shout, rage, persist, get angry, hit back. Later on, she will learn what is expected of her, and what she is not expected to be and do and say and think. She'll hear about it at home, from her parents, relatives and siblings, from television programs and advertisements, and she will see those images all around her as she grows up and goes to school. Everything in her world will be colored by what she as a female person is supposed to be and do.

Still later, she will learn those traps which young women are thrown into when they become sexually aware and/or the targets of men. (Regardless of the women's own sexuality. It is assumed that all women belong in men's sights.) She will be introduced to the simple traps first, the societal double standard, the iconography that makes her a redeemer or a temptress. Later on, if she persists in her curiosity about herself and her own desires and fantasies, and if by chance she does not easily fit in one predetermined role or another, she will trip wires which make her invisible, or unworthy of record, or dangerous. And that may be the most insidious trap of all; the one which isolates and then turns the blades of fear and rejection inward.

There is a deep human need for society, for the security of community. On a personal level, it is that drive to find, learn about and sometimes be with those who are "like me." To hear their voices, each word and experience a soothing reminder that we are not alone, and that we are not as isolated as we sometimes feel; this is a hunger as basic as any survival mechanism. When the subject in question is religion, or politics, or sports or any kind of hobby, it's easy to find others with whom to bond or socialize. The libraries are full of books, the shelves full of magazines and journals, the hotels packed with conventions and meetings, fan clubs and craft guilds.

But when the topic is sexual behavior, it isn't so simple. Too much is hidden, or doesn't exist at all. There is a lot of posturing and declamation by men from psychoanalytic and sociological fields, and a smattering of judgmental acknowledgement from the more pop-culture researchers. It is far too easy to get buried in an avalanche of the too simple (and not helpful) or the overly technical and scholarly. Will reading Comfort's *The Joy of Sex* do, or will slogging through volumes of charts and case studies in Kinsey's works be more suitable? Do you believe in the Hite Reports, or look toward the lab observations of Masters and Johnson? Do Bell and Weinberg hold the answers, or Foucault?

And when it comes to SM - sadomasochism, leathersex, power exchange, bondage and discipline, dominance and submission, restraint and pleasure, or whatever cute code phrase conjured up in any particular year ñ well, it's hard to get any information at all, let alone hear the voices of other women.

Women do have sex, the various sources are proud to tell us. But...

They can't have anything but a (choose one) clitoral orgasm or a vaginal orgasm. (Unless they had a G-spot, named for the man who "discovered" it; and now, if they do not seem to have this mystical spot, there is a new way for them to feel inadequate!) They shouldn't have sex too many times, or with too many men. ("Too many" defined according to the prevailing number of horny-but-not-getting-it men in her vicinity.) They shouldn't really have sex with women, but if they do, they should definitely not have sex with men at all. (According to other women who have sex with women. Heterosexual men, of course, believe that women have the right to be sexual with other women until the right man comes along.) Women, we find, are inherently monogamous. (And men may learn to be monogamous too, if only their women would be better sex partners.)

Women may not do anything sexual for money, nor may they be public about their sexuality. They are not sexual before they exhibit secondary sexual characteristics, and as they get older, their sexual "drives" slow down. But that's all right, because it takes them longer to orgasm anyway, and by that age, they probably don't want to bother. They don't fantasize. Or if they do, it's usually about movie stars and romance. They don't exhibit any signs of having fetishes, and they certainly don't actually do anything like practice sadomasochism, unless they are being paid for it or manipulated into it. And if they do, they are cruel, amoral killers who use men as tools until (can you guess?) the right man comes along. And he will alternately cure or kill her.

It's easy to laugh at some of the generalizations I listed above, but remember that not only were they taken seriously and accepted as truth, but they still remain part of the social consciousness. In fact, even as SM slowly creeps into the mainstream as SM (and not disguised in what Mary Daly calls Sado-rituals, those aspects of mainstream culture which incorporate pathological social sadism), these same old stereotypes about sexuality are becoming more and more pervasive throughout the media. And while some small percentage of women may fit one or a few or even all of the stereotypical identities depicted in sexual studies of various sorts (even the killer, I suppose), it is vital to recognize - and learn about - those who do not.

Some women were different, are different, will always be different. There is an invisible society of women who are united only by a negative definition. Whatever they are, they are not what the stories and surveys and books and the media have concluded. And because they didn't fit, their answers and their lives were discounted, left under-recorded and in many cases just ignored. When they do receive attention at all, it is usually of the sensational kind ("She Liked Rough Sex" screams a headline), or within the propaganda of those who disapprove of them.

In the past two or three years, I've seen some new books which have addressed the "SM/leather community" by publishing essays or excerpts from interviews. Fill the shelves, as I have said before; keep people reading and learning. But the need for something more specific still remains. Women, we who are that slightly more than half of the general population, we who bear almost all of the sexual totems and taboos, are still fighting uphill battles from cradle onward. Women should search among themselves for the voices to tell them that they are not alone, and that they are not going to be easily shunted away to the back pages, or buried underneath the weight of a two-to-one "balance" of male and female writers. Nor shall they be rendered invisible, either by the far right or the far left, for being politically, socially, religiously or culturally incorrect. Women are correct in their own lives and experiences, proper in their skins and minds.

Women don't write about their sexual experiences, shouldn't tell about their secret joys, can't speak for themselves, may not band together in groups to pass their tales to the next generation?

Some women do, should, and did.

(And many more will.)

In the Name of Art

(First published in *Virgin Territory 2*, edited by Shar Rednour)

I was sitting in my comfortable leather armchair with a beautiful girl wedged under my legs, bitching about the work I should have been doing at the time - namely, writing this story for an anthology about losing various virginities.

"Trouble is," I moaned, "half the things I did for the first time I don't remember - buried, as they are in a haze of bad rock music and excellent drugs. Approximately one quarter happened before I was old enough to even mention these things, let alone write about 'em later, and the final quarter are just too damn personal."

"You mean they're about your current tricks," she replied, reminding me that I do tend to fall for smart girls.

"Whatever," I groused. "But anyway, I have to write this thing now, or I'm in deep trouble. Got any suggestions?"

"Write about the first time you did SM with yourself."

"Too young."

"The first time you fucked a woman to unconsciousness."

"Too violent."

"The first time you slept with a woman? Got tied up? Cross-dressed?"

"Too young!"

"All of them??"

"In the same date, no less," I said with justifiable pride.

"Cool," she said, suitably impressed. But I was no closer to an idea for the story. So, we brooded for a while longer, and then she suggested, "The first time you brought someone home from a bar."

"I've never brought someone home from a bar," I admitted sheepishly. It's true. I'm just not good at that sort of thing. Meet you at a sex club, sure. But bring you *home*?? Before I know what your relationship with your mother is? I do have some standards.

"Well, let's go out and pick someone up, and then you can bring her home and write about it tomorrow," the bright girl said, shifting so that my boot landed right next to her crotch.

"That would be cool," I said. "Then, I could write off the evening's entertainment as a writing research expense. Say I was 'interviewing a story prospect' or something like that." I laughed. "Cute idea."

"No, it's a great idea!" she said, rearing up and grinning. "Let's do it!"

The things I do in the name of my art.

The first thing to do was to examine the listings for the various dyke hot spots the city had to offer. We scanned the newspapers and magazines and compiled an assortment of bars, dance clubs, performance art spaces, gyms, theaters, coffee shops and restrooms. It was fairly impressive, especially since I'd only been to two of them.

"You'd think you didn't live in the greatest city in the world," the girl said. "Don't you ever get out?"

Yeah, well. I smacked her, we got dressed up, and we hit the city. Our goal was clear - to eliminate one aspect of virginity in yours truly, before dawn.

Of course we had to start at the Club, the first time I'd been there for pleasure. (Business has given me the most interesting assortment of bedfellows.) If you've ever been to the Club, you know about the thumping, throbbing pulse of the music, the miasmic blend of sweat, smoke, booze and girl, and of course, the stirring panorama of stripped-to-the-waist dancing dykes gyrating and shaking until the very walls seem to shimmer with the rising heat. If you haven't been there, you've missed all that, and what a shame. I admit I was captivated, apart from the isolation that the sound system enforced on me. I clutched a cool beer bottle that was sweating as much as the Brooklyn born Amazon I was giving my cruise of death to, and was startled to find that I was being hit upon from another quarter entirely. The girl had gone off and brought back another girl, and was shouting into her ear and nudging her toward me.

My, my, how industrious. I'd have to reward her later. No girl had ever gone hunting for a another girl for me before. What a fascinating sense of erotic power it bestowed. What a feeling of personal contentment. I glowed, I flushed, and when the time came for the new girl to saunter up to me and say hello, I realized that there was no way this one was coming home.

I mean, shit, the girl brought me another girl! You know what I mean - a skirt, a flirt, a girly girl. Yeah, a femme, if you must. And if I remember one thing from my way to early to write about experiences with women, you don't put two girls together, unless you enjoy having your body ripped to shreds like some bad Greek myth. It's not that they'll automatically fight or anything like that - but let's face it. Girls like attention. They live for it. And they're like little accountants, adding up every moment when you slighted them and weighing them against every second of single-minded, dumb brute adoration. And they remember.

Six months later, they'll remind you. "You liked her better," they'll say, leaving you wondering which "her" was being singled out this time. "It was that ecru mini-dress with the double straps and the plunging neckline," they'll add, knowing that your entire mind will be occupied by the question "what the hell is ecru?" for the precious moments they need to get you sucked in deeper. By the time you've figured out that they're talking about that babe who winked at you at the annual Dyke Drama Ball, they're accusing you of sneaking off with her to the nearest laundry closet for a quickie. Or at least entertaining continual fantasies of same.

This new girl was a walking slab of future troubles. Her leggings were skintight and low across her midriff, and the mingled chains that made a kind of belt spangled and called attention to the way the soft material mounded up between her legs, an erotic invitation to stroke the raised portion of her flesh and find out whether it would make her purr. The black lacy bra she had retained was just barely necessary to prevent a series of bounces with every sharp breath, and it mounded her breasts together in the way which I now knew meant one of those Wonderbra things that made even the most boyish chest look all girly and soft. But her lips - ah, perfection. Wide, but soft and just a tad on the full side, creamy lips, perfect for nibbling, sucking, wonderful lips framing a mouth that was meant to be kissed for hours.

Danger, Will Robinson, danger.

Naturally, I couldn't tell the new girl that I was worried that a half a year later she would return to spoil a dinner and a romantic evening, so I was polite and distant until she seemed to be responding to that. I had never been so desperate not to pick someone up before. I tried to act bored, and she sighed. I imperiously told her to fetch drinks, and she scampered off with a look of excitement in her eyes and a sexy little twitch to her walk. My girl looked at me and raised an eyebrow. "Not your type?" she asked.

What was I supposed to say, "too girly"? I looked deeply into her trusting eyes and crooned (at the top of my lungs, because the music was very, very loud), "She can't compare to you, sweetie," and kissed her to stop any reply she might make. (Especially of the cutting, sarcastic type. Nothing ruins those moments more than a scoffing "I can't believe you said that!")

And for the first time, I actually left a club to avoid someone I was supposedly flirting with. I hated myself. All the way to the bar.

At the bar, dykes were packed in so tight it made the Club look like a square dance. The tiny dance floor was a milling assortment of women who shifted back and forth to the loud Melissa Etheridge songs, and the line for the bathroom was easily mistakable for the line to get to the jukebox. I grabbed my girl to keep her from wandering off to find another sweet thing I would have to reject on sight, and swept her onto that minuscule square of parquet in front of the music machine and wrapped my arms around her. I had never danced with a woman in such a public place before. It was unexpectedly exhilarating, and memories of my early days of coming out of the closet swirled and mingled with the incredible pleasure of swaying back and forth with such a fine woman in a dense crowd of dykes.

She seemed confused for about two seconds, and then molded her body to mine, and we both sighed. Isn't it nice when that happens? I was thrilled by these new sensations, the flooding of my brain and body with information and response codes. I forgot that I didn't know how to dance, and rocked and moved with her, my hands caressing her back, her shoulders, the curve of her ass. As our legs brushed together, I wondered why I hadn't thought of this as something erotic, only something as a prelude to eroticism. I ran my fingers through her hair, and as a slower song came on, struggled with my instinct to flee. I didn't want this to end.

How strange.

For thirty minutes, maybe longer, I forgot why we were out, intoxicated by this newly discovered pleasure. We claimed our little square of space, and never noticed that we were constantly surrounded by women also trying to find a way to hold onto each other. Nothing mattered, except that I was holding her and she was holding onto me, and wherever our bodies touched, streams of tingly pleasure worked their way through me.

I felt her nipples pressing against me, and pressed her body into mine until they were erect and hard underneath her little black dress. Every time I swayed and brushed against them, she moaned, and every time she arched her back, I pressed my thigh between her legs and rocked her back forward. My fingers found a tangle in her hair and wrapped around it, and with every sharp tug, we both ground against each other, private pain amid one woman's voice after another. We fucked at each other during hard, rocking songs, and caressed each other during slower country songs, and I wanted to cover every inch of her during one ballad that was so sweet that it redeemed all of popular music for me, forever. And I was shocked to find that I was tremendously excited - aching with desire for her, wet and hard and crazy. Just from dancing! I was wondering why I had waited so long to do this, when her voice took me back to the present.

"I need you," she whispered sharply in my ear. As usual, those words sent an immediate message to my body, and I was ready to lay her down right there, except that there wasn't any room. The line for the bathroom hadn't abated one bit, but there was a sex club just two blocks away...

I flung the money at the woman at the door and we hit the darkened backroom like a pair of closet cases after summer vacation with the family. Instantly, we were sucking on each other, her hands tearing at my fly, mine holding onto her hair while I explored her own perfect mouth. I heard the presence of other women, several of them talking and none of them fucking, but I didn't care. It didn't matter that I'd never been there, didn't know anyone, and hadn't ever just fucked like a sex starved lunatic in front of perfect strangers. It didn't matter that it was dark and uncomfortable and I preferred well lit warm places with slings and towels and a quiet, appreciative audience.

She raised her skirt up over her hips and for the first time I didn't even take a moment to admire what attractive lingerie she was wearing. I grabbed onto my dick, and felt the warm slipperiness that my own body had pushed past the straps of the harness to moisten the base, and slid my fingers up and down, my own brand of precum making me wet, shining my warm length before it slipped into her. She tried to grab for it, and I let her. For this one time, I would allow such a brazen act. She moaned and straddled my body, and I leaned back against a wall, lowering my hips so she could climb over me, fill herself with me. When she settled with a hard slam, we both gasped, and our faces screwed up in what could only be the start of mutual orgasm. I didn't have time to reflect on how this was a first for me - I was too busy coming.

My head snapped back, and I didn't even feel the brick wall, I was so gone. I thrust up, deeper into her, and wrapped my arms tightly around her waist, pulling her to me like the perfect sex toy she was. It was violent and it was harsh, and every jerk of my body made me growl and her scream. As I panted, and fought to catch my breath, I was conscious of several pairs of eyes glinting through the darkness, and knew that we had become the entertainment focus of the room. But I didn't care. All I knew was that one series of spasms wasn't going to be enough for me. I turned, awkwardly, keeping myself inside her, and pressed her against the wall. She started to slide down, and staying with her, I ended up on the floor, braced over her, while she moaned and gasped, and started to whimper. Catching her legs, I pulled them up, her thighs now braced from my hips up to my waist. Her ass lifted off the floor, and I could see her cunt, split and filled with my cock, and the sight alone was enough to send me into yet another spiral of ecstasy.

"I'm not finished with you, girl," I snarled, pulling back to slam in again.

Her wails hit a new high note as I pumped, and the shifting position of my cock was just perfect for the arhythmic fucking style that would give me some more time before another orgasm made me insane. She tried to grab for me, and I caught her wrists and slammed them down against the floor. I knew what she liked. So did her body.

We fucked until I couldn't breathe any more, until sweat matted my shirt to my back and the pool of slickness between us seemed like a thin layer of oil spread over our entire bodies. When I pulled out of her, she screamed and clutched at the empty air, and I stood and watched her writhe in the final throes of an agonizing series of delirious shakes which almost - but not quite - got me horny again. I wiped myself off with my back pocket hanky and tossed it onto her body so I could tuck myself away.

"Cool," said a voice from behind me.

"Way cool," said another. And amid a few snickers, I heard gentle applause. I blushed, because of all the reactions I'd ever gotten while playing in public, no one had ever clapped!

The girl was in the bathroom, doing what she could to repair the damage to her clothing and body I had inflicted when a woman in an orange vest came over to me. She was tall, and dark, and oh so butch, and I wondered if she had liked what she'd seen enough for me to snag her number before the girl got back. Then, remembering why we were out, I began to wonder if she'd like the girl, and might like to replay this scene in private, later on. I smiled, relaxed, and she scowled.

"We only allow safe sex here," she snapped. "You didn't put a condom on that thing, so I'm going to have to throw you out."

"But - but-" I started to stutter, for once at a loss for words. And to my everlasting shame, me, the women who never fisted without gloves, and always carried condoms in her toy bag, was ejected from a sex club for having unsafe sex!

Well, I never!

The girl rejoined me about ten minutes later, all fixed up (it's amazing how they do that), and she soothed my hurt feelings with a reminder that the night wasn't over yet, and we had marked off several other places that might have potential. But I was devastated. How could this happen to me? I was not in the mood for any new adventures that night, so I told her we'd just go back to my place and tomorrow I'd write some short piece about some kind of first time experience. She, a smart girl, nodded and went home with me and fixed me a drink and soothed my ego and before long, we were on the couch, and she was kissing me, a sweet series of "let's go to bed" kisses.

Well, you know that was just the beginning. Although I started out feeling annoyed and snippy, I had to admit that her girly caresses were nice and I was not used to having someone make these soft, romantic overtures on me. Hey, even when I bottom, I don't like that. But for the first time, it seemed nice, it seemed right. I let her unbutton my shirt, and laughed at her. Usually, I would let her go only so far, and then roll her onto the floor and remind her who was in charge. But that night, I wanted to see how far the girl would really go.

So, I didn't stop her as she freed my tits and played with them, taking the nipples into her mouth and then running her fingers down my back. I moved onto the floor first, on my knees, and she followed me, running her fingers through my hair for a change, and I resisted the urge to laugh. I was determined to let her play until she decided she would like it better if I took my usual role.

She hesitated from time to time, and I knew she was waiting for me to make my move. But the longer it seemed delayed, the bolder she got. Soon, I was on my back - not an odd position for me. In fact, it's one of my favorites. But instead of telling her to get my cock up and into her and amuse me, I stayed silent, leaving it up to her.

She stripped her dress off, leaving the matching lacy underthings I didn't have time to admire at the sex club. Then, slowly, she mounted me, and slid her body down onto the cock that had previously been used like an internal bludgeon, making it into the sweet sex toy it could be. And slowly, she rocked on me, building until she was at a steady swaying movement that pleased her, instead of the rough, staccato thrusts which pleased me.

Different, definitely different. But not without its charms. I arched my back once, pushing up into her, and she leaned forward and caught my wrists, as easily as I had caught hers. My eyes opened wide - here would be the moment where I would wrestle free, turn her over onto her back and hurt her until she apologized for such a possessive, dominant move. But instead, I laughed and leaned back, surrendering.

"Go ahead, you little slut," I taunted. "Take what you can, now. You know I'll make you pay for it later."

She grinned. "If you can," she snarled. Oooh, I was real afraid. But I resisted the urge to put her down hard, and instead stopped all motion altogether.

"Go ahead and try to get yourself off," I said calmly. "You won't get any help from me. Go on, little girl, stuff that big cock into your cunt for me and show me what a whore you are. Jerk yourself off on my dick, and make it good."

She snarled again, this time in frustration, and then pushed herself up for better leverage. And while I infuriated her by smiling and keeping utterly still, she rose and fell against me, harder and harder, until I could see and feel the familiar signs of her approaching orgasm. And then, when she ground down hard and started to pant, I pushed up, and turned my body sharply, and pulled out of her.

She screamed and clutched for me, but the loss of balance put her well out of reach of my cock. Her hands flew down to her cunt, but I caught them and held onto them, and laughed out loud as her entire body shook and her legs pressed together in the shattering throes of orgasm-interruptus. I knew she was experiencing the beginnings of one, and knew that sensation of the start of the pulsing mingled with the swift fading of intensity, and the need for something more.

"You bastard, you motherfucker!" she was shouting, writhing against me, kicking me, clawing at me. "I hate you! I hate you!"

"You're going to hate me more in a minute," I said, my voice soothing, and my hands like the steel cuffs that would soon be replacing them. "But don't worry, sweetheart. I'll let you jerk off for me in the morning."

I'd never done that before - tying a woman so that she couldn't touch herself, gagging her, blindfolding her, and jerking off while watching her, listening to the whimpers under the gag, the twisting motions of a body in bondage. It was fun. I reminded myself I'd have to do that again sometime. And when I slipped the gag out of her mouth and kissed her good night, I fell asleep while she was begging me for a reprieve, promising that she would be good, so good, if only I let her come, just this once.

Well, I suppose there's a first time for everything. But not that night.

We Never Speak

Her eyes asked me, "How does it feel?"

How does it feel when you answer the phone and I can hear the joy in your voice? As though we were still courting, getting to know each other's smell and taste, and that for you, every phone call from me is a new chance to get to know me, a surer step toward Saturday night. I hear that you are always happy to listen to me speak, always flattered to know that I want to talk to you, and always disappointed when my voice is captured on your machine and you weren't instantly available to hear me.

I am so pleased when I walk into a room and you are there, wearing the clothes you know I like to see. I can imagine you standing in front of your closet, pulling the outfits out one after the other, holding things up to the mirror, wondering if they will be right. I see you tossing clothes on the floor in frustration, running to the bathroom to make sure your makeup isn't smudged.

And I know that you arrive at the bar hoping I'm there, waiting for me to come in, and that your attention is scattered and impatient until I come near you. I feel a hissing of breath between my own teeth when you stand for me, coming to attention of your own free will, and when I come close, I know that you will shudder at the friendly touch of my hand. I am awed that my recognition means so much to you.

And when I take my hand and grasp the back of your neck, feeling those two points that can bring you up to your toes or down to your knees, and I can feel the shaking, the tension and then the relaxation of your entire being, I am bemused. I can feel every shift in emotion as cleanly as a temperature gage. You make no effort to hide them. You make me smile.

I am always aware that your eyes are on me, your ears turned to hear my voice. When you follow me like a loyal dog, I know that you are hungry for the slightest nod, a touch, a word. I am careful when I grant them. I pull you close suddenly, to hear you gasp. I tempt you with my posture, sometimes unconsciously, and I see the need in you to fall at my feet, curl by my leg, draw your body in close by my side. When I finally do point or press your shoulder, I know that between your legs, there's a wetness growing and you are trying to control yourself. I know that when you stand, you want to kneel. When you kneel, you want to grovel. When you grovel, you want nothing more than to be utterly prone, my boot against the back of your neck, squirming against the floor.

I am always aware of that. So I control it, in myself and in you, so that each progression never loses its magic. And I delight in knowing that you know what I'm doing, and that you always struggle with your desires, trying to be strong.

I feel the great power that holding your dignity grants me.

And when we are alone, and you alternately lower and raise your eyes, waiting for me to take the lead, patient yet barely holding back your desire, I feel like a monarch. I know that you will leave me if I choose, unfulfilled in your lust but content to spend mere time with me.

I know that I can simply use you for my pleasure, or even lie back and command you to please me and then send you away, your cunt overflowing, your head spinning from the service you offer. And I know that you will remember every moment of those nights. That you will replay them over and over in your head, making them the crux of your most private orgasms, and you will love them with all your soul.

Or I may choose to put you through an ordeal, tormenting you with those things you hate, teasing you and causing you discomfort and pain, until your writhing tempts the real sadist in me and I can only push you deeper and deeper into the mire of your own fears. I can poke and thrust at you until you make sounds that shame you, until your body responds and fails you, until you cry out those words you hate and finally surrender, utterly. Not to me, but to the pain, to the shame, to the fear that you will break, and I will not find you interesting any more.

And although I cannot even imagine such a time, I feel the fear from you and when I am a sadist, I drink it like brandy. Or tears.

Or I may be kind to us both, and bring out those things which we both love, and feel the ease of play. I know that you will breathe in the rich scent of the leathers, eagerly hold your limbs for the binding, turn your body for the lash. I love to see your shoulders bracing against the heavy tresses of my whips. and feel the fire building beneath your skin. I am so proud when I hear the strangled cries of pain you allow to escape, knowing that you can remain silent if you choose, yet you will display these reactions for me. I know what they cost you. I know that you endure more than you should, to allow yourself the freedom of such grunts and sighs of pain.

I love it when your body is bared for me, and I can possess it, every inch of it. I can spread you out, wide open, your cunt a doorway for me, my fingers, my hand, my tongue, my cocks, my vibrators, the handles of the whips. I love exploring it, with gentle caresses and harsh slaps, with pins and clips and pincers and with silken ropes and wraps and brushes. I love it

180

when you strain against the ropes and the only thing I hold is a slender nylon rod, or when you squirm and twist under the touch of a feather. I love watching you, your hand slowly drawing near that open cunt, when I've told you to please yourself, and you close your eyes against the bright lights I have trained upon you. I tell you that I will take your picture like this one day, and you cum.

Oh. The rapture of your shameful obedience, your terrified lust.

I am captivated by the way your body welcomes me. When you bend and I can open your ass and slide in, I am mesmerized by your sighs, the easy way you accept this most intimate violation. When I fill you to the point of pain, I can hear your breath catch and hold, that little whimper of submission, acknowledging my right to hold you so, begging for just a moment to adjust. I know that you will take more, and I know that you allowing me to choose is but one sacrifice in a long line of sacrifices. I press inward, my eyes fixed on your opening hole, my ears on those little whimpers of fear and gratitude.

I am amazed at how much you trust me, that you will put your body and your mind into my care and deny me nothing. When I command you in an act you have never done, you are more than willing, you are eager to do it, and do it well. You are genuinely sad, sometimes angry, when you cannot take what I have planned, or complete a task I have laid upon you, or enjoy an act I request. And I am touched when I hear you try to hide your resignation, as though you think I don't know you. But I do know. I know that you will do as I say despite your pain or your shame or your distaste, until I tell you to stop, and then you will bask in the slightest reward.

I remember that I was once torn between commanding you to difficult tasks for your pleasure in performing them, or laying them aside in my respect for your tastes. Now, years later, I know that I will never stay a command for your sake. Doing so robs you of your chance for a masochistic, obedient martyrdom.

And sometimes, I feel confused. At the emotions you bring out in me, at the ways you've made me rethink. You make me into a tyrant, a monster, who dines on your suffering and drinks your strength. I am never so wonderful in your eyes as when I grind you into the dirt, leaving marks of scorn on your body and soul. You depend upon me for approval, yet wish for my anger. You always want and need more from me, yet as time passes, you make yourself content with less. I want to reward you, make you happy. But to do so, I must punish you, and make you feel like nothing.

I don't know how I do this. But somehow, when I am with you, it all comes out of me. I am overwhelmed by my own hungers, all responding to yours.

I want to own you, to possess you, to mark you with my spirit. I want to raise you up as my most precious thing, not my lover, not my girlfriend, not my slave, not my submissive, not my bottom, not my toy, my boy, my girl, my pet or my thing, but just absolutely MINE, for as long as we live.

I am honored by your devotion and loyalty. I am humbled by your patience and strength. I am awed by your faith in me, and your ready obedience. I am made whole by your love.

We tell each other these things every time we meet.
We never speak of them.

Coprolalia

(Published under a pseudonym in *Leatherwomen.*)

She's such a cruel bitch, you know? Always knows what to say, that mouth ready to snap back something nasty, cut you to long red ribbons in one verbal slice.

Makes me feel like shit.

So we don't see each other for days and then weeks and then months, and then it's nothing but a phone call in the middle of the night, "I need you, hot-stuff."

So out come the gloves and the lube, the straps and the rods, the dicks and the clips, and here we go again.

There will be kisses, hot and wet and long and deep. Tongues wrestling for dominance until we both have bruised, swollen mouths and look like we've been making acquaintances with brick walls. We hurt each other orally, biting and sucking and humming and slurping, until you'd think that her nasty, filthy mouth was too sore to keep up the battle.

It's only warm-up. I know that. I keep kissing her, hard, to forestall the main event. It never succeeds. She finds a way to escape my need and snaps at me.

"You're such a worthless little slut."

How common.

So it has to be followed by slaps, hard ones to hard parts of the body, shoulder, upper arm, back, upper thigh. Red marks against the flesh, punctuated by hard sounds.

The pain of the slaps makes me bite my own tongue, and her words are swift to follow.

"You're so fucking inept, I don't know why I waste my time with you."

Profanity so early?

Then she has missed me.

I grin, even as I flex for the next torment, the next round of words. It has to be the strap now, doesn't it?

Heavy, rifle-shot smacks and relentless bands of pain across a moving target, because we just can't stay still in this battle. Each move is another jarring crack, and her words punctuate the thrashing.

"Coward cocksucker! Shit-licker!"

I love it when she's at a loss for words. She's done so much better in the past. I'll never forget the time she called me an *excrescence*. It seemed such a nice way of saying I was a pile of shit. My cunt begins to throb in the rhythm of the strap and the words. I know there will be a change soon.

"You putrid dog-fucker! You slurp up dog shit for the taste! Fuck -" (Gasp of breath. Was she getting out of breath so soon?) "You bend over for dog packs! Like to howl...howl until they cover you with their slimy dog-cum! Then you try to suck 'em off to get some more!"

Very vulgar. And gross. The change would come now.

Steel bondage, always effective when someone just can't keep still, right? But first we have to wrestle, or else they're not going on. Snarls and more profanity flow between us, until the steel rattles closed, and kicks have to be dodged.

"You think you're worthy of my attention, you scabrous, syphilitic moron? You're a puss-sucking two-dollar whore, a wino's three-hole masturbatory toy!"

I really hate that. Some of my best friends are sex workers. I growl a warning.

"What's your problem, pussy-for-pay? Can't admit you trade gash for cash? Or maybe you're only taking beer bottles up the ass for quarters these days?"

The ass has to be targeted in time to that, of course. Pokes, and then heavy swipes with the rod, a snappy sound of latex, a glob of cold wetness, and slam, right up the old poop-chute with some kind of rubber thingy. Accompanied by appropriate dialogue.

"You like it up the ass, don't you - anything, anyone's fuck-stick! We can ship you to Tijuana and put you in the mule fucking show, you're sloppy enough to take two at a time! Then you can give your famous two-bit blow job. Hell, you can take on twenty or thirty cheap tourists in your sleep!"

Get on with it girl, this is getting old. But I'm so wet, I'm so sore already. The smell of us is all perspiration and sex goo and nasty things.

184

An opening is made for another rubber thing, and it slides home with an ease that makes us both take a pause to breathe. It doesn't last long.

"You degenerate...filthy...goddamnmutherfucking...son of a bitch, bastard, scumsucker! Slimy...perverted cooze, pussy-whacker, feeble jerk-off...."

Yeah, go ahead. Call me weak. Who's gonna outlast who, babe? I yowl in response to her words and motions, and she takes up the call with a series of sarcastic yelps and barks.

"That's it, little bitch...canine cunt! Howl to the fucking moon, you inbred, asinine, fatuous fuck-up! You ignorant, insipid...brain-dead bovine!"

Now she was getting personal.

It was time to change tactics again. We are so predictable. Tits get smacked and grasped until white, finger shaped worms appear, and our tight, reddened faces are thrust up against each other, and her mouth is against my ear, telling me all the things I hate to hear.

"You deformed, fucking-eyesore...repulsive slob, you fat, ugly...uh!"

Finally, I break. I hate it when she gets around to the physical stuff.

Letting one tit go, I smash my fist into her gut, and all her venom comes out in a rush of stale air in my face. Cuffed as she is, it's no fair fight, but I'm getting mine now. I turn and shove, and fill her mouth with my answer, the answer she always gets, until the only sounds she's making and grunts and moans, and the only way she can be taken is stuffed and broken and quieted at last.

When I finally finish, I push a gag into her, and leave her to watch me through angry, wet, hostile eyes. I know she's checking her vocabulary list for round two.

But how can she do better than *fatuous fuck-up*?

Don't Get Me Wrong

Let me make one thing clear before we start, OK? I am straight. That's right, a cocksucking woman, a woman who likes the feeling of a big, strong man pumping away in her, a bitch who's had cum spurt up her snatch, in her mouth, and up her ass. Yeah, I took it any way I could, and I liked it. Not like some frigid bitches who just lay there and stare at the cracks and water spots until the guy's finished. I mean, I got into it, the minute I felt a dick sliding into me. As far as I'm concerned, there's nothing like a big hunk of meat being shoved in and out one of my holes until I just cream all over the fucking place. I like guys. I like their cocks.

In fact, that's part of the situation, you know? Because I once had a boyfriend, and he had a problem with Aich, and his problem led to my apartment being a stash for all kinds of bad things. I wasn't stupid; I knew he was fencing the stuff he found so he could shove it up his sleeve. But he was in control, you know? He didn't have a problem with it. A lotta people don't know that most sess addicts, or like they say now, IVDUs, have real lives. They go to work and they have friends and kids and all that happy shit. They really just wanna be left alone, get some stuff in them, and keep right on going. But not everyone lives by the old live-and-let-live code, you know? And I guess Phil's problem was that he didn't always have the cash, so he'd pick up anything that wasn't nailed down and trade it for some green. So he was busted with some slightly used stereo equipment and I was busted because the rest of his stuff was topped off with a gun he thought he could trade for about a week of heaven.

I guess everything would have worked out if I testified against him. The DA offered me a nice deal, but you know, one week apart and all I could think of was how Phil was doing without the smack, and whether they're giving him decent meth, and if he missed me. But I swear to you, sister, if they got me that first week and made the offer, I would have walked and shoved my walking papers right up his sorry ass. But they let me sit too long, and I got to missing him.

See, that's how I figure I'm straight. But we got that settled, so let's move on.

Six months vacation guaranteed at a upstate correctional facility, with an option to renew if I was a bad girl. That's how my fuckin' court-appointed put it when he said "adios." Fucker. I went in figuring I needed a real badass attitude, because I never been up before. I caught a few overnighters downtown back when I was in the Trade, but you know the deal. My daddy had three bail bondsmen on call, and he would even pay for a cab home. But there's no future on the street. And when daddy got 'shroomed in the Bronx because a couple of kids decided to argue with their pieces, I just kinda drifted along, waiting for a new opportunity. And that's when I met Phil, see?

So anyway. I go to the island in that junky bus with the bumpy back seat full of PR girls talking Spanish and the evil looking black mama who took her man apart with a kitchen knife and five girls who got nabbed because their honeys are just bad news. They didn't talk to me, not much. I was too white, what with my red hair and everything. I heard the word "puta" when I walked down the middle and took my seat, and I shot back, "With your old man, slit!", and then one of the guards started banging his nightstick against the window bars to get us to shut up.

I was scared shitless, I can tell you that. All the way there, all I could think of was those shitty TV movies where some blonde white chick goes to jail and there's a million mean, mother-killing lesbians who fuck you up the ass with a broomstick or a coke bottle, or they catch you in the showers and beat the shit out of you for fun. And then there's the boy guards, who want blowjobs after dark, or in the laundry, and trustees who will make you go down on them for three days so you can get off of disciplinary reports. Man, I was ready to puke by the time we saw the outer gates. I was wondering how the fuck I could manage to stay in solitary all the time and not extend my six months into the usual year.

But you know, it's not like that, not really. At least, not a first. The first week, especially for a new girl, is all exams and getting to know your way around. They look at your eyes, they take your blood, they look up your snatch and up your ass, they even poked around in my mouth, checking for hollow teeth or some shit like that. I actually roomed alone for three days before they got me assigned to a regular cell, and that's when I met Candi.

With a name like that, you know she's a hooker, so we hit it off right away. She was black as night, but man, we had a lot in common. For the next two days, we swapped John stories, talkin' about our best and worst tricks. I mean, she brought back some real funny memories for me. Like the guy who didn't want to fuck, but liked to watch a girl jerk off. Now that's not so rare, I used to get a lot of those. They liked the red bush, you know? But this guy, he'd wanna play this really weird music while I was clit whacking. He'd bring this little Jap radio with him and put in a tape, and what played was that music they always play at the Fourth of July. You know, the one with the cannons and shit. And he'd yell a lot, usually "Yes! Yes!" over and over again, and tell me to hold onto the cum until some big bang.

Like I was really coming for him, right?

What the hell, he paid good money. Candi liked that story. She told me one about this guy who taught this reading class for these really white middle-class nerd-brats, and how every time one of them graduated or won an award or something, he'd bring the little rugrat in to see her. She said those boys had never seen pussy before, or got their dicks sucked, and they certainly never talked to no big black mama, and she had to keep such a tight hold on herself not to laugh in their scared white faces. But she sighed and told me that there was no cum in the world as sweet as a little white teen's first cum.

Candi showed me around, warned me away from the worst food, and sat next to me when we ate, to point out the troublemakers. "You stick with me, sugar," she'd say, "and you'll be outa here in six and not one motherfucking day more!" Hey, I was just fine with that. I didn't want to mess with no bad ladies.

But man, two weeks in and I was so horny my fingers were starting to get all mushy, like dishpan hands, you know? Candi thought I was a riot, the way I jerked off every night. She said no one could give her pleasure like her old man could, so she just didn't try when they were apart. I told her that Phil was a stud, and that I was missing him so bad that I was ready to start humping the fucking toilet. The truth was, I was always a horny bitch. Since I was just a little kid, I couldn't keep my hand out of my panties. Shit, I was getting off playing boyfriends with my pillow when I was about eight or so! And I did miss Phil, kinda. Even though it was all his fucking fault I was in this to begin with.

But just because I was horny didn't mean I was asking for what happened. I mean, you have to understand that; it's just like they say at all the women's shelters. No one asks for it, and I certainly didn't. What happened was just not my fucking fault.

What happened. That's the whole fucking point of this right? OK, I'm getting to it. Weeks go by, and I'm just fine. Candi's my friend, I stay out of everyone's way, I say the right things in the support group thing that

Candi said looked good in your file. I even went to fucking church on Sundays. What laugh, but you know, you gotta keep appearances up. I figured that by the time I was through, I was gonna look like a little choir girl right out of the Sisters of Mercy Sunday School.

But there's always a fuck-up waiting in the shadows. Just waiting for things to settle down, waiting for people to relax and think, hey, things aren't so bad. And then, wham! You get slammed real fucking good.

And none of this was my fucking fault. It was Candi's. Well, not really. I mean, she didn't ask for me to get involved.

Maybe I should tell the whole story. You see, Candi's old man had about six, seven, maybe eight girls, a real entrepreneur. And she was not his best bitch, not by a long shot. But she had class, and she had regulars, so she had steady employment. Then, the asshole gets a new bitch, and she is one mean motherfucker. First, she gets him to really whack away on the girls who aren't producing like she thinks they should, and then she starts ragging on the girls who are doing righteous work. The way Candi told it, this bitch was really just interested in keeping her own butt off cheap mattresses, even if it meant that the other girls were doing twenty five dollar blowjobs in commuter cars on their way out of the city.

So anyway, Candi gets up in this bitch's face about it, and let's just say they weren't best friends. But the next time Candi gets picked up and taken on the tour downtown, suddenly there's no lawyer, and no bail. Candi's no 'burb, though, she's got her own back up, and she gets her ass out the next day. And the first thing she does is get one of her steadies to pay a visit to the bitch. Now Candi wasn't doing this to scare the bitch, but to take her out. She wanted her man to cut her, like that model in the fucking newspapers, make some really scary bitch outa her. So you can't think that Candi was all sugar and nice thoughts. But when you're a hooker, the only heart of gold you know is the one your daddy wears around his neck, the one he bought with your cunt.

And the most messed up thing about it is that instead of hating your daddy for treating you bad, you hate his other girls.

So Candi sends out her man to cut this bitch that made her daddy leave her dry at the tank. Got that? But the bitch got a man of her own, and the boys gotta fight, and then there's a dead guy, and then the girls gotta get in on it, and the next thing is that everyone gets hauled in on murder and assault and all kinds of really heavy shit. Candi ends up with two years on an assault charge, and the bitch ends up in the hospital with some of those cuts that actually got made before the boys got to defending the honor of their whores.

And Candi is my cell-mate. And when the bitch gets out of the hospital, she gets in touch with her friends inside, and they decide to teach

Candi a lesson. And when they think about it, since the bitch's man bought it, they'd take out Candi's main squeeze.

Who they thought was me.

See how this stuff gets fucked up? I mean, just because Candi never turned down a snatch shoved in her face, they think she's lesbo, and so I must be too. Really fucking bright, right? She's not, and I'm not, but everyone's gotta assume things, make up stories to fit their ideas of what everything has to be.

They took me down after lunch, when I was supposed to be learning how to fold towels and sheets and shit. Yeah, it happened right where those shitty movies say it happens. And you know why? Because it makes sense.

You can't get into the cells when they're locked, unless you've got a few guards feeling good about you. And even then, the cameras and the sweeps will catch someone where they shouldn't be and wham!, you're doing disciplinary time. You can't do it in the library, the noise would be too much. You can't do it in the fucking rec room, because there's dozens of girls around, and if one of them doesn't like watching, the guards are in and you're fucked. (That doesn't mean no one gets whacked in rec, though. I once saw a bitch take about a dozen hard belly punches in the middle of the big commercial break during the Super Bowl. She was cheering for the wrong fucking team. When the guard asked her why she was puking her guts out all over the floor, she didn't say a fucking thing. One of the hard timers said, "Bad popcorn." Not a single bitch in the room even cracked a smile.)

But in the laundry room, you got noise. Holy shit, you got noise! The washing machines, the dryers, the whole mess, is nothing but hot and wet and noisy. And even though you got guards there, the last thing they wanna do is stand around in the heat and mess, watching women dump, sort, carry and fold. Besides, these girls had something going with the fucking guards. They had to set it up just right.

I was waiting for this girl to toss another pile of sheets in front of me. We were folding them together, see, but she kept on leaving me to go get more. I was standing between about six tables full of clean, hot sheets that smelled like some really nasty bleach. I was just minding my business. I was not looking for trouble.

But it found me, sister. In the form of three bitches from hell. I mean, every one of them was a hard-timer, and later on I found out that Rica, the leader, had fucking killed her own fucking kids. Seems that they couldn't shut up when she wanted them to be quiet. And the other two weren't exactly nuns themselves.

The three of them were the Sistahs. They weren't all black, though. Rica was some kinda mix, she spoke the lingo like a Puerto Rican, but she kept telling people she wasn't no spic. They called her Rica anyway. Her best buddy was Deshawn, who everyone called Dee, who was in for aggravated assault. You wanna know how aggravated? She had this neighbor who maybe stole some of her stash or some shit, right? So she goes over to the neighbors house, picks up a big lamp, breaks the bulb off, and cuts the neighbor lady into little neighbor-slices. Then, Dee takes out the two cats in the house, leaving chunks of kitten all over the fucking place, rips up the furniture and the curtains, and helps herself to a six-pack from the fridge on her way out.

I'd call that pretty fucking aggravated.

And then there's little Weasel. She's skinny and cute, and she's got two teeth that some weird dentist sharpened to points. The prison dicks wanted to have the motherfuckers pulled, 'cause they might constitute a weapon, but they never figured out how to do it legally. Weasel is the strangest one of the Sistahs. I mean, if you wake up one morning and there's a fresh pile of shit on the bottom of your bunk, you know it's Weasel that paid you a visit. She looks like any bitch can pick her up and break her in half, but when she fights, she moves so quick, you find your teeth living somewhere down your throat before you figure out where the little fucker went to. She's just as likely to slip you an extra cigarette as cut your good bra to pieces in front of your eyes so you have to wear one of the armor-plated fucking prison bras. She was in for a long time, something about knifing a guy in the middle of some kind of weird sex and drug scene, with kids and goats and crack all over the place. She liked to tell people that her mother was a priestess who could lay some serious curses on them. And then she'd flash those pointy teeth and lick them.

And the three of them took me down, hard, in between three tables of folded sheets.

I didn't even have time to yell "shit!" I was on the floor, with Weasel's arm around my throat and Dee's fist in my belly, and before I could even breathe again, Rica shoved a washcloth in my mouth.

"This Candi's cunt?" I heard Dee ask. You might be thinking that they had to whisper. Not on your fucking life. They had to talk real loud to hear each other over the washing machines.

I started to struggle, and shout. I thought I was saying "No, wait! I'm not!"

I guess it sounded like a bunch of muffled whimpers. Weasel clamped down harder, screaming, "It's her! Get the fucking tape!" And they wrapped tape around my head, pushing that fucking washcloth as far as it could go in my mouth. And then, Rica taped my eyes shut too. It pulled at my hair, real bad. But I wasn't worried about my fucking hair. I was worried about how I was going to fucking breathe! I mean, if I had a cold, Sister, I'd be dead. It's that simple. And every time it looked like I was struggling, Dee (I figured it was Dee) would just punch her big fat fist into my stomach. I finally gave up.

Rape is like that. I mean, it's not like that stupid joke, you don't just lay back and enjoy it, OK? But if you fight every fucking inch, all it will do for you is put you six feet under. And it was three against one. So I couldn't fight them off or even make them think it wasn't worth it. So they raped me. And more.

They had to drag me off the main floor. I ended up behind the folding tables, the ones that were already filled, and up against the back wall. We were as far away from the guards as you could get, and hidden by mountains of towels and uniforms.

They popped the buttons on the front of my dress when they pulled it off, and I could hear the little plastic knobs hitting the concrete floor. Funny how you remember things like that, isn't it? I just remember hearing the little click, click, click, and then thinking, oh no, how am I gonna get those things back on before someone notices? I shouldn't have worried.

I'm laying there in my panties and bra (one of my sneakers fell off back at the other table), with Weasel still panting in my ear and holding onto my neck, and I hear Rica.

"Your lesbo bitch messed with the wrong lady, Blanca," she said, to start off. "She lost her main man; so we gonna do the same to your cunt. She gets to see you messed up, girl, messed up real bad. That way, she know what it like to not have a pretty thing to fuck with!"

"This bitch ain't pretty," Dee said. She was so close, I could smell her breath; it was like old bacon. "I bet she dyes that fucking hair."

"Let's see!" Weasel said. Her voice was high, like a squeal. I could tell she was getting excited, because every time I shifted, she just clamped down harder and giggled.

Dee was probably the one who tore my panties off. I guess she was disappointed at my red snatch. She showed it by punching me right there, right between my fucking legs.

If guys feel like I felt when they get kicked in the balls, no wonder they get so pissed. I thought I was going to die. But I was so wrong. I was so fucking wrong. That was the nicest thing they did to me.

Before I could try to kick her, she shoved a few fingers up my cunt, and the three of them laughed. Weasel (her fingers were long and bony, I could tell it was her) grabbed hold of one of my tits, keeping her arm tight around my neck, and squeezed it, hard. Her fingers felt like they were gonna break right through that tit, just burst it open like a balloon. I screamed, and I heard it all in my head, but not outside the gag.

Those fucking cunts just laughed some more. And kept right going. With someone fucking my snatch open, I felt hands all over my body. Both of my tits were clamped down on, like someone was holding onto them like a bag caught in a subway door. I felt something cold spill on my crotch; it was this gloppy shit we used to get the really bad stains out of sheets, you know, like shit stains and blood. And Dee grunted and snuffled like the pig she was as she just started shoving this glop into me.

"We gon' get you nice and wet," she yelled at me. "Gon' get you wet for good nasty!"

She had about three fingers in me, I guess, then four, and I started to really scream. My nose was getting clogged, and to breathe I had to snort out the snot, which was really disgusting, but what could I do? The bitches laughed again, called me names, told me I was just a little snot-nose cheap puta, a kiddie whore, a sucker of diseased cocks. They told me I was gonna get sick, die maybe, but first I was gonna get ugly. When they started in on that shit, they began to hit me again, on my tits, on the side of my head. One of them kicked me, down at the bottom of my leg, my calf? Over and over again. It was gonna look like someone backed a fucking taxi over it by the time she was through.

And then Dee started really slamming into me, all her fingers at once. And then, she started folding them up. Sister, I felt like I was giving birth. It hurt like a motherfucker! I was screaming so loud, even with the gag so tight, I just didn't know what the fuck was going on. It just felt like someone was shoving a bowling ball up my twat, and I couldn't breathe.

My sister, Linelle, she gave birth once, she had this way to do it without it hurting a lot? But she said, even with all the fucking panting and blowing and relaxing and pushing, she was sweating like a fucking pig and screaming for mama, Jesus, and all the saints for hours. And she didn't have a fucking washcloth in her mouth, either.

"Ey, look! I gotta cunt on my hand!" I heard that like it came from another room; I was that far gone. It was like their bodies and their hands were all over me, but their voices were a million miles away. When Dee started slamming her fist in and out of me, that slimy glop squishing around, falling out and pooling all around my ass, and more of it being dribbled all over my crotch, I started choking. Suddenly, the hands on my tits, the pain in my leg, even the cut I could feel on one side of my head, they were all nothing. Soon, even the fist in my cunt was nothing. Only one thing mattered. Air! I knew they were gonna fucking kill me, fuck me to death, make me choke to death on a fucking washcloth. Snot was just all over my face, I couldn't breathe any more! And I started to get dizzy, and then I tried to fight them one last time.

And then, I just went limp. I couldn't do shit anymore, so I guess my body just flopped back to die.

That's when they took the gag off. They just ripped the tape away, pulling out hair and skin, and dragged the washcloth outa my mouth. My tongue felt like it was three times the normal size. I couldn't have screamed if I wanted to, but someone smacked me hard across the mouth anyway. I realized, while sweet, hot air was hitting my chest, that there wasn't anything in my cunt any more and I thought that maybe they were finished.

They weren't. They just turned me over, onto my hands and knees, and someone slammed my head against the floor. I ended up bent over like a Muslim guy at prayers, my ass up and my head down. My lip and my forehead were both bleeding. Something fat and cold was shoved into my snatch.

"Thas it, pipe fuck the bitch," someone yelled. They were shoving a heavy pipe, the kind most inmates would love to keep for self defense purposes, right into me. And sister, let me tell you, it was still nicer then Dee's fat fist, OK? But they had other things on their mind, too. Someone scooted down in front of me, and grabbed my hair. I could hear Rica's voice in my ear.

"Since you so friendly with the cunt, maybe you like mine!" And she dragged my face down into her crotch.

I keep telling you I'm not a lesbo, right? Well, that means I never ate cunt before. I used to have a trick or two that liked to do it, but mostly, it just wasn't something I got into, from either end. Like I said, I like to fuck.

But sister, I dove in like an old bull-dyke on fresh bait. If it was gonna keep me alive, I was gonna do it, OK?

I never had my face in a cunt before. Rica smelled bad, real funky, like she hadn't showered last night. And you better believe that the State don't provide fucking feminine hygiene kits to the bitches, OK? I mean, this was no springtime fresh pussy. But at least she wasn't on the rag, and if it smelled funky, it still smelled like pussy, so I just did what I guess anyone thinks you should do when you're down there. I stuck my tongue in and licked. Sister, I almost gagged to death at first, but I got used to it. I had no choice. Whenever I pulled back, she just slammed her fist into my head and pulled me into her, grinding my face into her shorthairs.

And in the mean time, I had this pipe being shoved in and out of my cunt, like a piston, and someone was dumping more glop on me, slathering it down my ass crack. So you know, the next thing I feel is the pipe sliding out of my cunt and into my ass.

Did I say sliding? Being shoved in is more like it. I mean, I like a nice stiff cock up the shit chute on a good day, with lots of greasy lube. But cocks got skin on them, they got fat. And they're smooth, and rounded. But a pipe is just hard, and it doesn't have a nice smooth end, and it doesn't bend and sqoosh to fit in right. I was crying into Rica's snatch while her girlfriends shoved this pipe up my ass and giggled.

By the time Rica got bored, they were all ready to switch. With a few hard punches to keep me quiet, they maneuvered around me and I found myself face down in another dirty cunt. And while I ate this one out, I felt Weasel's hard, bony fingers squeezing into my pussy. Soon, she had her fist in there, and I was getting screwed every way possible. My mouth was full of cunt, my ass full of steel, and this scrawny bitch had her fucking fist in my snatch.

They kept changing places, fast, hitting me harder and harder every time they switched. Sometimes, it felt like I had nothing but pussy all around me, ooze and sweat and blood and piss, until my mouth was full of this filthy soup and my ass and cunt were nothing but two huge open wounds. I began to taste the goop on their hands and their cunts, and when that became too much, I finally lost everything, I mean I upchucked my lunch all over some bitch's lap. I guess it was Weasel, really, because Dee had to pull her fingers out of my asshole to pull me back and slam my head into a table leg. They all got up then, and kicked me, someone landing a really hard one just over my belly, another one right between my legs. Their expressions of disgust were mixed with more laughter as Weasel took her revenge by standing over me and pissing all over my face and tits.

And then they left.

The whole thing took less then a half hour, or so the guards swore at the hearing, because they couldn't have been away from the room longer then that. I don't know. It seemed like forever to me.

I spent four weeks in the infirmary with a cracked rib and a mild concussion and the little piece of my cunt that needed a few stitches, plus the fact that I picked up a real nasty yeast infection and then had a motherfucker of an allergic reaction to something in the laundry goop. I sang like a fucking canary, and all sorts of people were called in to testify, including Candi, and at the end, I was given a month in solitary and they shoved me outa there as soon as my first parole hearing came up. The Sistahs got a few more months added to their sentences, and Rica ended up transferred to another facility. But I wasn't gonna take no chances. When I got out, I was ready to move, sister. I wasn't gonna stay in town with the friends of these bitches waiting to take me down.

I met with my parole officer four times before I got word from my sister that she'd lend me the money to move. Phil was still in jail; and besides, he hadn't written to me once, the prick. So I headed west with nothing but my clothes and about a hundred dollars. But my cunt was all better, so traveling money wasn't a real problem. I just needed enough to put down some money on an apartment. I wasn't gonna live in the streets, that's for sure.

And that's how I ended up here, see? I mean, I didn't intend to come to this city. I was thinking I'd rather go somewhere warmer, like L.A. or something. But everyone said I had to see this city, with the hills and the pretty houses and the bay and everything, so I figured what the hell? And even though there are so many queers here, there's still plenty of business for me.

And I got a boyfriend. I told you that, right? He is fine, truly fine. He looks like what's his name, Kevin Costner, and he's got this amazing business, sending dead flowers to people. No shit, that's what he does. And he's hip to what I do for cash, it don't bother him. In fact, when we're doing the nasty, he likes me to tell him what a stud he is compared to the tricks I see, how much bigger his dick is and how much longer he lasts, and how much more interesting and talented he is. And when he fucks me, I feel like I'm goin' to heaven. And that's the truth. He is one hot stud.

But there's this thing; I'm not queer, right? And I like him a lot, and I love doing sex with him.

But godammit, I just keep thinking about what happened in prison. I don't think about it during the day, or when I'm working. But when I'm alone and jerking off, or when I'm with my boyfriend and we're going at it like two cats in an alleyway, I keep thinking about me, on the cold, concrete floor, a pipe up my ass and a fist in my cunt and my mouth slurping all over some dirty, smelly snatch. And I cum, sister.

It's the only thing I think of when I cum.

Mandarin Style

(A Marketplace story, from *The Academy*.)

She was like a knifeblade in twilight, attractive and dangerous and oh, so obvious in her presence. I felt for her like I sometimes feel when I stand on the edge of a balcony, like I should really bend my knees and launch my self out and down, to my certain destruction.

I dampened my jockeys right through to the seam of my 501s, and turned away before I leapt.

I was late for the seminar, the booklet folded back in my hands, slipping and sliding among the dozen handouts and schedule updates, glancing down from time to time to make sure I was in the right place. The hotel hallways were crowded, and I could barely make it from one room to another without running into ex-girlfriends, former bottoms, current fuck buddies and assorted community acquaintances who all had to be acknowledged. Hugs and back pounding, kisses and casual gropings, promises to meet later, later, after the next one, before the contest, at the dungeon.

How many people have I slept with, based on a relationship that lasts ten minutes at a time, while we're both on our way to something else? I amused myself by trying to count while I scanned the room looking for a seat behind someone not too tall.

As usual, the presenters weren't ready, just milling around at the front of the room, playing with the microphones and pouring glasses of ice water. I stuffed the papers into my vest pockets and settled my dick comfortably against my right thigh. It was itching today, probably too dry. The straps of the harness settled up tight, and I sat up straighter to relieve the pressure.

Finally, with nods all around, the leader of the seminar coughed and tapped the mike, and people began to settle down. I waved at a pal across the room, and they turned the tape recorder on, and the man introduced the topic.

"Twenty-four-slash-seven, or, Do People Really Live This Way?" There was scattered laughter; I smiled a little. The amusement didn't make me feel comfortable. I pulled the program booklet out of my pocket again to check the description of the seminar. It said:

"An examination of the possibilities in a full-time D/S relationship. Presenters will discuss the realities of this most difficult lifestyle."

I tried to sit tall while they introduced themselves. Yes, yes, the middle guy has been in the scene for twenty years. He has two lifestyle "subs" under him. Yes, the woman at the end has been in the scene for *thirty* years, and she is up to her third slave. The two leathermen have been together for five years, and they are master and slave. I read it all in the program. Let's get to the point. How did they meet? How did they know? What did they do - and how can I find someone to do that with me?

Well, isn't that the point of all these things? I mean, I had fun watching the fire demonstrations earlier, but really, I'm here to hook up. If not for tonight, then maybe - maybe much longer.

As they took turns explaining how real their relationships were to them, I was dismayed to find my mind wandering. Yes, it's sweet that you love each other so much, I said mentally, but what does it say in your contracts? Do you really do anything you want with your lover? What does it feel like? And why weren't there more bottoms on the damn panel?

Instead, I began to hear how compromise made things work for them all. The same stuff I'd heard before, last year as a matter of fact. This one had a trick for making sure that his slave knew that certain things were his right to do - but that he didn't have to exercise that right. Another one sat down with his slave once every quarter, to discuss things like equals, just to make sure things were going great. Not that she couldn't ask to do that at any time, he added quickly. It was just to make sure that they both had a safety net. That started a discussion on the burdens of being the top in a full-time relationship. Nods of agreement all around.

I stifled a yawn, and wondered when the dungeons were going to open that night, and whether there was a women's party.

As my mind wandered, so did my eyes. And that's when I saw her slip into the room, followed by this tall blond haired man who looked like he would be more at home posing for an advertisement for milk.

But she was the one who grabbed me. Barely five foot two was my guess, with spiky ink-black hair that looked like it ran down between her shoulderblades. Her high cheekbones and narrow, dark eyes spoke of an

Asian background, but she wasn't obviously Chinese or Japanese - maybe Filipina? She was wearing faded jeans and tight chaps with a silky leather uniform shirt, aviator glasses hanging from a correct loop in the front. There wasn't a ring of keys dangling left, but what looked like a silver snake of a collar, with a lock hanging tantalizingly low on her thigh.

I instantly saw myself crawling to her and rubbing my face against that thigh, pushing that loop of silver, begging for it to embrace my throat.

I turned back to the seminar and pressed my lips closed. Swallowing hard, I then had to take a deep breath, because a wave of dizziness had washed over me.

You got it bad, baby, I thought to myself. Calm down! Jeeze, you'd think you weren't getting laid often enough!

But I didn't dare look back at her. I stared at the presenters, waiting for wisdom, or at least a clue.

"You have to recognize that your sub is a human being, with feelings and needs just like you have," one of the guys was saying. "Sometimes, she's going to need some time off, maybe to just chill out and take inventory. It's your responsibility to provide her with that time."

"And what if you should require that person's services during that time?" came a voice from the back of the room. I knew who it was. This time, I was not the only person who turned to look at her.

She was still standing, and the blond guy was behind her and to one side, looking kind of casual, but attentive. And very cheerful. She, on the other hand was dead serious.

"Well, what do you mean? Like to talk or something?"

"No. I meant, what if, when you have dismissed your slave for this free time, you realize that there is a task which needs completion, or that you wish to have sex with them. What if you have an unexpected guest whose comfort requires the services of your slave? What if you are merely bored and wish them to come and act as a footstool while you take tea?"

Her voice was low pitched, but clear, and there was some kind of accent there I couldn't recognize. She made short gestures when she spoke. Little, sharp movements which emphasized words, added ironic accents to her phrases. The room swayed as attention went back to the panel.

"I'll take that," the woman on the end offered. "It's simple - the agreement I have with my slaves is just that - an agreement. In it, I have made promises, too. I have to uphold them, on my honor as a mistress. If I have to deal with a minor inconvenience from time to time, it's my responsibility to deal with it."

There were noises of agreement, affirmation.

"Then why do you call them slaves? Would a slave not be pleased to be used by their owner? Would a slave not be utterly available, at all times, even if this is inconvenient to them - because that is their purpose? Does not an owner have the right to use their slave, so long as such use does not cause them to be incapable of serving?"

I was beginning to flush. Every line from her made my cunt throb and pulse, and by now, I was so wet I wondered if the seat was going to be spotted. But I was also shaking. When I turned back to the panel, I grabbed hold of the laces on the side of my vest and wrapped them around my fingers to keep my hands from trembling.

"Well, I guess it depends on your definition of slavery," one of the men countered. "The way I see it, I have just as much responsibility as my sub. More, in fact. As a dom, I have to make sure that she is safe, and - "

"Happy?" The woman asked.

"Well, yes, of course," he admitted, with heads bobbing up all around. "What's the point of doing all this unless both partners are happy?" asked another one. There was some applause, and then the room swished as heads turned back to the woman in the rear. A few hands danced and waved, trying to get in on this, but it was obvious that they were going to have to wait.

"It seems strange to me," the woman said, this time allowing a thin smile to show through, "that you will spend all this time and effort to create happiness when a man or woman who truly wishes to be a slave will be happy once they become one." She made an abrupt gesture to one side, and Blondie stepped away, opened the door, and she slid through.

"Hey - don't leave - you can't do that -" came an outraged cry from the podium.

"Oh, that was nice," the woman on the end snapped. "Come in, say your piece, and then leave before anyone can argue with you. That was useful."

"Well, let's just say that that sort of judgmentalizing doesn't help anyone," the leader said, regaining focus. "Slaves and masters are whoever they decide themselves to be. Now, let's get back to the real topic, OK?"

I heard one person down the row from me whisper, "Do you know who she was?" I saw the head shake, no, and then I gathered up my papers and made my way out.

By the time I got to the hall, she was long gone.

I saw her again, skirting the edges of the room where the fund-raising auction was held, but lost her in the crowd. In vain, I looked for her at the dungeon space, even loitering in mixed space for two hours, asking people if they'd seen her. Almost everyone had - but not there.

I didn't know what I would say to her. I didn't even know how I'd say it. But that night, after a few halfhearted friendly scenes with some other girls, I fell asleep alone, twisting under the covers, hot but unable to jerk off. It was like being lovesick, except that I didn't even know her name, or whether she liked girls, or shit, even if she'd take one look at me. It hurt, real bad. And no, not in a good way.

On Sunday, after the last of my marked off seminars, I packed and stowed my luggage at the front desk. I would have three hours until I had to take the shuttle to the airport and then home. Because of that woman, this had been one of the strangest conferences I'd ever been to - I hadn't taken anyone new to bed, and I hadn't bottomed to anyone new, and I didn't even come, not once. I was wondering how long this was going to last.

"Excuse me," came a voice from the door. No, it wasn't her - it was him. Blondie. I turned and jumped a little - but she wasn't next to him. He flashed a smile. "I'm sorry, I don't know how to address you," he said easily. "Is it Miss, Ma'am, or Sir?"

God, you could hear the capitals when he talked. "Jessie," I said, clearing my throat. "Jessie is just fine."

"Thank you, Jessie. My mistress has asked for the pleasure of your company if you are currently free."

My heart beat out the rhythm of a tango. I stood without thinking and nodded, and he held the door open for me. How did he find me? Why did she want to see me? How did she pick me to see? I walked with him to the elevator, where he punched up the penthouse suite floor, naturally, and I began to feel a little giddy.

"This is like being in a book," I said out loud.

"Yep," he agreed.

"I mean, wealthy, mysterious woman who I don't know asks to see me the last day of a conference. This doesn't happen on a regular basis."

"Nope!"

I wiped my hands against my jeans legs and looked at my traveling clothes in horror. I was as vanilla as you can be, not even packing. I didn't even look like a dyke, let alone a tough, butch bottom leatherdyke.

The elevator door slid open and Blondie waited for me to exit, and then kind of sailed across the hall to tap on a door. He opened it slowly, and ushered me in like he was going to announce me.

She was sitting in one of the big wing-backed chairs by the wall of windows that gave a great view of the city. She was also not in her leathers - she was wearing a man's tailored white shirt, French cuffs and gold at her wrists, and one of those fancy silk ties that cost more than what I make and will never, ever be used for makeshift bondage.

"So," she said right away, before I had a chance to even step into the room. "What do you want?"

My mouth went dry, and my mind went blank. I stared at her for an incredibly long moment and then mentally shook my head to get the cobwebs out. "Er - you sent for me," I managed to say.

"You sent for me, what?"

"You sent for me - Ma'am." This time, I put in the capital. It was real easy.

"Sir," she corrected genially.

"Yes, Sir," I whispered.

"You were looking for me, and now, you've found me. Tell me, little girl with a big cock, what it is you were going to say when you followed me out of the workshop yesterday."

"Well," I started.

"No, wait! First, straighten your back. Place your hands in the small of your back, and push them forward. Do not, do not fidget, yes, do not fidget. Look at me. Tell me."

I did as she said, and my hands burrowed into place before I figured out how to do it. "I wanted to tell you," I said, shaking, "that I liked what you were saying. Sir."

"Yes, you did. And you wanted what else?"

"To - to see if you knew - to find out if you might -" I lost the nerve. Sweat was covering my body, and I was trembling too hard to concentrate. It all seemed to so stupid, that I was standing there like that, so scared yet so fucking turned on that I couldn't even move. I hung my head, and took deep breaths.

"You must say it, or I will have Andy open that door and send you on your way."

I looked back up at her, and felt my knees shaking. There was only one response to that - I hit the floor, hard, and she made a hissing sound that was almost like a whistle. "Then come closer and tell me," she said.

Flashback to that moment in the seminar - but now, I was there, literally crawling to her on my knees, crossing that hotel room in an agonizingly embarrassing halting shuffle, until I was as close as I dared to be, her curious, hard eyes following my every move.

"I want to be a slave like that," I choked out, bowing my head again. "Sir. I would be happy if I were a real slave."

The scissoring whisper of steel caught my attention, and like magic, there was a knife in her left hand and her right hand was gripping the collar of my t-shirt. "Everyone says that," she said, catching my eyes with hers. "Whose slave would you be?"

"Yours," I gasped. Anything else was cut off as swiftly as she swept that knife along the front of my shirt, stabbing it down below where her fist was, and then cutting straight through the straps of my bra, and not stopping at my waistband. Instead, she switched grips and pulled my shirt from the jeans and finished severing it. I felt a tug from behind and gasped again, but it had to be Andy, pulling the newly made rag from my shoulders, along with the remains of my bra.

She reached down and pinched one of my nipples, gently. "You would be my slave? I have enough slaves. Be my toy, right now, and show me how much you meant what you claimed."

This is crazy, I thought. I have a plane to catch, and I don't have anything to wear down to the lobby, and that was a good bra!

"As you wish, Sir," I said, shaking.

To describe what we did would be fairly pointless. If I told you she spanked me, how would you know that every blow of her hand made me want to cry, not because of the pain, but because she was telling me with every heavy swat, that spanking was for children, and only with my tears would this end. And every time I felt that, I fought the battle with never wanting it to end and wanting so much to give her what would please her.

How could you know that?

And if I told you that I crawled and whimpered on the floor, following her boots with my tongue as she parted my legs with a slender and wicked cane, leaving so many slashes on the inside of my thighs that the very thought of pulling my jeans back on was terrifying, would you realize that I didn't care about the pain or the discomfort? Would you believe me when I said that my thoughts were only on the boots which I had been commanded to shine, and that until they were gleaming with my spit, nothing, nothing would distract me? Could you possibly understand how pleased I was when she braced her heels, one at a time, against my back, and pronounced the job done to her satisfaction? That I came, grinding my cunt against her foot, only to repeat the exercise, knowing that this was a trap set for me yet also understanding that I was to fall into it, eagerly?

It's impossible to describe.

And when I say she possessed my body, you may think that her fingers in my mouth, in my cunt, in my asshole, were all just that - fingers, penetrating and opening me, spreading me wide to examine and tease, to empty and fill again, until I squirmed with ecstasy and groaned in pain. But to me, she was taking possession of me - marking her territory. I begged for more, not with words, but with every time I arched my back, every time I relaxed to take more, every time I cried, or moaned or licked hungrily at her offered fingers in gratitude.

The knife was in her hand again, but her other hand was indicating her fly. "Take me," she said, "take me well, and all that I wish to do with you, and I will mark you. And if I mark you, I will see you again."

I forced my hands into stillness as I worked the fly open. Underneath the expensive trousers, dampened with my tears, were silk boxer shorts, never so sexy on a woman before. I reached in, and felt the bulge I would have to take to earn her favor, and licked my lips desperately. It was large. No, it was huge. One of those black silicone things that doesn't look anything like a real cock, and as it came free of her clothing, I despaired of ever really taking it with any expertise. I could only hope to survive on sincerity. She passed me an unlubricated condom, and slowly, I worked it over the tip, using my lips to push it on.

"Eeeee- yes," she sighed, watching me. "That is good, *ma petite*. I know you cannot swallow all of me. But make love to it nonetheless. Do not allow what is happening to you to distract you."

What was happening to me? I wondered about that for scarcely a moment before I felt my thighs being spread wider. It had to be Andy again, and his fingers lightly touched my cunt, and I shivered.

I had not had a man touch me there in years.

The cold shock of that made me stop what I was doing - exactly what I shouldn't have done. What she said she didn't want me to do. Instantly, her hand was in my hair, jerking my mouth off of her cock, and turning my eyes to hers.

"You are not a virgin," she stated with the assurance of one who has already had access to my open holes. "You may be a lesbian, but you are my toy right now, are you not?"

"Yes, Sir," I said, feeling a wash of betraying tears. The fingers had left me, and I shook, half in fear and half in anger at myself.

"And if I choose to have my toy penetrated by my hand, or my fist, or my cock, that is my right, is it not?"

"Yes, Sir!"

"Or any hand or fist or cock. It is of no import who or what they are attached to. I wish it done - you will accept it."

I felt a word dancing around in my mind, and captured it before it could escape. Safeword, I was thinking. Dammit, safeword! I want you, not your boy-toy, I don't want *any* man's dick in my cunt.

But I want to be a slave, your slave, like you said, serving you -

But I don't want anyone else -

But other women, that would be all right -

But I could be happy -

She pushed my head back down, and speared my mouth, expertly. I choked at the intrusion, and almost fell backward, but caught myself with a fist wrapped around each of my ankles. There was no intruding hand between my thighs this time, only the hard, slick cock of a woman, the pounding and sliding penetration that no flesh and blood phallus could duplicate. I set my lips around it, and pushed back, taking as much as I could, coughing and gagging as she took me. I didn't know what to think, and soon enough couldn't. At one point, she held me suspended on this gag, filling me until I couldn't breathe, and laughing as I swayed back.

And then, I was on all fours, and that big, awful cock took me, first driving into my cunt, slick with the dampness of cum and sweat and every drop of lube my body could possibly manufacture. By the time she spread my ass cheeks, I was near blind with confused pleasure, drunk on endorphins, exhausted with the strain of holding my own body up. I felt the tearing pressure as though it came from outside my body, and when she sank her teeth into my neck, pinning me to the floor, I screamed and thrashed around in something so shattering it couldn't be contained in the word orgasm. Think of one mind-blowing electrical shock that zaps you from head to toes. Now, sustain it until you can't breathe.

I lay there, panting and oozing, clutching at the carpet fibers, trembling. I felt a weight on my back, and a sharp cut on my shoulder, and cried, sobbed, really, when I realized that she was marking me.

Then, I felt Andy lifting me up, and allowed him to lead me to the glorious bathroom. He bathed me like an invalid, wiping me down, and left the room with me sitting on the john, utterly wiped.

I stood, and turned to see my back in the mirror. On my left shoulder was an odd mark - two vertical lines, one with a shorter line flying up on the right side, the other with a line extending from the top at perhaps a 30 degree angle. They were trickling blood. When Andy came back, he put a bandage over both. He brought my clothes with him - at least my jeans, socks and boots. A conference t-shirt was with them, probably his, since the woman's would be too small for me.

I realized that I didn't even know her name.

I walked into the room, unsure of what to say, or what to do. Should I kneel again? What would happen now?

"You may go," the woman said. She was placing a business card on the table by the door.

I stood still. Confusion must have been quite apparent on my face.

"You are not ready," she said, with a shrug. "*Ce la vie*. But you were fun to play with, and so I have given you a souvenir. Perhaps you will be ready one day, and then you will call this number, and I will see you, and if you prove suitable, I shall finish the cuts. But do not dare call if you are not prepared to give me everything."

Tears came quickly - how could I still have them to cry? And she shook her head at me.

"There is no failure with me, little girl-boy, only partial success. You have been entertaining, and so we part as so many do, mm? Without rancor, without tears. Surely, you will find other happiness, even if you never call me."

I hated her, with every fiber of my being. I hated her for teasing me, for playing with me, for cutting my shirt and making me miss my fucking flight, but I hated her for making me leave, oh yes, that was the worst part. Stiffly, determined not to make a scene, I strode to the door. My back and thighs and ass and cunt and tits ached, and I thought, well, at least I have that. I picked up the card in shaking fingers and put it in my pocket. Andy was holding he door open and I was almost through it before I turned and hit my knees again, this time bowing my head all the way to the floor.

"Yes," I heard her say. "You are welcome."

Andy took me to the airport in a big shiny rent a car. We didn't say much to each other. And I didn't look at the card until I got home. It was very plain. It had a New York telephone number on it, and the initials KM. She had written on it, "When you are ready."

I slid it into the frame of my mirror, where I see it every morning, and every time I check myself out before hitting the bars. I don't exactly know how I feel about this readiness, what it really means, and whether I'll ever call that number.

The price of freedom has never been so low.

The Catalyst

Introduction

From the garishly lit lobby of a theater in lower Manhattan, a steady stream of adults spilled onto the sidewalk and the streets beyond. It was a chilly evening, mid-winter, and the crowd evidenced a curious mixture of well-worn leather jackets, sensible down parkas, and elegant fur coats. People gathered in small groups around the displayed posters under the marquee, and there was a strong buzz of conversation all along the block.

"Disgusting," intoned a matron, husband tightly in tow. She was looking at one of the scenes from the film, a single moment's image of a woman in a tightly laced Victorian corset, bound helplessly inside a doorway, her breasts displayed, her mouth filled with what appeared to be a ball on a strap. The woman's husband only nodded in agreement as he meekly followed her toward the street.

Four people looked after the two, and laughed. They too studied the series of photos from the film. "What about you, Guy?" one of the two men said, pointing at another picture. "Did you think it was disgusting?"

"Oh, absolutely! So disgusting, I can't wait to get home." Guy slipped an arm around his wife. "I can think of a few more disgusting things as well...shouldn't we get going?" Allison giggled nervously, and nodded her head toward the movie poster hanging nearby.

"I think we'd better go, before Guy gets any strange ideas," she said, rubbing one hand across his back. "He might begin to think of himself as one of those leather master types."

"OK...your place or ours? We went out to you last time." William slipped an arm around his own wife and glanced down at her. "Shall we try our house for a change?"

"Yes," she replied, softly. "It's closer."

"Whoa, I hear that!" Guy smiled and winked. "In this case, your wish is my command, Terri. I can see that movie is having the same effect on you as it has on me. Let's not waste it!" He began to walk steadily toward the nearby parking garage where they had left his car. The other couple followed after one more lingering glance at the posters and promotional photos.

"It wasn't a movie, it was a film, an art film," Jen explained for the tenth time. "You're not supposed to take it literally!"

"Oh really? Then what does that mean?" Lisa, Jen's lover, pointed at an excerpt of a review, blown up to seven inches of lettering around one of the framed posters. It read, "The most explicit exploration of the dark side of sexuality ever filmed!"

"Explicit doesn't mean allegorical," Lisa said pointedly. "And it was still full of patriarchal violence against women. The degradation! The humiliation! How would you like it if you were made to wear a dog collar and crawl around like that woman was?"

Jen sighed, pulling her lover away from the theater. "Lisa, you're making a scene."

"Damn right! This is just typical of you...you drag me to some trendy movie, and then expect me to wallow in the obvious manipulation on the screen and thank you for the experience. This was terrible...what about the scene with that, that, dildo!"

"Lisa," Jen ground her teeth together, trying to keep calm. Why did every fight have to become a production number? "Lisa, there were plenty of scenes where men got treated like that too, remember?"

Lisa tossed her blonde hair in an angry turn away from the theater, and shrugged her lover's arm from hers. "Yes, but it was clear that they wanted it."

"That's a double standard...Lisa, Lisa, wait..." Jen ran to catch up with her.

"Oh god, that was soooo gross!" A dark haired woman in a stylish jacket too light for the weather mimed one of the scenes from the film with an expression of exaggerated glee on her face. Her friends, a group of six women all of an age and somewhat dressed alike, all shrieked in laughter. Their shoes and dress suggested that they had gone out after work on this Friday night.

"No, wait, what about the scene where the red-haired woman dances on the guy wearing those spiked heels! Like, I couldn't even walk in those, let alone dance on someone in them!" More laughter.

"Come on, the best part was that orgy..."

"That wasn't an orgy, it was a gang bang!"

"Yeah!"

"No! It was an orgy, you could tell."

"Oh, maybe *you* can tell, Gina!" The young women erupted in laughter and fell into good-natured ribbing as they began their walk toward the nearest subway station. They were loud and friendly, as only a group of women out on the town could be.

"I liked the part with all the rubber stuff."

"No way!"

"Oh, you would, Margaret."

"Well, at least I didn't, you know, moan out loud during the scene with the feathers."

"I did not!"

"Did too! The whole row could hear you!"

"I liked the part with the maid."

"Oh, god, Rox, how could you?"

"Yeah, that was so silly."

"Like, that guy looked sooo stuuupid!"

"If some guy pulled that on me, I'd just barf!"

"Hey, look girls...there's someone who can't wait 'til they get home."

Their attention all turned toward a couple, the man pressing the woman against a nearby building, pushing her skirt up her leg while he passionately kissed her. The woman's arms were locked tightly around his neck.

"Oh, god, I mean, can't they hold it?"

"I think she IS holding it!"

The young women laughed together and began to head for home.

"That was a hot movie."

"Yeah."

Mike and David left the theater lobby and stopped by the promotional display. They scanned the reviews posted up and read out loud.

"'Perverse'!" David snickered. "Yeah, it was certainly perverse."

"But it was also 'Powerfully erotic,' like it says here," Mike looked at the color photos of some of the more notorious scenes. "There wasn't much gay stuff in it."

"Well, we knew that. Besides, you know where to go to look at boys in leather..."

They said it at the same time, "The Shaft," and laughed together.

Looking at the crowd and the shortage of taxis, Mike said, "Care to walk across town? We can get home in about twenty minutes."

"I'm not in the mood to go home yet." David stuffed his hands in his pockets and looked carefully at the ground. "But let's walk. I need to talk to you."

"About the movie?" Mike's voice was low and seductive. David looked back up at his lover's eyes and nodded.

"Yeah, me too. Let's take that walk."

They too, passed the couple making out alongside the building, but they were too interested in each other to notice.

Two other people who decided to walk home were Nicole and Eve, who only had about six blocks to go to get to their shared loft. Nicole paused to light a cigarette and coughed when she saw the spectacle of two people practically screwing in plain view of the entire street. She tugged on Eve's arm and pointed.

"See," she said, with a slight giggle. "We weren't the only ones to get the message!"

Eve laughed and nodded, her black eyes dancing. "Well? What do you say?" she asked. "Shall we go ahead with plan A, or not? Let's face it, we're never going to get this psyched again."

Nicole bit her lip and continued walking, a little more serious. "I don't know, Eve. I mean, we have no idea if he's even into this stuff. He could have a girlfriend we haven't seen, you know. Or maybe he's gay! I mean, we really haven't thought this out very much."

"Where is your sense of adventure, girl?" Eve demanded, catching up. "If he's unavailable, he's unavailable. But in the meantime, we haven't done this in months! And I tell you, I know the signs! He's definitely into this!"

Nicole looked at her dark friend, pretending hesitation for one more moment, and then laughed again. "OK, OK, you win! But I get him first!"

"No way, sister, if I do all the work, I get the payoff!"

"We'll flip for him!"

They walked home, their pace increasing as they went.

"Well, so that was the movie everyone's talking about." Marsha pulled her coat tighter around herself, keeping a watchful eye out for purse-snatchers.

"It was...different."

"Ha! You can say that again." She took her husband's arm as they walked out under the marquee. "Do you remember where you parked the car?"

Bob looked back at her patiently. "Sure, down that way a few blocks. Do you want to wait here, and I'll pick you up?"

"No, no, let's just walk. After all that sitting, I need the exercise."

"Odd mix of people in this crowd, wasn't it?"

"Well, it is the hottest art movie playing right now. I guess it's all the desire to be trendy...I mean, we wouldn't have come if Steve and Brenda hadn't been pushing us for so long."

"Well, it wasn't so bad. Just...weird."

"Yes, it was certainly weird."

They walked in silence for a moment, hearing snatches of conversation and the shrill laughter of a group of women who seemed to be comparing favorite parts of the film. As they passed the couple who were making out against the neighboring building, Marsha gripped her husband's arm tighter. She waited until they were out of earshot and said, "I think it's terrible what some people think they can do in public. Couldn't they have waited?"

Bob nodded, thinking of their warm bedroom at home, and he bent down to gently kiss her cheek. "I can hardly wait."

It worked. Marsha relaxed on his arm and pressed closer to him. "And I want you, honey. Let's get home."

They walked a little bit faster.

"I don't fucking believe that we came all the way out here to see that fucking sick excuse for a movie," Greg reported. Profanity always served as his punctuation when he was pissed.

"Hey, it was all right," Alan said, scooping the last of his popcorn out of the bag. "Some of it was hot. I liked the part with that rack thing. Think we could build something like that in the living room? Couldja imagine trying to explain it to la date de jour?"

"Yeah, sure. Come on in, darling, oh that? It's a, a coffee table!" Greg mimed ushering someone through his arms. "Yeah, that's it, a coffee table! It doesn't mean I'm kinky and want to tie you up and do disgusting things with you, no way!" He shook his head again. "Stupid fucking movie, a waste of time, money, and now we have to get all the way back home, and I swear, if Annie wants to see this fucking thing next week, I'm gonna give her a ticket and go play pool down the block."

"You would. You know what you are, Greg? You are one uncultured motherfucker, that's what you are." Alan tossed his balled up garbage into a trash can and began to dig through his pockets for a subway token. "That was a hot movie. I know I'm not ready to hit the sack yet. Wanna watch that sorority babes video again, and work it off with me?"

"I got nothing to work off, asshole. You watch the babes, I'll be sleeping like one!" He laughed at his own joke. "How you can get anything out of that sick shit is amazing. Maybe I should warn what's her name. Tell her what a fucking pervert you are."

"I'd rather be a pervert then a moron, dickface!"

"Asshole!"

Mark pulled Thea's skirt up higher, so that it almost bunched around her waist. It was only his knee pressed into the hot wedge between her legs that kept her pussy shielded from the passersby. From time to time, he whispered overheard comments into her ear, telling her how many people were seeing them, and what they thought of her. "You're a slut, you know...displayed like a cheap 42nd street whore, and all these people know it."

She moaned and squirmed under him and gripped him tighter. "Do it, do it now! Let's just do it in front of everyone, please!"

He slipped a hand between them, sliding it along her wetness, teasing, pulling on her hairs and making her arch against him.

"You'd like it now, if I fucked you, wouldn't you? You'd love my big dick slapping into you right out here on the street, with everyone watching? Tell me, say it right."

"I want you...I want you to fuck me, oh, god, please..." Thea pushed her hips forward into him. She shuddered in erotic anticipation, reaching for him, holding his hand between her thighs. Suddenly, he laughed, and pulled away from her, his hand glistening with her juices. Casually, he wiped it across her face, and then raised that same hand to hail a cab, leaving her to smooth her skirt back down across her thighs, allowing a few people a glimpse of her bare pussy.

As the two of them got into the cab, no one, including them, could believe that they just met barely two hours ago.

As the crowd thinned and the marquee lights dimmed and went out, once again the cashier noted how the people leaving this particular film always seemed to be in a hurry to get home.

Chapter One:
The All-Americans

The ride on the Long Island Expressway was a little more silent than usual, but there was no real discomfort between them. Bob kept glancing at Marsha with loving concern. It was rare enough for them to get out of the house together, and the decision to see that particular film had been a difficult one. But then, there wasn't much of a choice, really. Everything else seemed designed for teenagers - big budgeted, violent, loud movies without the burden of a plot.

Not that this one had any real plot, he thought, as he guided the sedan further east. Just a lot of different scenes of people doing things to each other. He remembered how silence kept sweeping through the theater, as though the audience couldn't exactly keep up a pretense of being nonchalant about the action on the screen. The film certainly deserved the X rating it almost got! But the company had decided to release it without a rating, and people were flocking to see it, compelled by the hauntingly mysterious advertising posters and the outrageous word-of-mouth.

Which was how he and Marsha heard about it. Steve, one of his coworkers, had gone to see it with his girlfriend, Brenda. The following day, he had taken Bob aside in the men's room and told him what a great night the two of them had after seeing this film.

"It was sick," Steve had said, leaning against the wall. "But some of the scenes were so hot, I swear I was as stiff a board. Brenda was so wet, we couldn't wait to get home. I'm warning you...some of the scenes aren't for everyone, you know? But I guarantee, you'll see it, take Marsha home, and fuck her brains out."

Bob smiled as he signaled for his exit. He liked any excuse to fuck Marsha's brains out. Even as she sat beside him in the passenger seat, her eyes softly closed, he loved the way her face looked, the way she breathed and the lift of her breasts. She felt him glancing at her and opened her eyes, smiling. When he saw that smile, he felt the beginnings of a swelling behind his fly and grinned.

"I know what you're thinking," Marsha noted. "Don't take too long with the sitter. I'll be waiting for you in bed."

"I love the way you read my mind, sweetie," Bob said.

Home was a two story brick house with a huge, sprawling lawn. Bob pulled into the driveway, and waited for Marsha to go inside and pay the sitter. The high school student came bouncing out, after what Bob knew was a night watching MTV, eating the chips they always stocked for her, and chatting with her boyfriends. He drove her home, politely chatting. She used to linger a little while with him, stalling perhaps, or flirting, but he never gave her encouragement. He heard from other men about their affairs with various young women. College and high school students, tutors and baby-sitters, au pairs and even a swimming coach. But he was never tempted to try something like that.

He had a girlfriend at home, waiting for him.

So he bade her a good night, avoiding her questions about how they liked the movie, and broke speed laws heading back home.

By the time Bob had turned back into the driveway, Marsha had already checked on the kids, turned the thermostat down, and gone around the house making sure everything was all right. Mark, their firstborn, was asleep in a tangle of blankets, toys scattered all over his floor. At eight years old, he was just becoming interesting to her. She could see his father in him, and a little of herself, and she liked to watch him work things out for himself.

Then there was Cathy, restless until her thumb found its way back into her mouth. At five, she was a real cutie, with her mother's curly blonde hair and her father's laughing disposition. "You're going to break some hearts some day," Marsha whispered as she worked her daughter's thumb out of her mouth. "If your teeth grow in straight."

She heard the sound of the front door opening and closing and smiled as she headed toward the master bedroom. She folded down the bedcovers and turned down the lights, casually killing time until Bob came upstairs.

He paused in the doorway, a deliciously lustful glint in his eye, teasing her until she laughed. "Ready for me?" he asked, already unbuttoning his shirt.

"More than ready." She reached out to him and they hugged warmly. He took the bottom edge of her sweater in both hands and slowly pulled it up, over her head, and kissed her bare throat. While his tongue danced on her neck and around her ear, she purred and pushed his shirt back over his shoulders.

"You're so hot, baby," he murmured, pulling her tightly to him. "I want to sweep you off your feet and fuck you silly."

"Mmmm. If movies like that make you feel like this, we should go out more often." She cupped his hardness with one soft hand as he wrapped one hand in her hair to kiss her firmly. When the kiss finally broke, they were both flushed with sexual warmth, and they moved together toward the bed.

"Did you like the movie?" he asked, pushing her gently back and unfastening her skirt. "I couldn't tell." He eased the skirt over her hips when she raised them off the bed, pulling her pantyhose down at the same time. He leaned over her to plant a kiss on her navel, and then slid his tongue down to the ridge above her pubic mound, making her shiver in delight.

"I...I thought some of it was hot," Marsha said finally, as he tossed her clothing aside, leaving her in panties, laying back against the bedspread. "You liked it."

"Yes." He stretched out next to her and reached for her nipples with one hand, propping himself up with the other. He caressed one softly, watching and feeling it become erect under his fingers. "I liked a lot of it. But I like you more."

She gasped as he pinched her nipple, and let a moan escape, and then rolled to face him, reaching again for the bulge in his pants. He suddenly grinned and moved out of her reach. She looked at him in surprise.

"I think you liked it more than you're saying," he whispered. "Tell me."

"You tease," she said. Then, she leaned up on one elbow and looked at him squarely. "Do you really want to know?" He nodded. "I liked the part where that woman in the miniskirt was all tied up and the man with the mask...you know." Suddenly, she found herself blushing. But Bob seemed to find that as arousing as anything else that evening, so she moved closer to him again. "What did you like?"

He avoided answering her for a moment. "You liked it when that woman was tied up and raped, huh?"

"She wasn't raped! She enjoyed it. And it was so good...you could tell." Marsha blushed again, both at the memory and the quick feeling of wetness between her legs as she spoke about it. "Come on, what did you like?"

"I liked that part too," Bob admitted. "But I also liked the spanking scene."

"Which one?" Marsha asked warily.

He smiled. "All of them. All I could think of was how it would feel to lie under you while you rode me, and feel my burning ass against the bed."

"What?" Marsha sat up in surprise. "YOU want to be...spanked?"

He sat up too. "Well, if I'm going to tie you to the bed, you should do something for me too," he said, seriously.

She smiled through her amazement. "Would you really tie me up? Do you think we should?" Marsha asked, looking around the room. "It's so...kinky. I don't know...they seemed to have a lot of, well, stuff, in that movie. Paddles and things...and honey, what if I hurt you? What if you don't like it? What if the kids..."

"Listen," Bob took her hands in his and looked into her eyes, "You would never hurt me." He kissed her again, slow and lovingly. "And," he said, when they broke the kiss, "I bet we can find anything we need right here. I say we do it. If the kids didn't wake up the night we rented that Kama Sutra tape and tried some of those positions, they won't wake up now." She giggled at the memory of that night, the pillows on the floor and the "love lotion" everywhere else. Then, she looked at him again and nodded.

"Good. Let's see...I'll go find stuff to use on you, and you find stuff for me. I'll meet you back here in...ten minutes?"

"In ten minutes." Marsha got up and threw her robe on, and purposefully left the room quickly. Bob chuckled, thought for a moment, and then slipped a sweatshirt on.

Marsha found herself in the kitchen, standing in her bare feet and looking at the utensil rack. Once, when she had been small, her mother had used a wooden spoon on her behind. For what crime, she couldn't remember. She never struck her own children, but she did have a full rack of things her mother would have probably loved to utilize. She took one wide spatula down and swatted it against her hand. Instantly, she yelped. It stung! She would have to be careful. She took two more, and then went back upstairs, suddenly inspired.

Bob slipped out to the garage, where he spent a few minutes uncovering the items in storage for spring. Coiled neatly in a net bag was about fifty feet of soft but strong clothesline. He sprinted back to the house, and turned off the kitchen light that Marsha had left on, and then softly walked upstairs. She wasn't in their bedroom...he briefly wondered where she could be and then stashed the clothesline under the bed. Waiting for her, he dug into one of her drawers and took out a silk scarf he had given her while they were still dating. It smelled of her, of her perfume. He tucked it under one pillow, and then stripped off the sweatshirt and his shoes.

Marsha was tiptoeing through her son's room, looking for a bright red box she had noticed earlier. When she found it, she opened it silently, and felt around inside for what she was searching for.

One scene in the film had depicted a caning. Marsha remembered flinching as she watched little lines form on reddened skin. While she was standing in the kitchen, she had been wondering if the handle of a wooden spoon would work like that. It seemed too hard, too thick and brittle. The cane in the movie had been whipper-thin, and so supple it could be bent into a circle. Then, she suddenly had a flash...there was something in the house like that...the wand from little Mark's magic set.

She pulled it out with a flourish and quietly left the room. Her last visit was to the hall closet where she stored the summer items. There, in a box with a pile of white plastic balls, were two matching ping-pong paddles. She took one.

If he wants a spanking, she thought, good-naturedly, I'll give him a spanking he'll never forget! As she headed back to their bedroom, she had a moment of doubt. Could she really do this? Hit her husband on his bare butt, hurt him and make marks on him? Would he really like it as much as the handsome actor did in the film?

A sudden wetness between her thighs gave her the answer. Whatever Bob felt when it actually happened, she was turned on by the very thought. Even if it didn't work, she would end up tied to the bed with his big cock slamming into her welcoming pussy. She took a deep breath and walked into their room, holding her handful of improvised implements.

She was surprised to find him already there, his bare chest quietly rising and falling in the deep rhythm that signaled a strong but quiet turn-on. He was standing by their bed, still wearing his dark slacks, his feet bare. He immediately noticed her burden and came forward to help her.

"No," she stopped him on an inspiration, "just stand there, exactly like that. And remember, this was your idea."

Bob grinned and stood still, watching his wife empty her armload of objects onto the bed. Carefully, she separated them and laid them out next to each other, arranging them in what she felt was an order of severity. As she did this, she glanced around the room, trying to figure out what Bob had brought. To her dismay, there seemed to be nothing different about the room. What is he planning to use, his ties? She frowned slightly, more than a little annoyed. Couldn't he think of anything?

When she glanced at him again, he was still grinning, and she realized that her disappointment at his seeming lack of preparation could be used in the game they were about to play. Not returning his smile, she stood straight and asked, quietly, "Do you expect to take your spanking over those pants?"

Bob noticed the swift change in mood, and stammered. "Uh, well, I guess not. Do you want me to take them off?"

"No." Marsha got another inspiration. She sat primly at the edge of the bed and straightened her robe over her thighs. "I want you to drop them to your knees and drape yourself across my lap." She half expected him to balk. This wasn't exactly what had happened in the movie, and she didn't think it was what he had bargained for. But her fleeting doubt was banished in an instant. Behind the dark material of his trousers, Bob showed her proof that he found what she was doing exactly right. As he moved to her side and ran the zipper down, his cock was hard and curved against his stomach, trapped by his clean jockeys. He started to run a finger around the waistband of those too, but she stopped him again.

"Just the pants," she said, a surprising hoarseness in her voice. She loved the sight of him, erect yet contained, and wanted to keep him that way, for just a little while longer. Without showing any disappointment, he did as she told him and pushed his pants down around his knees. Then, a little awkwardly, he bent forward over her lap, and shifted his body until he found a position he could stay in. She felt his manhood tight against her thighs, and was glad that her knees were close together. If they weren't, she would have actually dripped on the floor.

Marsha took a deep breath and examined her husband's ass, and the backs of his thighs. She ran her hand lightly across his cloth-covered ass, and he shivered against her, a delightful sensation. She tickled the hairs curled on his legs, and ran her fingers across his taut muscles. He wasn't the college athlete she had married, but he was a strong man, in good shape. Having him across her lap and in her power was a thrill.

"Are you ready?" she asked, her voice a little more assured.

"Yes. God, yes!" Bob's voice sounded strained, and it wasn't just the position. Marsha immediately knew that he was having the same emotional charges that wracked her mind, and in response, she raised her hand and slapped it once against his ass.

The thin cotton muffled the sound, but the sensation was amazing! Bob jerked under her hand, and ground his still-hard cock against her legs. The slight sound he made was like a sigh. Marsha raised her hand again and struck the other cheek, and Bob's reaction was the same. This is easy, she thought, delighting in the game. She began to spank him regularly, first one cheek and then the other, until he began to squirm.

Bob was trying not to lose control. The details of making up his mind to ask, asking, and then planning for this had kept him too busy to really think about how it was going to feel. It was wonderful! His hot dick was pressing against Marsha's lap, feeling ready to spurt every time she whacked him. The position he was in raised his ass up, and tightened his balls against his body, causing sweet torment with every move. And Marsha was enjoying it! He could tell by the way she aimed her swats and kept pausing to run her fingers across his ass. Pretty soon, he wouldn't be able to hold back! He tried to think about other things, tried holding his breath, counting, thinking about work. Nothing was working.

Then, Marsha stopped. He relaxed his body for a moment and panted.

"That's hard work," Marsha commented, shaking her hand out. "Maybe we'd better switch tactics." She reached for the line of household objects on the bed and picked up the wooden spoon. Aiming carefully, she brought it down sharply at the very center of his ass.

He yelped in shock, and jumped. That thing hurt! Marsha also reacted to his reaction, by pulling back, thinking she had gone too far and had really harmed him. "Oh," she started to say, feeling bad, "did I..."

"I'm all right," Bob said. "It just surprised me." That was true...the sensation was already fading away. "Go on...please." Impulsively, he bent further and kissed her calf.

Marsha hastily rubbed her husband's butt where the spoon had hit him and smiled as she felt his lips against her leg. Then, she abandoned the spoon and picked up the ping-pong paddle, judging it to be too wide to cause such a sharp pain. She was right. The first smack with the paddle made Bob nestle firmly back into her lap, and fairly purr with satisfaction. She used it for a while, liking the feel of the broad paddle against his ass. Liking the way it pushed his cheeks forward, and loving the feel of him rubbing his cock against her again.

Then, she stopped long enough to hook her fingers into the waistband of his shorts and pull them down to his thighs. His ass was slightly reddened by her attentions. She couldn't resist running her fingers across the redness, and he shivered again when she did that. Joyfully, she laughed, and used the flat of her hand again, spanking him with enthusiasm.

When her hand was sore again, and he showed no sign of wanting to stop, she used one of her spatulas, making small, rapidly reddening marks all over his butt, until she sensed that it was too harsh for him. She switched back to her hand for as long as she could stand it, and then picked up the magic wand. For effect, she swished it back in forth in the air above him.

"Are you ready for this?" she asked.

Bob felt ready for a repeat of the invasion of Normandy. He felt he could lead it, too. His butt seemed to be afire, an all-through warmth that had alternately wilted and strengthened his prick until he could barely stand the sensation. It was almost free now, the head poking out of the pushed down waistband, and nestled against the flesh of his wife's thigh, where her robe had been pushed aside. He lifted his ass a little more, and knowing what he was doing, Marsha parted her legs, allowing his cock to edge neatly between them. It sprang free of the confines of the shorts, and Bob gasped as he felt the heated moisture that had been trapped inside Marsha's tight delta. If nothing else, her arousal made him even more eager to shoot his load, but he wanted to do that inside her, while she was tied down. That image almost pushed him over the edge! But he didn't want to stop. He remembered the caning scene too, and he wanted to feel that wand.

"Keep going," he whispered, bracing himself.

Marsha raised her hand and brought the wand sharply against Bob's upturned butt. The black plastic whistled as it flew, and left an immediate white line behind it when she pulled it away. Bob's body jerked against her, and his breath expelled in a gasp, but he found the strength to say, "Yes, do it, keep going!", fearing she would stop. Made bold by his plea, and excited by the sensation of his manhood trapped between her thighs, she did as he told her and left another white line, and then another. These lines rapidly turned red as they added up, and before long, his entire ass was a crosshatching of red and white lines. He squirmed and wiggled against her, biting the inside of his lip, trying desperately not to come! But he had too, his balls were full, and the strain of holding back was unbearable.

"Oh, Jesus, oh God...Marsha, I'm gonna come, you sweet bitch, you're making me..." He gasped and then felt the explosion build.

Marsha heard him, and dropped the wand in her excitement. Not knowing what to do, she tightened her thighs around him and hit the underside of his ass with her bare hand.

That did it! Bob came like a roaring freight train, bucking against her lap, and holding onto her leg. His come spurted out of him, hot and thick, splattering her legs.. He had never looked at his cock when he was coming, at least not from this position. The tension on it, trapped between her satiny thighs, was too much. Out of breath and slightly out of his mind, he could only whimper and stretch against her.

She understood immediately, and opened her legs again. The scent of her own arousal was overwhelming. Bob just relaxed and allowed his body to roll off her lap, hissing when his ass touched the bare floor.

Marsha giggled at the sight of him. "I guess you liked it," she said, softly, leaning down to flick his jism off her calf. "But now what?"

"Now what?" Bob repeated. "Now, I get to do things to you." He pointed at her solemnly, and she giggled again.

"It's going to take a little time," she said mischievously. "Since you couldn't wait..."

Bob pushed himself up and ended up on his knees in front of her. "Fucking isn't the only thing I have in mind for you, sweetie." Suddenly, he pushed her back onto the bed and grasped her right hand as she fell. She struggled a little, more out of confusion than fear, and her struggles allowed him to get that hand under her body, at the small of her back, where he held onto it with his left hand. Then, firmly shoving her thighs apart, he ripped the front of her soaking panties down, bent into her and took a long, loving taste of her.

Marsha's breath exploded from her in a moan that almost seemed loud enough to wake the kids. Bob thrust his tongue deeply inside her, washing her inner lips with broad strokes, lathering the sides and the sensitive top, where her pleasure nub was prominent and awaiting attention. She moaned and squirmed, his firm hand holding her down more in her imagination than in reality. But she arched her back and pretended that he was holding her down all the same, and when his lips and teeth finally found her aching center, she was totally unprepared for the thrust into ultimate pleasure. Her hips moved against her will, and a spurt of new wetness met her husband's tongue as she thrashed and came into his mouth.

It was a sudden, swift, and harsh orgasm, and as she found herself on its wave, she also found herself crying out to her husband, over and over again, as though his name made it better for her, taking her over the top. "Oh, Bob, Bob, do it baby, do it!" And as her pleasure peaked and her body shook in the tremors of passion, Bob pulled himself up onto the bed, dragging something with him. He left his crumpled trousers on the floor. Before she knew it, heavy rope was looped around one wrist. Too weak to move, she let him drag her other wrist out and up, and smiling, he tied them together.

"You...you cheat..." she managed to say, as he pulled his knots tight. "You got me when I was too weak to fight."

"That's the idea. Come on, my lady love, up to the head of the bed. I'm not finished with you yet." With that, he proceeded to tie her wrists to the wooden headboard. Then he pushed a pillow under her ass and running the rope under the bed, he tied her ankles spread apart. Casually, he untied her robe and spread the sides, letting them fall. Pushed up by the pillow, her loins were on display, partially hidden only by her wet and crumpled panties.

He reached over to her and pulled those panties back up, and she emitted a sad groan. "You kept mine on for quite some time," he explained, smoothing the cloth over her. "Now, its my turn." She moaned in anticipation and tried to arch her back even more to get pleasure from the touch of his fingers. But he pulled them away, and thrust one hand under the remaining pillow at the head of the bed. When he pulled out the scarf, she trembled.

"This one is for your eyes." Awkwardly, he managed to blindfold her, tying the knot by her ear. Then, he pulled a chair near the bed and sat to look at her.

He had been honestly shocked at the enthusiasm she displayed while she was spanking him. The feeling he got when he sat down was a reminder of that! But he had never taken the opportunity to really look at her, like this, her body bare and on display, waiting for him. He loved the gentle swell of her full breasts, the roundness of her thighs and the way the dark golden hair, now hidden under those soaked panties, curled upwards toward her belly. She was every bit as beautiful as she was when they first began to go out together. He sat still, admiring her, and remembering the feel of her hand against his bare ass, until he felt a stirring that signaled he was getting close to full recovery, and then he slowly moved toward the bed. Without warning, he reached out and pinched her nipples.

Marsha bit back a scream. She had been laying there, loving the wait, loving the feeling of him still in the room, watching her. But at the same time, she was itching for his touch, wanting to beg for his cock. She had kept silent because she couldn't decide what to do! The sudden sharp feeling in her nipples scared her and excited her at the same time. She moaned her appreciation as Bob gently kneaded them, bringing them to little twin erections. She felt his body settle near her on the bed, and gasped as he leaned over her and took one nipple, and then the other, into his mouth, to suck and nibble on. Then, he began to run his tongue against the sides of her breasts, under her collarbone, and around to her shoulders. Wherever he left this trail of wetness, she shivered. He worked his way across her face, nibbling on her earlobes, kissing her lips and the curve of her cheeks, until her moans began to intensify with urgency. He brought his body far up on the bed, and planted his knees on either side of her chest, his cock now hanging inches over her gasping mouth.

"I want you," she declared, writhing in ecstasy. "Stop teasing me!"

"I'll tease you as long as I want to," he replied, settling into position. "Maybe all night."

"Damn you! Please, Bob, please..." She shuddered as he reached behind his back and pinched her right nipple with one hand. His hand brushed his still hot ass cheek, and his cock stiffened immediately, almost drawing him down to ease into her mouth. But still, he held himself back.

"Please what?" he asked, balancing over her. "Tell me what you want...and make it dirty."

"Let me suck your beautiful cock," Marsha moaned instantly, shocked at how easily the words came to her. "Let me have it in my mouth, let me taste you, let me please you, oh, god, Bob, please..."

"Whatever you say." Bob lowered his waiting cock into his wife's open mouth and she immediately wrapped her wet lips around him, engulfing him in hot, soft pleasure. He gasped as she drew him in, swallowing him to the root in one delicious slurp. Ecstasy flooded his nerves and almost made him cry out. He gently began to slide his cock past those tight lips, back and forth, back and forth, rocking, holding himself up by grasping the headboard.

"Oh, yeah, that's it, baby, take it all...so nice!" He groaned in delight at her eager mouth- and throat-work, the way she pulled and caressed him, and the way she followed his movements as though she were afraid he would take this treat away from her.

"That's good, sweetie, so good. I love your mouth on me like that...I might let you do this all night, wouldn't you like that?" Bob was also getting off on the sheer power of the situation; having Marsha helpless under him, yet so hot for him she was taking him in like a pro! She gasped and he drew his cock back for a moment.

"Yes! Yes, give it back, I'll take it all night, I'll make you feel so good! Oh, Bob, this is so hot! Please, and Bob...make it hard! Fuck my mouth, make me feel it!"

He cut her off by thrusting his impossibly hard cock straight into her mouth. No gentleness here, only hard, fast face fucking! He couldn't take it anymore, both Marsha's overwhelming erotic response, and her willingness to take even more from him. He shoved his cock neatly to the back of her throat and felt the contraction around the head that meant that she had gagged. He eased back slightly, to let her breathe, but then shoved his way back. She made muffled, sharp sounds of pleasure as he plundered her throat in a way he never had before. Could this be her gentle but imaginative lover? Her partner and the father of her children? She gulped him deep into her mouth and lavished all the attention she could on that relentless piece of flesh that battered and so wonderfully filled her. Finally, he pulled back all the way, and drew his cock from her lips, glistening with her spit.

"No, no, give it back!" Marsha pleaded, bending her head up, seeking it. "Don't stop, please..."

"I told you I'd do what I want, right?" Bob asked, moving down the bed. "Well, now I want to fuck you. Any complaints?"

Marsha only moaned, and he reached out to grasp the waistband of her panties, and tugged at it until they tore off, exposing her delicate but soaking wet mound. She gasped in surprise. Her pussy was displayed before him, splayed wide open, glistening with her moisture. He gently touched the soft hair and began to tease her again, making small circles with the edge of his finger.

"Oh...yes...right there!..." Marsha pulled and strained against her bonds, amazed at the intensity of every touch. "I want...I want you to fuck me! Come on, Bob, give it to me! I'm so hot...so ready!"

"Oh...you want this?" Bob slid down the bed and lowered himself to her, and then edged just the head of his throbbing penis into her. She gave a sharp, high pitched squeal of pleasure, and he felt her close around him, spasming in pleasure. He pressed his thumb against the engorged nub poking out from behind its protective hood, and forcefully, skillfully, brought her to levels of pleasure she had never even imagined before. She thrashed against the bed, her hips churning, and when she had spent all that energy, he thrust his cock into her as far as it could go.

If she had the breath, she would have screamed. Instead, she gasped and tightened around him, and as he began to fuck her in earnest, she brought her hips even higher, to meet each thrust. He was unstoppable, hard and eager, and he soon forgot that he had already come not so long ago. Her furious passion drove him, harder, faster, deeper, and she met him with a loving acceptance that brought him immediately to the brink. There would be no trying to hold back now.

"I love you, sweetie," he gasped, driving into her, the taste of her on his lips, the feel of her spanking still burning his ass. She groaned even as she nodded and began to convulse in yet another pinnacle of pleasure. The feeling of her tightening and kneading his manhood was just what he needed. With one final push, he emptied himself into her, shooting with a raw strength that left him gasping, stretched out over her body.

It was at least ten minutes before either one remembered the ropes. And as they finally slept, wrapped in each other's arms, they both realized that the kids had blissfully slept through the whole thing.

Chapter Two:
Sappho's Solution

Jennifer and Lisa lived together in a two story walk-up in Park Slope, and on this Friday night, their trip home on the subways was more tension-inducing than usual. After walking away from Lisa in front of the theater, Lisa slowed down as she usually did, and allowed her lover to catch up. But there was an insistent wedge between them, and all the way home, Jen kept wondering how long they were going to last if they could never disagree without it turning into an argument. They could never argue without it turning into a highly personal and hurtful fight.

And then on top of it all, damn it, Jen found herself thinking about some of the scenes in that stupid movie she had dragged Lisa to see. That part of Lisa's complaint was true; Jen was often the one to suggest new things to do and see. Lisa was more of a steady person, she liked things to be comfortable and predictable. But even she had admitted that they could only rent *Desert Hearts* so many times. Jen closed her eyes briefly and remembered the leather harnesses, the silvery image of chain, a black glove casually slapped across a man's startled face...and absently substituted Lisa's pouting face in that man's place. Surprised at her own fantasy, she opened her eyes and shook the memories from her mind. She had something that had to be dealt with tonight, or else the two of them would slide helplessly into that cold "we're not fighting" mode, where they just stopped talking to each other.

As the train rumbled through Manhattan into Brooklyn, Jen found herself silently watching Lisa as they stood near the doors of the subway car, occasionally swaying with it like the native New Yorkers they were. They made a good couple. Where Jen was a dark haired, (kept short for convenience) deeply tanned and curvy woman, Lisa was tall and willowy, with long, straight blonde hair and flashing green eyes. Right now, Jen was wearing her beat-up motorcycle jacket and boots; Lisa was wrapped in a colorful down ski-jacket. Their differences were part of what made them work so well together, except for this one thing.

They could never settle a fight.

When they reached their stop, Jen purposefully took Lisa's hand in hers, so they could exit the station together. Lisa tensed for a moment, and then tightened her grip on her lover's hand, and as they walked through the street   said, softly, "I told you I wouldn't like it."

Jen frowned. That wasn't what she had hoped to hear. Would it be too hard to say you're sorry, she thought angrily. But she said, "You never know until you try, hon."

"I knew." Lisa took her hand back. "You just didn't listen."

"Oh, come on, Lisa, give me a break!" Jen stopped walking and stared at her. "Are you telling me you didn't like one single minute in that entire movie?"

Lisa hesitated, but then said, firmly, "Yes, I am." Her mouth was set in the way that betrayed more storms ahead, and for a moment, the two of them looked about to square off. But then, Lisa turned and began walking fast again, and in that fashion, the two of them got home at last, in silence.

Jen slammed the door shut, knowing that Lisa hated it when she did that, and the two young women headed off to different ends of their one bedroom apartment. Jen went to the kitchen, where she pulled a beer out of the refrigerator and sat by the window to drink it, ignoring the plaintive meows of Lavender, one of their resident cats. Lisa headed off to the bathroom, and in a few minutes, Jen could hear the shower running.

The running water reminded her of several scenes in the movie, especially the one that took place in and around an old-fashioned Victorian style bathtub, the kind with feet. Although she always called herself a plain and simple lover ("I stick with what I do best" she used to say), she knew about all sorts of variations, and watersports was not a new idea to her. She'd always thought of the actual practice as a little sick, though. Dirty. But somehow, the scene in that movie made it hot.

Jen leaned back and stuck her legs out, inviting Lavender to climb up to her lap. As she stroked the purring animal, she imagined Lisa in the shower, her small, perfect breasts covered in creamy lather. Water running down the center of her back and down her long legs. Closing her eyes, she could see Lisa's body twisting under the showerhead, trying to get the soap off. Her hands wiping water away from her body in long, slow strokes.

If I were there, Jen thought, taking another drink, I'd watch her through the curtain first. Then, I'd ease it open slowly, and surprise her. She'd give me a "how dare you" look first, but then she'd see the look in my eyes, and she would reach to turn the water off. But as she bent over, I'd just step in behind her, and push her down on her knees, under the stream of water, do it just like a waterfall.

Just thinking about it made Jen aware that fights or no fights, no one in the world got her hotter than Lisa did. If only she were more...amenable. Open to negotiation. Because if she were, Jen thought, still stroking the cat, she'd just go down for me and look up, trusting and hot for me. And I'd spread my legs and pull her in tight, and let her love me right there, under the water...and then I'd pull away, and make her watch as I...

"Do you want the shower?" Lisa stood in the kitchen doorway, wrapped in a towel, another one around her head. Her voice was low and slightly sulky. Jen sat up, startled, sending Lavender streaking away in the petulant fit only a cat can have. She had been so lost in her fantasy, she hadn't heard the water stop or the door open.

"Yeah," she said, simply. She would have said more, or tried to, but words just wouldn't come. So instead, she left her half full bottle of beer on the table and stiffly walked toward the bathroom.

As Jen started to strip off her clothing before ducking into the steaming bathroom, Lisa stood by the kitchen and watched her. The shower had done wonders for her stiff muscles, partly from the cramped theater seat and partly from her indignation during the movie. But there was still a kernel of annoyance at the entire evening. Why did they have to go and see THAT movie? And why did Jen have to be so stubborn about everything? Lisa knew, deep down that she had been unfair and rude to her lover. But she buried those feelings as well as she buried the feelings that had unwillingly run through her body during certain moments of that sicko, perverse film. People really didn't do those things, did they? And enjoy them? They couldn't enjoy them! It was wrong to enjoy them.

Why couldn't Jen just let things be? There was nothing wrong with the way they did things, especially in bed. They didn't need all that weird dress up stuff, and they certainly didn't need dildos, or high heels, or whips, or men, for that matter! That kind of film is just made for men, Lisa decided firmly. Maybe Jen thinks that she hasn't been interesting enough, maybe she thinks we need to spice things up a little. Well, I'll have to tell her I like things just the way they are.

She went into their bedroom and found Lace, their second feline houseguest, curled up in the middle of their futon. That was nothing new. Both cats liked to sleep with them, and in the winter, two girls and two cats made a nice warm combination. She doffed the towel around her body and put on an oversized t-shirt, and then sat down to comb out her hair. In a few minutes, Jen walked in, without the benefit of a towel anywhere, and casually looked through her drawer for a similar t-shirt.

Lisa looked at her lover in the mirror, admiring, as she always had, the tattoo on Jen's right shoulder - a stiletto thrust through a bunch of red roses, and the words, "Sappho's Brigade" on a ribbon wrapped around it. Jen had sold her bike and given up the open road several years ago, to settle down and find a steady job and a steady lover. Lisa remembered her last ride as Jen's passenger. Treasured it because she knew that Jen had partly given those things up because of her, and the apartment they were going to get together, and the life they were going to share. She looked over her shoulder and said, "Would you feed the cats?" and then almost bit her tongue. She should have said something lover-like, not something so common. But Jen merely grunted, tossed a t-shirt over her head, and stalked back to the kitchen, the cats chasing her as she went.

By the time Jen got back, beer bottle in one hand, Lisa had convinced herself that the evening's difficulties had all been Jen's fault. All that was left in Lisa's mind was the fact that Jen had taken her to see some kind of porno movie, when she should have known that Lisa would have no interest in such a thing. And such a movie! Where everything was costumes and whips and chains, and degradation...it was almost too much to understand. So when Jen casually walked back into the room, Lisa turned to her and said, "I'm going to try and forget that you forced me to see that piece of filth tonight."

Jen stopped in mid-motion, bottle still tilted in her hand. She could hardly believe that Lisa was still trying to push the issue...and pin the blame on her as well! She stared at the blonde woman in exasperation.

"You never give it a break, do you?" she began, her voice strong and slightly nasty. "You agreed to go...you agreed to keep an open mind...and you just don't want to admit that you found some parts of it hot. I admit there were some parts that went too far, like that gang-rape scene..." Lisa's eyes flashed in angry agreement. "...but damn it, there were some good parts too! What about the bathtub? What about the scene outside, with the tree, and the ropes? This isn't about the movie. It's about how you can't stand to give one little bit...to admit that part of something I said or did was right, or good. You just can't let go of anything, not an hour later, not a day later, and not even when we're about to go to bed."

Lisa flushed, her expression a mixture of anger and confusion. "It figures you liked that deviant movie. Just because you're a pervert doesn't mean I should be one too! You just probably want to play some of those disgusting games with me, and that's why you dragged me to that thing. Well it's not going to happen! I never complained about the things you were doing, so there was no reason for you to think that I needed you to do...that stuff..."

"What?" Jen was incredulous. "You think I took you to that movie because I was insecure about MY lovemaking?"

Lisa flushed again, nervously. She said nothing.

"You have got one hell of an ego, girl," Jen said, draining the rest of her beer. "I took you because we both heard it was a hot movie, and who knows, maybe we could have learned something from it. But honey, learning how to play kinky games so I could amuse you was NOT on my agenda." She slammed the bottle down on their chest of drawers and walked over to the bed. "You just think the world revolves around you, don't you? If you ask me, you could use something from that movie. Something to take you down a peg."

Lisa stood up. "Just what do you mean by that?"

"I mean you need to be bent over and have that cute bottom of yours paddled until you said you were sorry, just like a little brat." Jen flipped the covers back.

"You...you!" Lisa sputtered, standing on the other side of the bed. "How dare..how could..."

"Yeah, yeah, like I would bother." Jen sat down on the edge of the futon and stretched. "You coming to sleep or not?" The anger in her voice was almost gone, and she spoke in a weary tone that suggested that she expected Lisa to sleep elsewhere, as had happened before, on a number of occasions.

"You wouldn't dare to ever do such a thing," Lisa said in an odd voice. "In fact, I dare you."

Jen looked over her shoulder at her lover, standing there, her voice trembling...in anger? Frustration? Fear?

Interest?

"Don't say things like that unless you mean them," Jen cautioned, looking directly at her. "Just because you don't want to apologize to me is no reason to keep this up. Now, are you coming to bed, or not?"

"I meant it. And if you want an apology, the only way you'd get it from me it by forcing it. Because I'm not sorry for a single thing I did tonight!" Lisa tossed her hair defiantly, her pouty face an invitation that Jen couldn't ignore. In a flash, she sprang up from her side of the bed, rolled over the top and took hold of Lisa's t-shirt with one hand as she righted herself on Lisa's side. The entire move took seconds - Lisa was so shocked, she didn't have enough time to fight.

Jen tightened her grip on Lisa's shirt and gave a savage tug that pulled the surprised blonde down and over, falling onto her stomach on the futon, the air expelling from her in a "whoomph." In another second, Jen scooted up next to her, and hooked one firm, tan leg over the small of Lisa's back, pushing her t-shirt up around her waist.

Lisa was effectively pinned to the bed, her legs over one side.

"I'll show you what it means when I'm not kidding," snarled Jen, laying the flat of her hand against Lisa's round bottom cheeks. "I'll make you apologize to me!"

And with that, Jen drew her hand back and soundly slapped it against Lisa's butt, making a sound so loud that it startled both girls. But she ignored the initial sound and began to spank her girlfriend in earnest, just as she had threatened...just like a little brat.

Lisa gasped at the first spank and then howled! She tried to kick out, using her long legs to an advantage, but Jen casually hooked her right ankle around Lisa's left and dragged the women's legs apart, exposing her dainty asshole and splaying the lips of her sex. Then, as if in response to the attempt at fighting, she redoubled her efforts and struck even harder, aiming at the center of her lover's twin globes, striking the part where they met the inverted "V" of her thighs, in a harsh, relentless rhythm that broke through Lisa's outraged howls and made her realize that what was happening was far more than painful.

It was embarrassing!

"Oh, oh god, wait! Wait! I...ow! I didn't, ow, stop it! I didn't mean it!" Lisa whined, and struggled and ended up pounding her fists against the futon in frustration. Being held down and spanked like an unruly child was almost too much for her.

"You meant it when you said it," replied Jen, never stopping her chastisement. "And I'm going to make sure you never say anything like that again unless you really mean it!" The hand kept rising and falling, sending Lisa's body pressing into the bed, as though she could escape the seemingly endless slapping. The blonde girl had totally lost her pouting expression.

Jen was totally consumed by what she was doing. At last, she had her whining, complaining, and just damn bitchy girlfriend in a position where all her sniping and pouting could do her no good at all. I am taking you down a peg, she thought, even as she brought her hand down firmly against the very center of Lisa's white ass, now turning a uniform red. And you do deserve this, you've had it coming for a long time...

"Haven't you?" Jen rasped, unaware that she was speaking out loud. She realized that she had, and continued. "You needed this, didn't you, you stuck-up bitch? Always getting on me. Always afraid to try new things, go new places, always making it my fault if you don't have fun..." Jen felt her anger rise, swell, and begin to dissipate, even as she continued spanking her lover. "Well, here you are, getting spanked, just like a naughty, whining brat, your bottom getting all red, and I'm not going to stop until you say you're sorry!"

Lisa had already stopped howling in outrage, and as Jen made this pronouncement, something inside of her broke. She sniffed and then began to cry, the steady beating on her behind making her gulp and gasp as she wailed.

"I...I didn't mean anything!" she managed to say between swats. "I'm sorry, really, please, stop, please, I'm sorry!" She was suddenly aware of a warm pleasure spreading in her loins, a pleasure that she had briefly imagined during one special segment of that movie. The one part that had made her hesitate when Jen asked her what she thought. Now, her legs spread shamelessly wide, her ass a hot mass of flesh, she knew the answers to the questions she had asked herself before, the ones she had lied to herself about. And in all this, the spanking continued, and she cried out again, both in release and pain, "Please, Jen, Jenny, please stop, I'm sorry, I'm really sorry!"

Jen almost didn't hear her, but the message did finally get through, and her arm ceased its machine-like movements and she was suddenly aware of a burning and stinging sensation in her own hand. Her palm was as red as Lisa's ass, and it hurt like...

She had hurt Lisa! As if she were suddenly aware of something she had done in her sleep, Jen held her own hand and gazed at the reddened butt of her lover in astonishment. How could she have done that? She was not a violent person! She loved Lisa!

"Oh, jeeze, oh, Lisa, come on, baby, it's OK, I didn't...oh, hell" Lisa was limp on the bed, tears streaming from her eyes, the bedclothes bunched in her fists. Jen quickly unhooked her legs and ran to the bathroom, where she wet a washcloth with cold water and came back to find that Lisa had not moved. Tenderly, she laid the cloth over that bright red bottom, and found out just how tender it was.

Lisa stifled a yelp as the cold water touched her burning behind, but allowed Jen to soothe the area while her tears were reduced to sobs, and her sobs to sniffles. Jen tried to be as gentle as she could, and carefully wiped away the excess moisture and dropped the cloth on the floor.

"Shhh, shhh, it's OK, I'm going to make it all better, just lay there, and I'll make it all better..." Jen tentatively brushed her lips over the warm area that covered Lisa's upturned butt, and Lisa shivered at the touch. Undeterred, Jen began to gently run her tongue around the globes of Lisa's ass, and then the rounded swells of it, kissing, soothing, and licking. Trying to get into position for a better angle, she braced one hand on the edge of the bed, and discovered a real surprise.

There was a very, very wet spot on the edge of the bed. Jen brought her hand up a little, to the triangle of downy golden hair between Lisa's legs and found that Lisa was very, very, aroused.

"Well, well, it wasn't that bad, was it?" she murmured, allowing her fingers to gently play with Lisa's delicate outer lips. Then, she planted a long kiss on the underside of Lisa's butt, and began to work her way down to the inside of her thighs. Spreading them wide apart with her hands, she began to plant little sharp kisses on each thigh, nipping tiny little folds of flesh and nibbling at the places she knew Lisa loved to be touched.

Lisa moaned, deeply, and shifted on the bed, just a little, raising her butt higher and allowing Jen a greater view of her pubic delta. Jen appreciated the view, and ducked her head deep in between her lover's legs and began to "soothe" her in the way she really did know best. In less than a minute, Lisa was writhing in pleasure, and Jen quickly pulled away. Over Lisa's moan of disappointment, Jen grasped her legs and pulled, bringing Lisa closer to the edge. Then, Jen twisted her around so that she was on her back, her legs up and over Jen's shoulders, while Jen's mouth descended into the sweet depths of Lisa's pussy.

"Oh yeah, oh yeah, that's it, lover, that's it, " Lisa sighed, opening herself to Jen's attentions. "I'm sooo sorry, you were right, I'm so glad you still love me..."

Jen looked up for a moment, and sent her fingers to replace her dancing tongue. "I do love you, hon. And I'm sorry I did this, I really shouldn't have..."

"I wanted you to" Lisa admitted, stretching backward like a cat. "I wanted to get you angry enough to do it right."

"Why, you little slut..." Jen abruptly ducked back down and attacked her lover with a quick and vicious mouth, her tongue doing exactly what her hand had done during the spanking...lashing away in a tight rhythm, this time where it would do the most good. This time, when Lisa howled, it would be in sheer pleasure, not in outrage. And as it happened whenever Jen concentrated on doing what she did best, Lisa came in a thigh twisting, body shaking explosion of pleasure that made the futon frame rock.

"Now listen to me," Jen said as she pulled herself up, laying her body on top of Lisa's. "Don't you ever...and I mean EVER...try to manipulate me into getting angry to get what you want!"

"I...yes, I'm sorry," Lisa breathed, her mind and body still enjoying the aftershocks of her powerful orgasms. "I just couldn't...I mean, it's so, so...dirty...I just couldn't ask for it...I wouldn't know what to say!" She giggled and wrapped her arms around Jen's body. "I mean, how do you describe this? I want you to spank me like...like..." Her voice trailed off, and the blush already on her cheeks heightened.

"Just like a naughty little girl, huh?" Jen filled in. "Yeah, I can see how that would be hard...but if you don't ask, I might just decide to do whatever I want to do! Like this!"

She lifted herself up and slid three fingers neatly into Lisa's snatch, harder and faster than she ever had before. Turning on her side, Jen angled her hand and began to firmly thrust her fingers in a steady rhythm, in, out, back and forth, turning them to spread Lisa open. Lisa arched her back and whimpered, easily taking the sliding fingers, spreading her legs as wide as she could.

Jen laughed, and leaned comfortably on one elbow. "Yeah, come on, babe, give it all up, let's see you take some more, huh?" She drew her fingers out in order to shape them together with her thumb, and then pressed into her lover's pussy, feeling the silken walls expand under her efforts, the flood of moisture all over her hand. Slowly, all her fingers and her thumb vanished inside Lisa's welcoming depths, and her hand naturally formed a fist.

"Oh my god!" Lisa cried out hoarsely, barely able to lay still. "Oh, yes, fill me, I love it..."

"Yeah, I bet you do, you've never taken my whole hand before," Jen chuckled. "Ready to be fucked silly?"

"Yes, yes! Do it!"

Steadily, sitting up for better leverage, Jen began to mover her hand around, in the same motions that she had made with her fingers earlier. Lisa moaned and then began to make harsh noises, torn from her throat in the nonsensical reactions of an animal in heat. She thrust her hips up, welcoming the invading fist, and began to pant. Taking it all, moving with it. Feeling herself tighten and expand around it.

"That's a good girl," Jen said, amazed at how easily her whole hand had slipped into Lisa, and thrilling to the sensations flooding her body. "Is my little baby gonna come for me again? Is there another come in there, can we get it out?"

Lisa heard the words and the tone of voice, and Jen felt her reaction all the way up her wrist. She grinned and pressed on, gently fucking her hand back and forth until Lisa's breath came in ragged sobs and gulps, and her moans became near-incoherent pleas, and then the spasms began all along her inner walls. Jen kept on, relentlessly, until the rhythm and the sensations caused Lisa to scream her pleasure.

"Yes, yes! I'm coming, oh yes, fill me, take me, make me...! Yes!" Lisa's body shuddered with explosive release, her cunt clamping around her lover's wrist and hand. She rode the ecstasy as long as she could, and then collapsed back, weakly, on the edge of the bed. Her body was covered with perspiration, her heart beating so fast and hard she heard echoes of it in her ears. She barely had the strength to squeal as Jen edged her hand out of her pussy, leaving her suddenly empty.

They lay there together for a few minutes, breathing and recovering. Jen got up in silence to go to the bathroom and turn out the lights. She stood by the bed for a moment, seeing the outline of Lisa curled up on one side of the futon, her breathing finally back to normal.

And then Jen climbed onto the bed, took her lover by the hair and directed her head down. "In the future," she growled, her tough voice softened by her lust, "you can just tell me what you need. Like I'm doing now. Get down there and eat me, honey, before I die waiting."

Which Lisa did, happily, and which eventually made their first real reconciliation such a joy that even the cats knew enough celebrate with them. They all slept entwined, like the loving creatures they were. Before they all managed to fall into their dreams, Jen murmured, "Tomorrow, we take a shower together," to which Lisa whispered a happy agreement.

Chapter Three:
Swing Your Partners

Guy Hutchinson drove to William and Terri's house like a man with a mission, and the two couples laughed at his obvious eagerness. Like the old friends they were, they were comfortable with each other, and they all knew each other's roles.

Guy was clearly a leader. It had been his idea to see that particular movie, just as it had been his ad that William and Terri finally answered, after months of fantasies. Well, his and Allison's, at least. Terri, although willing to experiment and intrigued by the thought of swinging, had always drawn back, half afraid at what kind of people actually did that sort of thing. When they got up the courage to actually answer ads and meet people, they were amazingly lucky to meet with Guy and Allison after only two very uninteresting encounters.

Allison herself had some history as a swinger, even before she met and married Guy. She often told them raunchy, lusty stories about times at Plato's Retreat, New York's old notorious swing club. She and Guy met after that place was closed, and tended to keep their activities low-key, finding other couples through carefully worded ads and national conventions. They too had some dull experiences before they met the Hutchinsons.

But now, they were a certified hit, all four of them. They occasionally looked into getting other couples to join them, but never regretted it when things didn't work out. They were genuinely friendly, happy with their friendship, and mutually interested in each other. Their weekend meetings were always planned with some sort of erotic special event to get them started. This week, it was the movie. And if the conversation and mood in the car were any indicators, they were all in for another hot night at William's house.

"OK, let's get comfortable folks...who wants what?" Terri glanced around the living room, taking drink orders.

William was laying some tinder in the fireplace. He looked up and said, "I'll have a beer, sweetie. Same for you, Guy?"

"No, I'll take coffee, if you don't mind," Guy said, taking a seat.

"Same for me," Allison added. Terri vanished into the kitchen.

"Whew, that was one hot movie," Will noted, as the tinder caught fire. He gently blew at the flames and added some sticks. "I think I almost came right there in my seat once or twice."

Guy and Allison laughed in unison. "You think you almost came?" joked the black haired woman, leaning forward from her seat on the couch. "Don't you know when you're going to come? I do!"

To the continued laughter of the couple, Will colored, and busied himself building the fire. When it was comfortably burning, he turned back to them and smiled. "Well, at least I can admit what turned me on, Ali," he said. "Can you do the same?"

"Oh, wait, I want to hear this," Terri called from the kitchen. "Let's all say what turned us on!"

"Great idea!" Guy agreed. They waited until Terri returned with their drinks on a tray, and then settled down near the fireplace and looked at each other expectantly.

"Well, since Will challenged me, I'll start," Allison said, grinning. "I liked the whipping, especially the part where the mistress in those really high heels whips that guy with the straps across his chest, and those rings in his, um..." She blushed and drew her fingers across her chest. The three laughed, and Guy trembled in a mock shudder of horror.

"Oh, don't remind me," he said. "My nipples ached just by looking at it!"

"Yeah, well, I like what the woman did to him. And I liked the way he treated her. With respect! I think women should be treated like queens by their men! Don't you, Terri?" Allison grinned teasingly at her husband, and he laughed. Terri blushed.

"How about you, Will? I said what I liked. Now it's your turn."

William stared at Allison intently for a moment, as if making up his mind. Then, he leaned forward and said, "I liked that part too."

There was silence for a moment, and then they all started laughing again.

"Really?" Allison asked, her smile taking on that devilish aspect that told them all she was getting turned on. "You mean, you wanted to get whipped, right? Not do the whipping?"

"Uh-huh." Will nodded. "To tell you the truth, to be handled and to serve a beautiful mistress has always been a fantasy of mine...sexually serve her, at least. And you are beautiful, Ali."

"Well, that has its possibilities! Maybe we can put on a little show of our own, for the amusement of our mates, huh?" Allison looked eagerly at the other two.

"Now, wait a minute, we're not finished here," Guy said firmly. There are two more people here who haven't told what they liked, and frankly, we'll need something to do while the two of you are playing games...why don't you go first, Terri?"

Impossibly, Terri's blush got deeper, and she dipped her head for a moment. "I'll tell," she began, "but you have to promise not to laugh."

"We promise!"

"Come on, Terri!"

"It's just a game, Terri!"

Assured by their interest, she looked back up and said, softly, "I liked the part where the women was tied to the bed and that guy in the mask brought strangers to look at her."

Guy leaned back with a satisfied expression on his face, even as Will turned in astonishment to look at his wife. "Really?" he asked, his eyes wide. "That would turn you on?"

She nodded, and looked at Guy. Guy couldn't hold it in any more, and he grinned, a huge, broad grin. "Well then, now we do have ourselves a little show. Allison gets to play mistress with you, Will, and I get to play master with Terri!"

"Oh, this is too good!" Allison exclaimed, standing up. "I can't wait. What should we do? How do we do this?"

"Everyone in the movie seemed to have costumes," Will mused. "Maybe we should change."

"Into what?" Terri asked.

"I don't know...wait, how about that little red thing you bought for Valentine's Day?"

Terri's eyebrows shot up and she blushed again. Then, after thinking a moment, she turned to Allison and said, "I think I have something for you, too! Let's go into the bedroom!"

Guy stood up. "Yeah...you girls get changed, and Will and I will do something about the equipment situation. You have some rope around here, don't you, Will?"

Will nodded, and the two men went through the kitchen toward the back of the house.

Their wives headed in the other direction, to the master bedroom, where Terri began to rummage through her closet.

"This is going to work," Allison said, as she looked at herself in the mirror. She picked up a comb and began to comb her short black hair back, making her hairstyle more severe. "Are you really into this, or are you going along because you thought Guy would want it?" she asked, suddenly.

"I think this is going to be the hottest thing I've ever done," Terri said suddenly, emerging from the closet with a giggle. "This has been a fantasy of mine for ages!"

"Oh good!" Allison turned away from the mirror and gasped when she saw what Terri was holding. "Oh, Terri! It's perfect! Will it fit me?"

"I think so...we can always tighten it with a belt." Terri smiled and then opened one of the dresser drawers. "I'm going to need your help with this..."

"Why are you cutting the rope?" Will asked, as he dug through his tool chest for some electrical tape. "Can we use pieces that short?"

"This isn't for bondage," Guy said, sawing another length off. "This is for the whip we'll give to Allison." He gathered the six pieces of rope together and took the roll of tape that Will found, and began to tape the rope together at one end, making a handle. "I think it's soft enough so it won't hurt...too much." He winked, and noticed that Will had fallen silent. "Hey, Will...are you OK?"

"Yeah, I'm fine...except...Guy, do you think...I mean, is it OK..."

Guy mercifully interrupted. "Do you mean, do I think you're a wimp for doing this?"

Will glared at his friend. Guy laughed disarmingly. "Hey, it's OK! No, I don't. I mean, this is all pretend anyway...and besides, this is the modern age. No need to go all macho about sex, you know? Let's just relax and have a good time. Maybe if this works, I'll try being the slave next time!"

Too relieved to admit that he was relieved, Will nodded and the two of them went back to the living room, where a surprise awaited them.

Standing proudly in the middle of the room was Allison...a very changed Allison. Her hair was brushed up and back, and she had changed out of the jeans and sweater she had been wearing. Now, she was dressed in Terri's black leather miniskirt, over a pair of black stockings. Her breasts were barely covered by one of Will's vests, and she kept her boots on. It wasn't exactly like the mistress in the movie, with her corset and heels, but to Will's startled eyes, she was amazing. He nearly dropped the makeshift whip he was holding.

Meanwhile, Terri had also changed. Now, she was wearing a bright red teddy, its frilly ends just touching her waist, the lace up front barely tied at her nipples. Her loins were creamy white against the matching lace panties. There was a red ribbon tied around her throat to complete the ensemble.

Guy whistled in appreciation. "Jesus, now we look like a couple of bums! What are we supposed to do for costumes?"

Allison grinned, and pointed at Will. "For starters, Will can get undressed! Shame on you, for being dressed in front of me!" She struck an arrogant pose, and Guy and Terri both started to snicker, but Will immediately dropped the whip he was holding and began to tear his shirt open. His fingers flew over the buttons, ripping one off in his haste. There was a look of total concentration on his face.

Immediately, the other three knew that the atmosphere in the room had changed. Guy stifled a giggle and walked over to Terri, who was wide-eyed at her husband's rapid transformation into an eager slave. By the time Guy was standing next to her, she was almost afraid to look at him. But warm memories of his big cock and his powerful hands made her turn her sweet face up to gaze at him. She was startled to see the scowl on his features.

"Are you planning to let Ali and Will have all the fun?" he asked, harshly. "Planning to stand there and stare all night?"

"Uh...um...no!" Terri almost squeaked.

"No, what?"

"No...master," she said, immediately feeling a wetness between her thighs. This was going to work! She could feel it!

He nodded, and then said, "I want things to tie you up with. Scarves, ties, something like that. Go get some, and come back here right away."

"OK...I mean, yes master!" She stumbled back and headed toward the bedroom at a run. Guy watched her retreating form with admiration. By the time he turned around, Will was naked and standing in front of Allison. The man's dick was already stiff as a board, curving up from a tangle of dark hair like a horn. Guy sat down to enjoy the show.

"I see you like this, Will...or maybe I should call you slave?" Allison was trying to think of what to say, and what to tell Will to do. At the sight of his passion for this treatment, her first thought was to throw herself on that cock, get it nice and wet with her tongue and mouth, and then get him to fuck her silly. But I'm a Mistress now, she thought. I should make him work for it.

Will, not knowing what to do with his hands, put them behind his back. He said, softly, "I think you should call me slave, Mistress."

"Think? Who said you could think?" Allison immediately improvised. "And who said you could suggest anything to me? I think you should be punished!"

"Yeah!" Guy agreed, turned on by his wife's performance. "Look, he even brought you a whip, although he had the nerve to drop it." He suppressed another giggle and looked over his shoulder got Terri. Where was the woman? When this scene got hotter, he was going to want a few things from her. He fingered the growing bulge in his pants and then leaned forward to take off his shirt.

"Go get that whip," Allison said, imperiously, pointing at it. As Will turned away from her, she added, "On your hands and knees! Like a dog!" The man hesitated for a second and then dropped to the carpet, and crawled slowly over to where the makeshift whip lay. Moisture began to gently ooze from the head of his cock. He was so turned on! So powerfully charged!

Without being told to, he bent his head and picked up the rope whip by the taped handle, holding it in his teeth. Then, he crawled back toward Allison, his head raised enough to see his own wife's wide-eyed look of surprise as he made his way across the living room floor. Somehow, knowing that she was witnessing his humiliation made it even better.

Terri had come back just in time to see her husband pick up the whip in his mouth, like a dog retrieving a stick, and then groveling his way back to Allison's feet. She paused, holding her scarves and two of Will's ties on her hands, and jumped when Guy laid one hand across her body to cup her breast.

"You sure took your time, sweet thing," Guy whispered to her. "I thought you were going to miss the show. But now that you're here..." His hand tightened around her tit, his fingers searching for the nipple. She hissed her breath inward, leaning back into him as he began to pinch and massage the delicate nub. Then, he brought his other arm around her, holding her in a hug, and cupped both her breasts, teasing her and bringing twin erections to her nipples. She arched her back and felt his hardness against her ass. He obligingly pressed it against her, the fabric of his pants a thin barrier. She moaned.

"You know," Guy whispered again, "This isn't fair. While your husband is there groveling at my wife's feet, you can see him, but he can't see you. Let's see what we can do about this." He suddenly dropped her breasts, and swept the tangle of scarves and neckties from her hand. He pushed her down to her knees, and sorted out two long scarves.

Neatly, he tied one around each ankle, and then, using the living room couch legs as anchoring points, tied her ankles wide apart. She gasped and fought to balance herself, her thighs drawn so open that the split crotch of her frilly panties gaped open, exposing her sex to the room.

Guy then gently pushed her back, and she fell backwards until the cushions of the couch supported her shoulders. She was now drawn exquisitely backward, like a bow, her breasts thrusting up against the sheer fabric. She dropped her arms down to continue steadying herself, and Guy knelt beside her, fingering the lace closures of the scarlet teddy she wore.

"I love this thing you're wearing," he said softly. "But compared to poor Will, you're overdressed. So let's get it off." One by one, he slowly untied the pretty bows down the front, until the material shimmered back of its own accord.

Meanwhile, Allison had finally taken the whip out of Will's mouth, and maneuvered him so that she could watch what Guy was doing. She absolutely loved the picture presented, of Terri's pretty, slender body arched backward over the couch. She looked down at the man at her feet and noticed him also watching, out of the corner of his eye, and she barked, "I didn't tell you you could watch! Get your face down...and...lick my boots!"

Will dived for leather! His lips pressed into Allison's foot; she could feel his tongue right through the heavy leather. Like a thirsty puppy, he lapped at the boots, lathered them with his spit, and polished them clean. Allison almost moaned in pleasure...Will was actually massaging her feet, through her boots, using only his lips and tongue.

She didn't know how much more of this she could take.

Not knowing what else to do, she lightly swung the makeshift whip against his bowed back. In response, he shivered in ecstasy and licked even harder. Smiling, she began to do it harder and harder, laying the soft rope strands across his back and ass, spurring him to expend more energy on polishing her boots. Slowly, parts of his flesh began to show color. First pink, and then red. She licked her lips, her mouth dry with excitement.

She needed to come, and soon. She looked back at what her husband was doing, and discovered that he had partially stripped Terri, opening her teddy and spreading the sides of her crotchless panties even further. He was busy teasing her exposed sex with his fingers and making her lick them. He glanced at Allison and they both got the same idea at the same time.

Allison said, loudly, "That's enough, slave. You're very good with your tongue, let's see you put it to some practical use! Crawl over to where that slave is tied." She pointed with the whip.

Will looked confused for a second, and then obediently did as Allison commanded.

"Now, roll over on your back."

Everything was clear now! Will eased himself onto his back, wincing at the touch of the carpet against his reddened ass and shoulders, and tucked his head in between his wife's obscenely spread thighs, as Guy moved out of the way.

"That's it. Now eat her! Lick her...get your tongue deep inside her!" Allison's voice was husky with pleasure. "I want to see her squirm! I want to hear her moan! Eat her out, you worthless slave, or you get no pleasure for yourself tonight!"

Guy orally attacked his wife's glistening cunt lips with the same passion he had bestowed on Allison's boots. He reached up and cupped her ass cheeks as he ran his tongue around and over her mound, tasting her, getting the scent and feel of her all over his lips and cheeks.

Terri didn't need to be told to squirm and moan...at the first touch of Will's tongue, she gasped and sank a little down to better provide him with surfaces to worship and pleasure. She closed her eyes in rapture, thinking of herself, tied, spread open and pleasured by her own slave/husband for the amusement of these two powerful people. She threw herself into the fantasy, and felt the inevitable orgasm building, until she realized that there was something...someone...standing over her face.

She opened her eyes to see Allison's pussy, framed by tight, curly reddish brown hair, poised right over her mouth.

Sure, Allison and Terri had shared touches, caresses, even kisses from time to time. Guy and Will massaged each other when the women were too tired, and never minded when their group gropings brought the men close together. But they had never really considered being so...blatantly bisexual!

Terri gazed at her friend's beautiful cunt, and marveled at the differences between women, and then hesitantly lifted her head to kiss the top of the mound. The soft flesh yielded to her lips, and she caught the rich scent of Allison's arousal. Allison settled down so that Terri could reach better, and spurred on by the wonderful pussy lapping Will was giving her - at Allison's command, she realized - she flicked her tongue against the older woman's clit.

Guy watched, highly amused and turned on by this scene of bisexual lust. Allison's expression changed from concern to purring contentment in one quick moment, as Terri began her tentative tongue-lashing. The man gazed at the mix of people, man on bottom, women tied over him, and then another woman on top of her, and decided that he had to get in on this. He quickly stripped off his pants, exposing his erection for the first time, and stood, one leg on either side of Will's body, right behind Allison.

Allison felt her husband behind her and arched her back, leaving just the top curve of her mound for Terri to lavish attention on. She braced her arms against the back of the couch. In a moment, she felt Guy's thick manhood pressing into her from behind, as he entered her more-than-ready pussy.

And so the tangle of three became four, as Guy gently fucked Allison, who was being frigged by Terri's tongue, who was being eaten out with gusto by William. Their groans, gasps and moans reached new levels of intensity.

His head securely surrounded by Terri's loins and thighs, Will was in heaven. His ass felt hot from his whipping earlier, and his back was deliciously tender in some spots. His cock jutted out from his belly, almost too hard to bear.

Terri, lapping and getting lapped, was deliciously torn by the sensations her husband was giving her and the delirious pleasure she was getting from pressing wet kisses all over Allison's engorged and hot clit. Allison sighed as Guy penetrated her, pushing her against Terri's inexperienced but dedicated tongue work, and Guy felt like he was king of the world.

Then, he shattered everything by pulling back and out. Allison, surprised, pushed back and took her mound away from Terri, who whimpered in confusion. The sounds of halted action above him made Will stop what he was doing, as well, and Guy had one hell of an attentive, (if not pissed) audience when he spoke.

"Hey, wait one minute here," he said in a serious voice, his eyes betraying his amusement. "That's my slave under there, and I'm not getting anything out of her."

"Oh!" Allison looked down at the panting woman beneath her and grinned. "Right! Well, I see something I can use, so let's switch places." Finally given the chance (and excuse), Allison lowered herself over Will's prone body and waiting cock, and neatly impaled herself on it, making him yowl in pleasure.

"I didn't give you permission to stop eating her, slave, so get busy! And you better not come before I do!" Carefully, she settled into a comfortable position, and began to ride him.

Guy wasted no time watching. He stepped up to Terri's face immediately and thrust his cock at her lips, still covered in Allison's sweet juices. "Come on, slave, show me how much you love this! Lick my balls! Kiss that shaft! Make me nice and wet!"

Terri obeyed these raunchy requests with the same gusto her husband had applied to her pussy. She brought her tongue eagerly up to wash the underside of Guy's nuts, and then the length of his dick, licking and nibbling, the way she knew he liked it. He moaned and grasped his thick cock in one hand and aimed it into her mouth, feeling her welcome it with wet warmth and slurping tongue. She was an excellent cocksucker, taking him all. Her mouth stretched around it, her teeth well out of the way. The bend of her throat accommodated him fully, and he let her fuck herself on the shaft, bringing her head up and then back again.

Allison rode Will's cock hard and fast, the way she liked it, and was the first one to cry out in orgasm. Throwing her head back and cupping her own breasts, she screamed out, "Oh yes! I'm fucking him...I'm coming now! Now!" She twisted on the shaft she had used for her own pleasure as the strength of her own pleasure shook her entire body. Will gave out a well-muffled gasp as her inner contractions actually milked him to his own come, and he spurted deep within her, his hips rising to meet her as she ground her cunt against him.

As Will gasped, he sucked Terri's clit between his teeth and gently bit down. Even as he bucked under Allison's magnificent fuck, he made Terri writhe into a long, sharp come. Her pussy quivered and clamped around him, her juices flooding his face, as she gulped at Guy's cock until it slid naturally into her throat, where the tightening of her muscles around it made Guy lean forward as if in pain.

It was an amazing chain reaction! In one moment, an electrical surge of ecstasy sped through the four people, their own reactions triggering pleasure in the next person! All together, they cried out in an orgy of splashing male cum and silky female wetness.

Guy fed Terri his load with a series of short thrusts that all bumped against the back of her mouth, and she drank him down like cool water, moaning around his cock. Then, sighing, he pulled it out of her mouth, dripping, and threw himself down on the couch, suddenly exhausted.

Terri also fell back, panting. Will finally let his head drop back to the carpet, his face well smeared with evidence of his wife's pleasure. And as Will's cock finally wilted, Allison lifted herself off of it and just rolled over on the floor, flushed and tired.

For a minute, there was no sound in the room except for the crackling of the fire and the sounds of four adults fucked to exhaustion.

Then, Terri said, weakly, "Um, could someone untie me, please? I'm getting a little stiff."

They all laughed suddenly, as if her request had broken the magic spell of silence that had taken them, and they moved to release her. She gratefully stretched her legs out in front of her on the floor, and cuddled up with Will, as he sat up next to her.

Allison kissed Guy gently on the mouth when he came to lay beside her on the floor, and they all watched the flames for a little while, still recovering. They would not forget this weekend for a long time!

Chapter Four:
Boys Will Be Boys

Mike and David walked together with the ease of two men used to each other. They touched rarely, but their strides matched so one never had to call the other closer to hear what he was saying.

David spoke first. "Did you ever do any of that stuff? The leather stuff?"

"Sure...didn't everyone?" Mike laughed. "Once or twice, I guess, to see if I liked it. But a lot of it was so...fake. All postures and clothing. So I never really got into it. I think I'm regretting that now."

"Oh?" Dave asked, teasingly. "Why is that?"

"Because I thought some parts of that flick were gonna make me explode, right there in the theater!" He laughed harder. "Of course, it would have been hotter if some big hairy guy was ordering that wimp around instead of the Barbie doll in lingerie, but you know, we all have our fantasies." He smiled encouragingly at his partner. "So, let's have it. What's on your mind?"

Dave ducked his head for a moment. It was one of the moves Mike always thought was so cute. "Well, you guessed it, Mike, I was hot for that shit too. All I kept thinking about was how great it would be if, well, if you, um, did some of those things to me."

Mike stopped short in the middle of the block. "Uh-oh. I guess we have a problem then."

"Huh? Why? You said you did it before, what's the problem? Is it too much?"

"Nope. But we both kind of want to be on the same side of things, I think. I never tried it from the master side, it always seemed too hard. Easier to just lay back and take orders, you know?" He shrugged helplessly, smiling at Dave's astounded expression. It was a slightly difficult admission to make. In their relationship, Mike was considered more top than bottom. He gave more then he took, and Dave liked it that way.

In fact, Mike mused, it's been so long since I was fucked, really fucked, I probably don't remember what it feels like. But the thought of it made him stiff under his jeans.

"So, I guess that's out for tonight!" Dave said, full of false cheer. "Let's just go home and party."

"No, let's not," Mike said, an idea forming. "Let's see if we can find someone to do us both. Together."

"Huh? A threesome?"

"Yeah! We'll go cruising, and find some leatherman who will master us both! It shouldn't be too hard, right?" They looked at each other and knew that Mike was right. They were young and handsome, city-bred hard, gym-worked to matching builds. They complimented each other and matched each other, and they had never had any problems getting either a third man or another couple to bring home and play with.

"How will we know some guy is real though? What if we get some queen in leather? What if we get some nutso?" Dave, ever the concerned one, mulled over the possibilities.

"We get someone we know," Mike said assuredly. "Let's go to The Shaft and look for...."

"Ron!"

They laughed together and headed for the West Side, near the piers. And they thought about Ron.

Ron was a leatherman they had both met on separate occasions. He had expressed an interest in the two of them before, but they never took him up on it. They had remained cordial, occasional spotting each other in bars and clubs, saying hello and moving on. He was a leatherman. Tall and muscular, he dressed in fine but aged leathers, the sign of a man long used to living in that world.

He was a real top. A man's man. A master. He would probably have no problem handling the two of them, and he was well-known in the community, so they could feel safe. Now if he was only at the bar tonight. If he hadn't already picked up some new boy to take home and torment...

But luck was with them, and they spotted Ron's ink-black curly hair over by the pool table in the back. The doorman/bouncer, his arms covered with biker tattoos and a thick cigar clamped between his teeth, had looked them over with derision when they walked in. Mike clearly heard the man say, "Fresh meat!" to a few of his cronies nearby.

Well, we probably look like slumming clones, he thought as Dave led the way through the crowd of men. Then, he gave a mental shrug. We are!

246

There was no game in progress, only a few men examining the scoreboards from earlier in the evening. The smell of beer fought with the heavier scents of sweat, piss, and leather. In one corner, a man in a cop's uniform was pressing another man to the wall, pushing an authentic looking nightstick between his legs. Mike gulped audibly, suddenly not so sure of himself.

And thn,e Ron looked up and saw them. His mouth curled into a smile under his heavy mustache, and he waved them over.

"Hey, good to see you boys," he said cheerfully, his voice a deep baritone. "What brings you out tonight? Ready to take me up on my offer?" He winked. He was wearing black leather chaps, neatly framing a substantial basket between his legs and drawing attention to it. His black t-shirt was skintight over his developed chest, tucked into a worn and faded pair of Levi's 501 jeans. A plain silver buckle adorned an old but shiny black leather belt around his waist. A leather vest and a tight armband on one bicep completed the picture, and David felt his balls tighten in anticipation at the sight of the man. He was hot!

Mike, usually the leader, had lost whatever it was he was going to say. They were really here, standing in front of this vision of masculinity, and they were going to ask him to...to...

Dave, seeing that Mike wasn't going to answer for some reason, took Ron's outstretched hand and shook it warmly. "Well, yeah, Ron, we are! How about that?"

Ron's surprise was genuine, but then his smile broadened. "No shit! Well, it's about time! I've had wet dreams about the two of you, you know. Or is it just one?" He looked back and forth between them.

"Uh, no!" Mike found his voice. "I mean, we both...I mean, if you think you can..." Why was his brain failing him? He tried to get a grip.

"We were wondering if you were serious about doing us both," Dave said, smoothly. "We just saw this movie..."

"Oh!" Ron nodded, cutting him off. "I know the one you mean. Hell, I've gotten three new boys this week from that flick. I should send them a thank-you card! But I'm real glad it gave you some courage. When do you want to set this up for? Tonight good with you?"

Dave nodded eagerly. "Man, I was hoping you'd say that. Where can we go?"

Mike thought, oh no, no tonight! Anything but tonight! But Dave was already arranging things. They would leave together, and walk to Ron's apartment nearby. Would they like to discuss some rules? Yes, they would, and would this take long? Mike barely heard what they were talking about. His mouth was dry, and his eyes seemed unfocused. They were really going to do this? Go home with this man in black and do whatever he wanted them to? Why, he could do anything! What made him think of this? What could possibly...?

"Hey!" That sharp word, clearly addressed to him, brought him back to reality. Ron was standing directly in front of him. He looked up into the man's dark eyes. "Hey, Mike...you with us here? Are you going to go through with this, or do you want to go home?"

The question was serious, and behind the harsh words, Mike could see that he was being given an option. He took a deep breath and looked back and then said, calmly, "Yes, sir. I'm going through with it, sir." And felt the immediate stiffening between his legs.

That was why he thought of this, he remembered.

Dave's hard-on intensified when he heard his lover speak like that. Maybe Mike was more experienced than he let on?

Ron nodded, satisfied. "Good attitude, boy. Now you go get me a beer while I talk things over with your boyfriend here." He gave Mike a push toward the bar.

By the time he got back, cold beer in hand, Dave and Ron were shaking hands over something. Mike held the beer out, still tongue-tied, and watched as Ron passed the bottle over to a friend of his standing by the rack of cues. "I don't think I need any more," the topman said, grasping Dave by the back of the neck. "I think me and these two boys have some business to discuss, elsewhere!"

There was warm but knowledgeable laughter as Ron herded the two men out of the bar, pushing them along from time to time. As they got to the door, the bouncer was almost in tears, he was so amused. "Hey, wadda you have here, Ron, two for the price of one?"

"You bet, Charlie, got 'em on sale." Ron stopped to pick up his leather jacket and shrugged it over his body.

"Yeah, well, remember...don't bruise the merchandise! You won't get your money back!"

Mike felt himself blushing even as his erection threatened to burst the zipper on his jeans. He left the warm confines of the bar with a gasp of relief, gulping the night air. In a moment, Ron was behind him again, this time with a hand on his neck.

"OK, you two, let's get one thing straight right now!" Ron's voice changed from genial to something more like a drill sergeant's growl. "You wanna know what it's like to do leathersex, and that's what we're gonna do. You're gonna do everything I tell you to, fast, and with no backtalk, and I'm gonna do whatever the fuck gets me off. Do you understand?"

Dave said, "Sure...but I told you -" He was cut off when Ron took a fistful of his hair and pulled his head back.

"Yeah, I know what you told me, boy. All that stands. Did you think I forgot? There's gonna be a taste of my belt on your ass for thinking I'd forget what I promised, kiddo. You better learn how to behave, and learn fast." He let the younger man go, and then pointed south. "Right this way, boys, and make it quick. I mean to teach you both a thing or two tonight."

Somehow, the three of them made it to Ron's walk-up without Mike passing out from the sheer, overwhelming pleasure. He glanced at Dave from time to time, and was aware that Dave saw the effect this strange scenario was having on him. Was it his imagination, or did Dave grin every once in a while? Mike's legs felt like rubber as he climbed the stairs and entered the cool, dark confines of Ron's apartment.

Ron closed the door behind them, and without looking at them directly, ordered them to strip. Dave and Mike glanced at each other in momentary confusion. Huh? was clear in their eyes, and only Mike's hands crept to the collar of his shirt. But Dave started to turn around to face Ron.

In a flash, Ron's large, warm hand was clamped onto the back of Dave's neck.

"YOU have a severe problem taking orders, BOY." Ron held onto the younger man and began to shake him back and forth, making him unsteady, making small, confused sounds come from his throat. "You didn't come here for chitchat, did you?"

"Uh...no." Dave managed to get out, trying to keep his hands from going to his neck. Out of the corner of his eye, he saw Mike watching them, tensed to move.

"What's this 'uh' shit, you little scum sucker? That should have been, 'Sir, no sir!' And you, dickface!" He directed this at Mike. "Why the fuck are you still dressed? I want you down to skin or jock, NOW!" Then, the leatherman pulled Dave closer to him. "I believe I owe you two punishments now, don't I?"

Dave saw his lover hurriedly shucking his clothing and groaned as Ron breathed heavily into his ear. "Yes," he said, weakly, "uh, I mean, sir, yes sir."

"You're still a fuck up, but I give you a point for trying. Get your clothes off and get your face down on my boot, and maybe I'll even take that as an apology." Ron walked past the two of them and sat regally in a wide, comfortable chair, beckoning Mike over as he walked.

Mike was down to skin - he almost never wore a jockstrap, unless he was working out. His excitement was painfully apparent, and as he approached the seated master, it only got worse. But Ron paid no attention to that symbol of manhood, only had Mike turn around and show off his body.

"You'll do, boy. Bring your tits over here. Let's see what you're made of." The black haired man patted his leather covered knee and Mike hesitantly moved forward. With Ron's guidance, he lowered his body, straddling that knee, his cock and balls pressed against the leather in luxurious torment. He tried to maintain his balance without putting his full weight on Ron's leg, and Ron did not move to correct his posture.

"Hands behind your back." Ron didn't wait for Mike to do it, but reached up and took hold of both of the young man's nipples. He gave them a sharp pinch, which made Mike gasp, and then began to work them back and forth between his fingers. They became miniature erections by themselves, and Mike arched his back, his thighs pressing on the sides of Ron's leg, his hands locked obediently behind his back. His head swarmed with sensation. His entire body gave itself to the intense pleasure/pain that the older man was causing him.

The only thing that called his attention back was the feeling of something ó no, someone, down by his foot. It was Dave, finally undressed, and crouching submissively at Ron's boot, his mouth barely an inch away from the leather. Mike saw the smooth curves of his lover's ass, and groaned again, his cock twitching, his hands aching to grab it. Ron roughly twisted his nipples.

"Keep your attention on me until I tell you otherwise, fucker, you got that?"

"Sir, yes sir!" Mike answered at once. Ron's slow, cold smile made him blush.

"And you! I told you what to do, fuck up, now do it!"

The room fell silent, until a slight, steady sound emerged from Ron's boot. Dave ran his tongue over the worn, polished leather, shining and cleaning, and worshipping. Mike couldn't take it any more, and twisted on his perch.

Ron laughed and pushed him off is knee. "All right, boy, that's enough attention for you right now. Get your ass into that room," he pointed, "and look in the closet. There's some rope in there, and a little black bag on the floor. Bring them here...but...I want you to crawl there and back. And, I don't want to see you carry any of that stuff in your hands. What you do when I can't see you is your business. But I want to see if you can be a good little boy for me. Get moving."

Mike dropped to his knees, for a moment right next to his boot-licking lover, and then crawled toward the room Ron had pointed to. He was awfully conscious of his engorged dick, hanging stiffly down, and his balls, heavy and already sweaty, exposed to the dark eyes of the man they had chosen to master them for an evening. A flush swept through his body again, and he continued to crawl.

Dave, in the meantime, had covered all of Ron's right boot with his spit, and polished it to a midnight sheen. He gasped as Ron's hand lifted his head by the hair and forced it back down on the other boot.

"Not bad, cocksucker. Now, while you do this one, we'll see to your punishments." Ron stood up and Dave heard the clanging sound of his belt buckle, and the terrible, slow hiss of the belt being pulled from it's loops. The novice tensed, and then actually trembled, as the belt was trailed gently across his back.

"Get your ass up, boy. Give me a nice target."

Exposing himself to the leather was the hardest thing he'd ever done, but Dave raised his ass up in the air, and instinctively drew his thighs together. His balls and cock were barely constrained in a white jock.

The leather belt smacked against his ass with a loud "crack!" and he jumped, pushing his face nearly off Ron's boot. A line of heat rose where the strap hit, and before he could react, another one was laid down. "Ow!" he cried out, unable to hold it back. In an instant, Ron bent over him, and grabbed him by the hair again, pulling him up savagely.

"What did you think this was about, boy? Did you think I was gonna let you snuggle up with my leather and jerk off until you came? This is about taking the pain and learning the discipline, boy, and if you can't take it, the door is right behind you. Your boyfriend knows the score, watch him. Get your face back down to my boot, and you finish that job, or you're outa here, got that?" He shook Dave again, and Dave felt actual tears forming. But he swallowed them and took a deep breath, his back tensing in anger. Then, he dived for that boot and attacked it with his lips and tongue as Ron got back up to swing the belt again.

This time, when it landed, Dave was ready. He grunted once, but continued his oral assault on the topman's boot, licking and washing until every square inch was lubricated and shined with his spit. And he took the belt rising and falling again, until his entire ass was a soft red, the white straps of his jock a sharp contrast. Behind the protective cotton mesh, his dick flagged and then rose again, stiffening in satisfaction as he finished the boot, and had no more embarrassing incidents. Ron dropped the belt onto his chair, and turned to look at Mike.

Mike had crawled into the bedroom and then, when he was out of Ron's line of sight, got up to open the closet door. As promised, there were coils of rope neatly hanging from hooks inside the door. Mike draped them around his neck, feeling their softness and wondering who had coiled them so neatly. Surely, Ron didn't do that himself? Mike imagined a small, hairless youth doing the task. Doing chores for his master.

The small black bag was on the floor, and the handle fit neatly into Mike's mouth. He closed the closet door and dropped back to his knees to crawl back, the rope around his shoulders and the bag in his teeth, and found himself watching his lover being beaten before his very eyes! He stayed on all fours, transfixed by the image, until Ron was finished and turned his gaze to him.

"Good fella," Ron said, pulling his booted leg away from Dave's mouth. "Now, let's see what we can do with you two."

Fifteen minutes later, they were tied back to back, their hands bound before them and secured to their waists, a rope across their chests holding their shoulders together. They knelt, their legs interlocking. Ron had taken a few strange objects from his little black bag, and now, he took his time, stripping off his vest and t-shirt and leaving the room to don a leather harness that crossed and defined his chest. But while he was gone, he also took his jeans off, pulling the smooth leather chaps back on. What had been hinted at under the buttons of a pair of Levi's was displayed in its glory for the two bound men. Both of them felt the same rush of lust and need.

Ron paused to let the two of them see him, and then picked a vaguely familiar red bottle from the bag. He approached Mike first, and opened the bottle.

"Here's a little gift for your tits, boy. It'll warm you up a bit." He shook the bottle over one nipple, then the other, and Mike recognized the smell. It was tobasco sauce! Ron rubbed the sauce into the sensitive nipples thoughtfully, and Mike began to feel a slight heat rising in them. He moaned, and Ron splashed some more on. The scent made his eyes sting, so he closed them.

Ron walked casually around to Dave and harshly tugged the jockstrap down, pulling the man's cock and balls from their covering. Splashing the burning hot sauce onto his palm, Ron then rubbed a generous amount all over Dave's hairy balls, working them between his fingers, until Dave cried out.

Ron carefully wiped his hands on a towel from the bag, and then brought out a handful of clothespins. Mike squirmed against his lover as the tobasco sauce really began to penetrate, and whimpered as Ron gathered his cock and balls together and hefted them.

"Well, your boyfriend has his balls on fire. You should have something like it," Ron said, as he began to pinch loose pieces of flesh. Swiftly, deftly, he fastened four clothespins on Mike's balls, and two, right on the ridge of his cockhead. Mike bit back a small scream, and bent forward, pulling Dave's head and chest back.

"Hold that position!" Ron said, stepping around to Dave. He quickly snapped one clothespin on each of Dave's nipples, to complete the set-up. "Good boy. Let him back now."

Now, the two men were in erotic agony. Each of them had both his chest and his crotch in burning pain, either from the crushing constriction of the pins or the slow burning of the tobasco sauce. Sweat dripped down both of their backs as they rubbed themselves against each other. The rampant state of their cocks made it clear that they were indeed taking pleasure from the leatherman's attentions. Ron smiled and dipped into the small bag again, this time to bring out a rolled condom. He opened the package and walked in front of Mike, holding the rubber over the head of his cock.

"Get this scumbag over my dick, little boy. Use your hot mouth to work it down, all the way." Ron planted his boots firmly down, making Mike reach for his task, and his reward. Pulling against a squirming and moaning Dave, Mike managed to wrap his lips around the condom and begin to push it back, unrolling it over Ron's endowment. He used his tongue to push the edges back, and his tightly closed lips to smooth it over the hard piece of manflesh that was so well framed by the black leather chaps. As he leaned forward, he felt the warmth of Dave's ass against his, and a drop of moisture escaped from his cock, even through the clothespins. He moaned around the thick cock in his mouth.

"Yeah," Ron sighed. "That's good, that's nice. You'll get the rest of that later, boy." He pulled his latex sheathed cock from Mike's mouth and then walked around to Dave, who was now literally shaking with the pain on his balls.

"Please..." Dave shuddered, even as the object of his dreams was aimed at his mouth. "Please!"

"Please what? You want me to take that shit off your nuts?"

"Yes! Yes!" Dave nodded, and the shook again. "I mean, sir, yes sir, please sir!"

"OK. But first, you'll take me right down to the root. And you're gonna suck me like you're sucking to save your fucking life...even though it's just your nuts. Swallow this, dickface." With a low growl, Ron slammed into Dave's mouth, giving him no chance to breathe. Dave felt the smooth intrusion sliding right over his tongue and banging into his tight throat, and fought to accept it. The pain in his tits and balls seemed almost forgettable now! There was nothing better than the steady, firm battering of his mouth, face and throat. He was not going down on Ron, he wasn't sucking his cock. He was being face-fucked, used for Ron's own pleasure. His whole body responded, and he threw himself forward, eager to receive what Ron was forcing him to take.

In what seemed like too short a time, Ron finally drew back, his cock dripping with Dave's spit. Smiling, the topman took a white cream and rubbed it all over Dave's burning nuts, and the intense heat began to ease. The two bound men sagged together, and Ron reached for the knots in the ropes. Within a minute, they were both bound together again, this time facing each other in a sixty-nine position. Ron reached between them and pulled the clothespins off of Mike's cock and balls, and off of Dave's reddened nipples, and the two men gasped as blood flew to those places that had been clipped for so long.

"Now for my good little boy," Ron said, dropping to the floor. He pulled and pushed at the two men until Mike was on top, his cock hanging stiffly near Dave's face, his own mouth over Dave's cock. "You get to take me right up the ass, boy. What do you have to say for that?"

"Sir, thank you sir, please fuck me, sir!" Mike raised his ass as much as he could, realizing that the harder Ron fucked him, the more likely he would be mashing his crotch down into Dave's face. But he didn't care. He needed this, needed it so bad! He felt Ron's hands on his ass, opening him, and squeezing cold lube into that hole that hadn't been fucked in so long. He realized that Dave could see this, was probably feeling droplets of sweat and lube on his face, and Mike's cock felt stiff enough to burst.

Ron's cock slid into him, riding the cool lube, until the man was in all the way to his pubic hairs! Mike moaned and cried out and invited the topman to take him, fuck him, sweep him away, and as Ron began to thrust, Mike began to feel like there was nothing in the world that could make him give this up, ever again. He dimly heard Ron order Dave to lick his balls, and then heard Ron strongly order both of them to contain their come.

"If either of you two come before me, it's over!" Ron snarled, his hips pressing into Mike's upraised butt. "You come when I tell you to! Understand?"

Their answers were unintelligible, but they both understood. Finally, Ron pulled out of Mike's ass and pulled the condom off. He got up, holding his dick in one hand, and said, "OK! Grab your dicks. Get ready, you cocksuckers, 'cause I'm gonna come all over you. And when I'm finished, I want you to shoot off into each other's faces, you got that?" He worked his cock, harder and harder, as the two men got their bound hands over their cocks, relieved and in ecstasy that they were finally able to handle them. Ron's back stiffened, and he aimed. "Here it comes, you fuckers! Here it comes!"

Thick, white come splashed against their backs and down their sides as Dave and Mike rolled together, pumping their own cocks furiously. Dave came first, splattering Mike's cheek, and then Mike, with a harsh groan, finally shot his load, right across Dave's chin and throat. They collapsed into each other, panting, and waited until Ron had cleaned himself off, stripped off his chaps, and put his jeans back on.

254

Then, the topman bent down to free them, and gave them a towel to clean themselves off. He vanished into the kitchen and came back with two bottles of beer and a bowl.

"So that's your introduction to leathersex," he said to Dave, as Dave pulled on his own pants. "How'd you like it?"

"It's intense," Dave said, grinning. "But I think I'd like to do what you do. I mean, this was great. I never came so much in my entire life. But it must be hot to be a top."

"It is," Ron admitted. "But the best tops come from the bottom. You got potential. I'd teach you." He drank deeply from one of the beers. "But your boyfriend there..." He pointed at Mike, who was still undressed. "He's a bottom. Probably always will be. You'd make him happy if you were his top."

Dave tried to object, but when he turned to look at Mike, he began to realize that what Ron had said was true. Mike was sitting on the floor, his eyes lowered, his face and neck flushed with embarrassment, but there was no doubt that he had not only taken well to Ron's treatment, but that simply being gazed at like this was getting him excited again.

Dave looked back at Ron, who sat down and placed the bowl on the floor. He then offered the second bottle of beer to Dave, and carefully poured some of his own beer into the bowl on the floor.

"Let's drink to a new friendship," Ron said, his dark eyes laughing. And as he and Dave clinked their bottles together, Mike wordlessly crawled over to the bowl and began to drink.

Chapter Five:
Maid to Get Off

Roxanne Ciccio was a woman with priorities. While other high school girlfriends were going steady and dealing with VD, pregnancy and prom night, she was getting good grades and holding hands with Richard Sarage, who was captain of the debating team. When they went to separate colleges, she avoided heavy romantic entanglements and had a short but satisfying succession of male friends she would never let get too attached to her, and spoil her chances for getting a good job. Now, working in the financial district of lower Manhattan, she had a gang of girlfriends who she went to movies and street-fairs with, and a few men who she occasionally went out with for dinner, temporary romance, and occasional hot sex. The sex part was OK, except for one thing.

She usually got bored after the third time.

It wasn't that they were bad lovers, as far as she could tell. And there certainly wasn't anything wrong with her. But somehow, the usual dinner, dancing and screwing combination often left her wondering if men really had any other speeds. So she listened to the stories of her friends in steady relationships and cheerfully received their comments about how wonderful it must be to be able to play the field, and didn't try too hard to look for "Mr. Right."

It had been Gina's idea to go see that movie everyone was talking about. Girl's night out, she had said with a wink. We'll get to see it before the guys drag us to it and try to get us into all that kinky stuff! The idea spread like wildfire, and their gang hit the theatre after an early dinner at an overdecorated and overpriced pizza joint. They had to stifle laughs and snickers during different parts, and Jennifer threw popcorn at Margaret when Margaret was staring so intently at the screen, but all in all, they'd had more fun at other movies. Giggles aside, there wasn't much discussion after they left the theatre and headed toward their homes, boarding different trains and hailing cabs with admonishments to do lunch sometime next week.

On her way to Queens, Roxanne switched trains at 42nd Street instead of further downtown, as usual. She just couldn't get those images and thoughts out of her mind! That slender man, dressed in a skimpy costume trimmed with lace, with a big bow tied around his waist, holding the apron on. His unsteady steps in those high heels, and the delightful blush that ran across his features every time he had to bend over...

You are sick, Rox concluded, although she stayed on the train. Here you are, with thousands of nice, macho guys available, and you want to see some stud in an apron and frilly panties.

But the image stayed in her mind, and she quickly got off the train and found her way above ground, where the sleaziest of New York's porn parlors advertised their wares in garish neon. Hesitating for a moment, she toured the notorious three blocks which made up the most concentrated collection of smut in the city, and chose one place that seemed at least halfway welcoming. Taking a deep breath, she walked in, past the guard at the door and the metal detector, and glanced hurriedly at the helpful signs draped across each row of materials. Video tapes abounded, and a wall of sex toys extended way into the rear of the store. Men wandered and looked, and seemed to do their best to ignore her. She rapidly found the magazine section, and browsed through it, her back straight, and all her senses on alert.

I have every right to be here, she thought, as her eyes passed huge glossy magazines covered with photos of tits and pussies. I am an adult women. One or two of the men began to watch her, but she soon found what she wanted. It wasn't glossy, but a tabloid paper, called *Mistress Monthly*. The picture on the front showed a man in the type of dress she had just been imagining, but with a collar around his neck, and something strapped into his mouth as well. He looked sad. But what she was really looking for was the banner across the top of the page that said, "Hundreds of Personal Ads!"

It cost five dollars. She brought it to the counter, paid for it, and the clerk stapled it into a plain brown paper bag. With no further delay, she left the store, the block, and got onto the train that would take her home.

All the way home, as she calmed down, the bag sat in her lap. I want to open it on the train, Rox thought mischievously. Imagine what the other people would think if I just slid it out and nonchalantly unfolded it and started reading. But she kept the newspaper in the bag, all the way home, and even took care to hang up her coat, sort through her mail, and make a cup of tea before she sat down and opened the bag.

The newspaper was revealing, in many ways. Rox read it all, literally, from cover to cover, amazed at the contents. Why, there were really hundreds, maybe thousands of men who wanted to be dominated by women! To be made to dress in silly clothes and do humiliating things, like licking boots or cleaning things with their mouths. And the ads! "Willing, able sissy maid seeks mistress to serve" and "Submissive gent wants to be your private servant" and "Naughty boy seeks corporal chastisement." There were even ads from the women, asking for some things that Rox had to imagine. Like, what exactly was a toilet slave? Did he clean them, or was he one? Was that the scene with the bathtub?

As she scanned the ads and drank her tea, she kept coming back to one in particular.

"Novice servitor seeks goddess. Will perform all chores and domestic duties. Ask only to be permitted into your presence and to receive the reward of a job well done. Use me to entertain your friends. Call: 212-."

Enterprising guy, Rox thought, circling the ad. He puts a phone number instead of a PO box. PO boxes take so long sometimes.

She looked around her house for a moment, and then back at the ad. Between her hours at work, and out with the girls, and at the gym and everything else, her home was a mess. It could definitely use some sprucing up, maybe some vacuuming, a little dusting...and it would definitely be a hoot to see some guy prancing around in silky nothings, calling her mistress or something. If she didn't like it, she could just not invite him back. And, if he was cute, she could get some more fun out of it.

It took almost an hour before she dialed the number, and listened to the answering machine message. The guy's voice sounded nice, his message was polite, but general. She said, into the machine, "This is in response to your personal ad in MM. Be available at this number tomorrow at nine AM." She giggled when she hung up. God, she thought, I hope that sounds dominant enough! She reread some parts of the newspaper again, and masturbated furiously before going to sleep. Visions of dancing boys in diaphanous pajamas wove their way into her dreams.

On Saturday morning, at 9:05, she dialed the number again, a few notes scrawled on a piece of paper in front of her. This time, the phone was picked up.

"Hello?" The man's voice was slightly high-pitched, as though he were nervous.

"Is this the man who placed the ad in MM?" Roxanne asked, in as firm as voice as she could manage.

"Uh, yes, yes ma'am! May I ask your name, please, ma'am?"

"Not before you give me yours, worm!" Roxanne got the impression that some of them liked to be called worm. The gasp on the other side of the phone seemed to confirm that.

"Please, Mistress, if I am permitted a name, um, I'm Scott."

Roxanne grilled the man for a few minutes, glancing at her notes and making more. Soon, she had his full name, his address, his birthday and where he worked. When he asked her why, she told him to just answer questions and keep his own to himself. In reality, she now felt more comfortable having a strange man coming over to see her.

"If I allow you to come and perform domestic chores for me, what can I expect? Are you good at anything?" She asked, unsure of where to go from there. He seemed eager to answer.

"Oh, I'm a very good houseboy, Mistress, very clean. I can also cook, and do the laundry, and I would love to have the honor of giving you a foot massage, if you like, or I can give you a manicure..." his voice fairly bubbled, as though no one had ever asked him what he could do before. "And I can type, if you need a secretary, and I am very willing to learn new skills, Mistress. For your pleasure, I can take some pain, or you may abuse me in various ways, or you can humiliate me in front of your friends. I can serve tea..."

Ah! That was familiar, at least. Roxanne interrupted, and asked, "Do you have a maid's costume?"

"Oh, yes ma'am!"

"And are you available today?"

"Yes Mistress! Oh, yes!"

Roxanne kept silent for a moment, and then threw the last of her cautious fears to the wind. She gave him her address, and told him to be there by noon. With exuberant thanks, he promised to be there, and she put the phone down with a feeling of excited anticipation. She was really getting one! But in her nervousness and glee, she realized that she had totally forgotten to ask him what he looked like. Hoping that he wasn't a real dog, she went into her bedroom to pick out something to wear for the occasion.

Her doorbell rang at exactly noon, and she drew herself up to meet her "experiment." She threw open the door with a dramatic (and, she hoped) dominant gesture, and prayed one last time that her maid-to-be wasn't a dog.

What stood on her front steps, if he had been a dog, would have been a cocker spaniel. From behind silver rimmed glasses, large brown eyes looked up into hers, framed by masses of curly light brown hair. He was standing one step down from the top, so he had to look up at her, and clutched in his arms was a knapsack. He was, Rox thought, as cute as a puppy. She smiled involuntarily, and then caught herself and tried to look stern again.

"Scott?" she asked.

"Yes, ma'am," he replied, nodding.

She continued to look at him for a moment. He looked a little skinny, but anything could have been hidden under the down jacket and heavy wool scarf he wore. Then, she stepped back, indicating that he should follow her.

"Oh, thank you, ma'am," he said, as he came through the door, "thank you so much for letting me have this opportunity to please you and serve you. I promise, you'll never find another houseboy as eager to serve as I am! I can't thank you enough..."

"Shut up!" Roxanne surprised herself with the force behind her order. But a flush of pleasure swept through her body when Scott immediately shut his mouth, and bowed his head. "Haven't you ever heard of speaking when you're spoken to?"

In her hallway, Scott had gained a few inches, and was now taller than she was. But his bowed head seemed to keep things a little more equal. She studied him for another second, and then pointed at the coatrack. "Hang up your coat, and come into my living room. Let's see what you got. I haven't got all day!"

To her glee, Scott almost ripped the coat and scarf off, and then neatly hung them up. He hurriedly picked up his knapsack and stumbled into her living room, to stand in what she thought seemed to be a very submissive way, in the center of the room. He had his hands behind his back, and his head was lowered again. She walked casually in, and stood in front of him for a second, before sitting regally in her favorite chair.

"OK, Scotty, look at me," she said. He looked up. "I called you because, um, I'm in need of a domestic servant. I want you to take care of some chores that I...that my last servant...neglected. And for which I had to send him away." She added to the tale with relish. "I like to see a man doing some meaningful work for a change. Don't you agree?"

"Oh, yes, ma'am!" He nodded, with that same puppydog eagerness. She found herself wanting to grin again, and held it back.

"So...let's get some ground rules. My name is Roxanne, but you will call me...Mistress. You'll never speak unless I speak to you, and you'll obey me in every way, and expect nothing from me. Got it?"

"Yes, Mistress!"

"Well, then, get out of those clothes and let's see what you brought!" Roxanne sat back, and coached the young man as he undressed. "No, you idiot, slowly! Let me see you do it like a Chippendale's guy. That's it, ease it up over your chest. Show off for me!"

Blushing, Scott slowly pulled his sweater over his head, exposing a flat stomach and a hairless chest. He still had some tan left, and all in all, Roxanne liked what she saw. She continued to encourage him as he unfastened his slacks and kicked off his shoes. Finally, he stood before her clad in a pair of black bikini underwear and his glasses, and Roxanne couldn't help but notice that there was definitely some interest straining the seams of those bikini shorts.

"Well? What are you waiting for, Scotty?" She liked the sound of that nickname. It suited him. "Get into your uniform."

He drew a tangle of black and white lace from the knapsack and sorted out the pieces. A teddy-like garment went around his torso and tied with a row of bows up the back, and a lacy collar went around his neck. Now as red as a summer tomato, he shook out what looked like a pair of crotchless panties and held them up for a moment, as though he was unsure about them.

"Real cute, Scotty. You should have put them on first," Rox said, with a giggle. "Get out of those boy shorts and put those on."

He bent over to work the bikini shorts down his legs, and she saw his cock, stiff as the proverbial board, slap against his thigh. As soon as he was free of the bikinis, he slipped his legs into the panties and slid them up around his hips, hiding his manhood again, this time even less successfully. Three little red bows kept the split crotch partly closed. Then, a little skirt with a white apron was tied around his waist.

He stood before her in a French maid costume, not nearly as pretty or authentic as the one in the movie, but damn close. His bare feet looked silly, though, and she pointed at them. He reached back into his pack and pulled out a pair of black pumps, and slipped into them.

"Much better." Rox stood and walked around him, and then reached out to cup one ass cheek in her hand. He trembled at her touch and gave a slight moan, and she grinned. "OK, Scotty, let's put you to work!"

Rox took the man on a tour of her house, showing him the rooms that had to be done, and where the cleaning supplies were. Then, she immediately put him to work. In no time at all, he had made her bed and gathered up her laundry, and took it down to the basement where her washer and dryer were. While she sat in the living room and tried to read the paper, he washed up what was in her sink, and started cleaning her kitchen counters and shelves.

She loved to see him walk through the halls, his butt poking out of that skimpy costume, the apron flapping against his crotch. He walked a little funny, probably because of the shoes, but she liked that too. When he came into the living room to dust, she made him bend over a lot, to get some imaginary dust that he had missed. Whenever he did, his cock and balls were clearly outlined against the sheer fabric of his panties, and the knowledge that she was looking at him made him delightfully hot and bothered. By the time he was finished with the living room, she could see sweat gathering in the small of his back.

Before he went on to another room, he came to her and knelt at her feet. She didn't know what to do at first, but then remembered that she had told him not to speak unless she spoke to him first.

I wish all men were like this, she noted to herself.

"What is it, Scotty?"

"Please, Mistress, may I be permitted to make you some tea?"

"Sure...I mean, yes, slave, you may!" Roxanne stopped him from rising on an inspiration. "But I want to see you crawl all the way to the kitchen. Go."

He turned and obediently crawled out of the room and down the hall. Roxanne watched him leave and felt the stirrings of pleasure in her body. I don't believe it, she thought, sitting back in the chair. This is really getting me hot! I wonder what else I can make him do?

By the time he came back with the steaming tea, she had a few ideas. She sent him again, on his knees, to put the laundry in the dryer, and then when he came back, she presented him with an old toothbrush.

"Time to do the bathroom floor," she announced, her eyes glittering. He gulped, but then crawled off to the bathroom, filled a shallow basin with hot water and detergent, and began to earnestly scrub the tiles with that little toothbrush. She watched him for a while, nearly doubled up on the floor, and coached him again.

"Not so light! I want you to get that clean, not wet! And don't miss the corners!" The more she scolded him, the harder he seemed to work, but there was a more clumsy edge to what he did, as well. Maybe I better leave him alone. He works better without me standing here, Rox thought for a moment. Then, she laughed at what she was thinking. Of course he wants me here, she reminded herself. This is part of his fantasy. So let's get into this stuff!

"You work is pathetic," she began, standing over him as he scrubbed. "You clearly need some incentive." She took a quick gaze around the room and plucked a washcloth off her towel rack. She dipped it into his basin, wrung it out, and quickly coiled it into snake. While he quivered on the tile floor, she snapped the wet towel across the back of his thighs, remembering the feel from Girl Scout camp. Apparently, it had the same effect on grown men. He yelped, and cried out, "Forgive me, Mistress, I'll do better!"

"Well, don't just say so! Show me!" She snapped the towel at him again, and he yelped again, but bent back to his task.

By the time he was finally finished with the floor, there was still the tub, sink and bowl to do. By the time she let him out of the bathroom, the backs of his legs were pink with red stripes up and down his thighs. The water had soaked through his thin panties, and they adhered to his skin in a way Roxanne thought was very erotic. She had not driven him to tears, certainly, but the look on his face when she finally let him crawl out was one of sheer gratitude.

She was startled when he dipped his head to the floor and thankfully kissed her feet, one after the other. Not knowing what to say, she began to walk back to her living room. "Go and get the laundry, Scotty. I'm not finished with you yet."

She heard his "Yes Mistress!" behind her, but didn't look back. When she sat down in her favorite chair again, she had a few things to think about.

What am I going to do with him now, she wondered. I don't want to let him fuck me. He's too cute to send away and never see again. He's real hot in that getup...I wonder if he dances? She imagined him in a harem costume, wiggling his little butt around the living room to sexy music, and the image was so hot, she almost groaned out loud. And she could just imagine having some of the girls over for lunch one Saturday and having him wait on them. They'd laugh, but he'd get harder every time they laughed, and that would be really cute to watch.

God, you can be nasty, Rox chided herself with a giggle. But who's getting hurt? He loves it, and it turns me on! But that reminded her of her predicament. Now, she was all turned on with no one to fuck, to coin a phrase. She thought about her options for a while, and then realized that Scott was gone longer than he should have been. She almost called out loud for him, but clanged her mind and as quietly as possible, tiptoed down the stairs.

Scott was standing by her dryer, a basket of clothing at his feet. But he was holding one pair of her newly clean and dried panties up to his face, and rubbing them against his mouth and cheeks. She stood on the stairs, surprised, for a moment, and then got angry. Then, as quickly as the anger came, it was replaced by an almost nasty delight.

"Is that the way you do laundry?" she purred, leaning over the banister.

He was so shocked, he dropped the panties before he turned to face her. The look of surprise on his face would have been totally comical if there hadn't been an edge of fear in it as well. But that fear made Roxanne's mouth go dry in excitement, and she licked her lips thoughtfully.

"I'm sorry, Mistress, I'm sorry! I didn't...I wasn't..." He moaned and dropped to his knees, picking up the panties and putting them carefully in the basket. "I was just coming upstairs, really, and I, I..."

"You got distracted." Roxanne walked down the rest of the staircase and stood in front of him. "Well, I don't remember telling you that you could do anything like that. Did I?"

"No, Mistress, you didn't, and I was wrong. Please, I admit I was wrong! Please don't punish me very much, Mistress, even though I deserve it, I do..."

"You talk too much!" Roxanne retrieved the panties from the basket. She looked around, found the measuring cup for her liquid detergent and wiped it dry with the panties. Then, she balled them up into a silky little ball, now wet with soap, and stuffed them into his mouth. He took the stuffing submissively, and then made a choking sound as he tasted the soap. "That's for using your mouth in a way I don't appreciate," Rox said, looking around again. She found the canvas bag of clothespins that she brought down here when summer was over and spilled a few of them out on top of the washer.

He made a sound behind his makeshift gag, and she knew she had made another good guess. She tugged the top part of his costume down and placed a clothespin on each of his nipples, and he squirmed. Then, she dragged him to a standing position, and pointed at his crotch.

"Get it out, Scotty," she said, sternly. He made his trembling fingers untie the little ribbons, and his cock almost sprang out from between the lacy edges of the slit. She examined it for a moment, and then carefully attached three more clothespins to the loose flesh behind his cockhead, hearing little squeaks of pain at each one.

"Now, lets get upstairs," Roxanne said, looking around one more time. "You've got to fold and put away the rest of this laundry before those pins come off. And just to remind you to keep working and not to get distracted..." She found a paint stirrer on her utility shelf that would do... "we'll use this." She swatted it against her hand, and then aimed it at his thighs. "Get going, slave!"

He lifted the basket and mounted the stairs, and made a thousand little cries as she kept up a constant barrage of swats and stinging slaps with the paint stirrer, all along his legs and his ass. He folded the laundry and put it away under her direction, and under the continuing series of spanks and whacks that made the pink color on his legs turn red. She occasionally, gently, hit exposed and pinned cock from time to time, whenever she felt he needed some encouragement to be faster.

And with every swing and connection, her own heat increased. Maybe it was the power, maybe it was the feeling that she was totally in control, but whatever it was, she was wet and ready to come. By the time he was finished, and she decided to get the clothespins off, she finally realized how she was going to take care of that personal itch.

She sent him into the living room, and told him to wait for her, lying on his back in the middle of the floor. Then, she went into her bedroom dresser and took out a favorite toy. And then, she changed some of her clothing.

He was lying on the carpet as she directed, the clothespins sticking up off his body. She took them off quickly, and watched him as he shook and jerked on the floor. He reacted to the ones on his cock like they were punches to his belly, his knees coming up and his face twisting in pain. As the blood rushed back to his nipples, they colored a deep red, almost as red as his ass. She watched him for a moment and said, "I guess you're not going to be playing with my laundry anymore." Then, she pulled his gag out.

He coughed and licked his lips and sputtered, "No, Mistress, I promise, never again! Thank you for correcting me..."

"You know, you still talk too much." With a triumphal gesture, she showed him what she brought with her. It was a plain, cock-shaped vibrator, with the speed attachment at the base. His eyes went wide as she displayed it to him, because although it was cock-shaped, it was a size not normally found in mortal men. She realized that he thought she was going to fuck him with it.

"Oh no, Scotty, this isn't for you!" She chuckled, and turned it over in her hands. "It's for me. You get to hold it." She pointed the head toward his mouth. "Lick it for me, Scotty. Get it nice and wet." She pulled his glasses off and put them aside. His eyes were wide with astonishment and pleasure.

He extended his tongue and lapped at the pleasure dong, wetting the thing from tip to base, until Rox had enough of watching him. "Put your hands under your back," she ordered, and when he did, she turned the vibrator on.

"It gets faster when you turn this dial down here, Scotty. So when I want it faster, you better think of a way to make it go faster, OK?" She demonstrated the dial with her fingers.

"But, Mistress, how...if my hands are behind my back, how can I..."

Quickly and smoothly, Rox upended the vibrator and stuck the base into Scott's open mouth. He quickly closed his lips around it, as she lifted her skirt to show that she had already taken her panties off. His eyes were wide as saucers as she settled carefully down over the vibrating dong, and therefore over his face.

The vibrations made his teeth and mouth ache, but her thighs on either side of his head and the scent and feel of her moisture drove him happily insane. In the dim light still available under her skirt, he could just see the outlines of her cunt as she slid gently up and down the pole that was anchored in his mouth. He still tasted the faint remains of soap on his tongue, but the new sensations were far more encompassing. He struggled to keep his hands behind his back.

Roxanne, as her favorite vibrator stretched and filled her, was in heaven. She had mounted him facing Scott's body, and she could see the erotic little dance his cock was performing, partly because of Scott's arousal, and partly because of the delicious squirming he was doing, keeping his hands behind his back and trying not to thrust with his hips. She moved carefully up and down, finding out how strongly he was holding the toy, and then called out, "Faster, slave!"

Scott fumbled for a moment and almost lost his grip on the vibrator, but then found that little dial with his tongue. He pushed against it as hard as he could and was gratified and horrified when the vibrations increased. For even as it made him happy to be able to do it, the vibrations increased inside his head as well, and made his ears tingle so much that it tickled. But then, above him, Roxanne began to more faster herself, and he felt her fingers clutch at his sore nipples. Despite the discomfort he was in, his hips moved involuntarily in response to his intense pleasure.

Roxanne began to feel the stirrings of orgasm almost as soon as Scott managed to get that vibrator really humming. She hadn't expected him to be able to do that! She figured that she would get off, and punish him a little more. Now, the unexpected surge of power nearly had her at her peak, and she ground her pussy down around his face. "Faster, slave, faster!" she cried out, twisting his nipples madly. She saw his cock jump and almost quiver, and then that unexpected surge of power and energy struck her again, and she allowed it to sweep her away.

"Yes! Yes! Come on, yes!" She twisted and then clamped tightly around the vibrating cock and it touched her in just the right way, like it always did, and she came, with all the power and strength that was missing whenever she had her previous relations with disappointing men from the mundane side of life. She gasped and moaned in ways no other lover had ever heard, and that this particular man could only hear dimly. She eased her way off the pleasure prick with a feeling of satisfaction that permeated her entire body, and sat down on the floor, plucking the vibrator out of Scott's mouth as she did so. He was gasping himself, and when his mouth closed, he moaned and whined like an animal in pain. She glanced at his cock, standing at attention for her, and then smiled.

"Go ahead," she said, pointing at it. "You earned it. Shoot for me."

His hands came from behind his back and his right fist closed over his rampant cock so fast she had to smile. It took only three hard pumps for him to relieve that almost painful hard-on, and his come spurted out generously, splattering his thighs and part of the carpet, while his body shook and trembled in release. He panted his exhaustion, and in between breaths, said, "Thank you, thank you Mistress...please, I have...something to tell you..."

"Yes?"

"I...I never really DID this before...I hope I wasn't too clumsy...you're so good...please don't send me away forever..."

She gazed at him for a long moment. "You should have told me that before," she said, coldly, regaining her power. "We're going to have to do something about that mouth of yours. If you're not talking too much, you're withholding information."

She got up and smoothed her skirt down.

"Clean up this mess," she pointed to the wet spots on the rug. "With that mouth of yours."

He turned over and began to lick at the carpet.

"Oh, I might keep you for a while," Roxanne said, picking up her vibrator. "But you're going to need some serious training.

"Yes, Mistress!"

Chapter Six:
Two for the Price of One

Eve and Nicole had found each other through the Classifieds. More specifically, Nicole answered Eve's ad for "Roommate wanted to share spacious, sunny loft." That Eve hadn't exactly found a spacious and sunny loft had not stopped her from placing the ad. She knew that two people would be better at finding a rental anyway.

There is little privacy in a loft. The one they finally found had a wonderful loft bed, just large enough for one, and they played poker for it. The space under it, which was draped with curtains, would go to the loser. When the game was over, Eve found herself the mistress of that raised platform, for which she immediately bought a sturdy pine ladder. She liked to sit on the edge of the platform and let her long legs dangle. From that perch, she could see the entire space quite easily, except for Nicole's little "room" beneath her.

Nicole hung translucent draperies of different colors, so that entering her sleeping space required a dramatic sweeping of diaphanous curtains aside. The two young women became friends easily, and due to the nature of living in a loft, they rapidly learned to share a lot of things. All the furniture except for Nicole's wooden chest and Eve's mirrored wardrobe was "theirs." They had one TV, one stereo, one microwave...why have two of everything, they argued as they shopped together. If they decided to move apart, they would arrange the details according to circumstances. In the meantime, two could indeed live as cheaply as one. They shared the grocery bill, and the electric bill and the telephone bill. They shared toothpaste and shampoo and umbrellas. They often shared late night take-out dinners.

And one of the things they occasionally shared was men.

It had started out with Eve's complaining one night.

"I can't stand that jive-ass idiot!" she had exclaimed, slamming the phone down. "This time he's gone too far. That's, it, I'm through. If he falls off the face of the earth, I'll throw a party to celebrate!"

"Man troubles?" Nicole guessed. Eve glared at her and then started ticking items off on her fingers.

"First, he makes a date and cancels at the last minute because he has a headache! Then, he makes another date, but cancels because he had some old college buddy in from outa town. Then, we finally make it out, and he forgets to bring his wallet, and guess who has to spring for everything until he can pay me back? And now, he 'forgot' that we were supposed to see the show at the Ritz tonight, so of course, he doesn't have the tickets, do I wanna see a movie? Save me from men!" She finished with a gesture that was very unladylike, and Nicole gave her a sympathetic look.

"Hey, so, he's a jerk. Dump him. But all men aren't that way. Doug is nice," she said, defending her boyfriend. "And what's more, in case you forgot, he's coming over here tonight. And we do have an agreement?"

Eve's face fell from anger to distress. "Oh, shit, I'm sorry...aw, no, you're going to make me leave?" Her voice scaled up to a slight whine, her eyes pleading for a break.

They had an agreement. They tried to schedule their dates (especially ones which could end up very late dates, or overnighters) so that they each had a certain amount of privacy in the loft before the other one would have to come home. So far, they had been successful, and this was their first serious conflict.

"Oh, come on, Eve!" Nicole replied. "Can't you go to a movie by yourself? I mean, its just for a while!"

"OK, OK, I'll find something," Nicole said glumly. "And I'm sure I'll have a great time, drowning myself in popcorn while you and your scrawny white studling ball your way across the floor." She stuck her tongue out in impotent fury.

Nicole made a dismissive gesture at Eve's assessment of her boyfriend. "You're just jealous because you won't get any tonight. And besides, Doug is NOT scrawny...where it counts!" She giggled as Eve snatched up the newspaper and began flipping through the pages to find the movie section. "In fact, for what I have in mind for him tonight, he's just right..." She stopped talking suddenly, her eyes taking on an excited gleam, as an idea began to form in her mind. Eve sullenly continued to look for a movie. It took her almost a minute to look up at Nicole's shining eyes and predatory grin, and Eve was instantly suspicious.

"What do you have in mind?" she demanded, putting the paper down. "I don't like it whenever you get that look in your eye."

"I just got a great idea!" Nicole jumped up and took Eve by the arm. "Don't go! Stay! And we'll both have him!"

"What? Are you out of your mind?" Eve laughed. "What makes you think I'd want a piece of his undernourished butt? And what makes you think you can plan this without asking him?"

"It's not his butt you'd be interested in," Nicole said with a grin. "And besides, isn't that every guy's fantasy? To be able to fuck two hot babes at a time? He'll go for it like a cat to tuna, you'll see! And we'll have a ball!" She giggled uncontrollably at her own pun. "We'll have two!"

Eve couldn't help but laugh with her. And it only took a few more minutes to convince her to stay and see how Doug took to the suggestion.

Nicole had been absolutely correct. Not only did Doug jump at the opportunity, but he performed with what they both agreed was an exceptional attitude toward pleasing them both. They eventually exhausted him, and that was the start of a series of shared adventures with assorted men who met their basic criteria. One, he had to look decent. Two, he had to be willing to go along with whatever they wanted. And three, he had to be convenient. No involvements, no marriages, no "pals" he wanted to invite in, no drugs...nothing that could distract him or them once they got together. Oddly, finding men who fit those criteria was not as easy as they once thought, but they had a selective list of past experiences that made good memories.

And then, Tony moved into their building.

Tony lived one flight up from them. They saw him leave in the morning, wearing nice suits and carrying a briefcase. They saw him dash home and out again with a gym bag, and they saw him running, his muscled legs pumping like oiled pistons. He was slightly dark skinned, just a little darker than olive, and had longish black hair that curled when he sweated. Both women agreed that he was indeed, very studly.

Eve was the first one to meet him, on her way to the laundry room. They chatted politely in the elevator, and exchanged professions. That evening, she had excitedly told Nicole that Tony 1) lived alone, and 2) was an investment analyst. On that night, they put him on their prospectives list.

That had been over three months ago. Since then, they had both met Tony on a number of occasions, in the halls, in the laundry room, at the tenants' meeting. Nicole invited him over for coffee one weekend, but as luck had it, the stock market took a sudden downward trend, and he had to do client work. Both women agreed that the financial world could be VERY inconvenient to romance.

And during their casual (albeit brief) meetings with Tony, it was Eve who discovered something she thought was very odd about him.

"Did you ever notice how polite he is?" she asked Nicole one night, as they were plotting and fantasizing. "I mean to women. In general."

"Hmm, yeah, I did. Never thought about it though," Nicole said, chewing on the end of a pencil. "Oh no! You don't think he's gay, do you?" she asked with sudden insight.

"No...no, I don't think so," Eve responded. "I mean, if he was gay, he'd have friends over, don't you think? And I've never seen a man coming to visit him. No, I think its something else."

"Oh yeah? What? A conscientious mother?"

"No, stupid. I think he's into S&M."

"What?!"

"Really! You know my friend Rica?" Nicole had met the slight woman at a party Eve took her to. She nodded, remembering.

"Rica's into all that stuff. She gets guys to pay her loads of money to step on them and call them names and all this shit. She told me some stories, girl...you wouldn't believe what some guys like done to them!" Eve began to think. "There was this one old white guy she told me about, he liked to have big things shoved up his..."

"Hey, hey, wait a minute there," Nicole interrupted. "What does that have to do with Tony?"

"Oh! Well, Rica says that one way to know that a guy is into that stuff is how polite he treats women. And that a lot of guys signal their interest that way, and hope that some babe recognizes it and takes over."

Nicole looked suspicious. "That sounds very, very iffy, my dear. How about the simple possibility that he was raised right?"

"What, in the 90's?" Eve laughed. "Honey, no one was raised right! I bet he just wants a woman to take over for him. Or two women," she added significantly.

Nicole refused to budge. "I think he's gay," she said firmly. "So let's take another look at...Carlos."

"Oh, his hair is too long!"

"Maybe his dick is too!"

They argued long into the night, and got up early to watch Tony go off to work.

Then, the movie came out.

And then, they found themselves standing in front of their building, gazing up at the lights that showed that Tony was home.

"OK, are we ready for this?" Eve asked, clapping Nicole on the shoulder.

"As ready as we'll ever be," Nicole said, now resolute. They kissed once for luck and got into the elevator. They stopped at home first, turned up the heat, and changed clothes. Eve got out the box of scarves and belts she had put together earlier, and placed it by their couch, on the floor. Nicole took out the canister that held their shared condoms and lube, and placed the bottle of lube in a towel over the radiator plate to warm them both. (She hated cool lube.) Then, she dug the toy they called their "secret weapon" out of its protective bag and dropped it into the canister with the condoms.

She gave a low wolf whistle as Eve climbed down from her loft bed. Eve had changed into a silky red wraparound dress that caressed her body and draped like a thin layer of strawberry glaze over creamy milk chocolate. Eve winked at the recognition and slipped into high heeled shoes, turning and letting the dress flare out around her thighs.

"Very nice," Nicole commented, getting up from her toy planting. "Very convenient too. What do you think?" She raised her arms to show off her own outfit, a plain black strapless minidress that barely covered the straps of her garter belt. Her legs were sheathed in sheer black stockings, and there were black and silver bracelets around each wrist. Some of the bracelets were leather, with little silver studs, and there was a matching one around her right ankle.

"Where...and when...did you get those?" Eve exclaimed, pointing.

Nicole smiled, and said, "Last week. In the village. I figured if you're right, he'd like them. Besides, I think they look pretty cool."

"U-huh!" Eve nodded seriously and then giggled. "Let's go pull this off, girlfriend."

When Tony opened the door, his eyes widened in a way that at last made Nicole believe, once and for all, that he was appreciative of female companionship. He recovered immediately, and smiled.

"Hey, good evening, neighbors," he said cheerfully. "What can I do for you lovely ladies tonight? Isn't it a little late for borrowing sugar?"

Nicole leaned forward a little, bracing herself lightly inside the door jamb. "Sugar isn't exactly what we were looking for...sugar." She fairly purred at him. He drew himself back for a moment, as if unsure he had heard her right. But there was no mistaking the deliberate way she allowed her eyes to scan his body, and linger over his crotch. He dry swallowed and looked at Eve.

Eve licked her lips and was immediately gratified to actually see a stirring underneath the soft pair of gym shorts Tony was wearing. His feet were bare, and a sweatshirt with the sleeves artfully cut off was the only other garment he was wearing. Eve liked jocks.

She winked at him and said, "We were wondering if you might be open to a proposition, Tony...Are you busy tonight?"

"Busy? Uh, no, not really...would you like to come in?" He took a half step back and swept his arm inward. "I'm sorry, the place is a mess...I can put on some coffee...tea?"

Nicole was already shaking her head. "No, I don't think this will take long," she said, shifting herself against the doorway. "Let's just say we have an offer for you. Wanna hear it?"

"Sure!" Tony stood, expectantly.

Eve leaned in toward him. "Let's say you come with us back to our place and we use and abuse you in any way our evil hearts desire."

Tony blinked, shook his head for a moment, and then looked back and forth between the two women who were seductively lounging in his doorway. The little recorder in his head played back Eve's words, and he looked at the two women again.

"You serious?" he finally asked, looking around. "This isn't a joke?"

Nicole stood up straight in anger. "Of course it's not a joke, dummy! We're offering you the chance of a lifetime! But if you want to be in the game, you gotta play by our rules. Now are you coming, or not?"

Eve was almost startled by her friend's vehemence. Nicole was always the one who seemed to lengthen negotiations, and she never wanted to rush things, at least not like this. But Tony responded by reaching inside his apartment, picking up his keys and stepping outside the doorway to join them, standing in the hallway in his bare feet.

"I'm in," he said simply. "Lead me where you will, ladies."

"Well..." Nicole said, with a slight pause. "That's more like it!"

"Good attitude," agreed Eve, with a muffled giggle. She grabbed Tony's hand and began to pull him to the stairs. "Come on, stud. Let's get this show on the road!"

Tony allowed himself to be pulled, laughing, into the girls' apartment. There, he was divested of his keys. ("For safekeeping," Eve promised.) He stood in the middle of their loft, comfortable in the rising heat, a smile on his dark, handsome face. Eve and Nicole dropped glances at each other, and they circled him, giving him what Nicole often called "the cruise of death." After a minute of that close and critical scrutiny, Tony began to fidget.

"Well," he finally asked, spreading his hands out. "What's next, girls?"

"Um," began Eve, glancing at Nicole.

Nicole took the lead and said, firmly, "First, you stop calling us 'girls.' It doesn't sound respectful." Eve nodded in agreement, and Nicole went on. "Next, you take off that top and show us what you've got."

Tony grinned and hooked his hands at the waist of his shirt, lifting it up smoothly over his head. His chest was everything the two women hoped it would be, pumped up and broad, with just a line of dark, curly hair running down the center, to flare at the waistband of his gym shorts. Nicole actually licked her lips in anticipation of what would be revealed when the shorts came off, but Eve spoke up first.

"OK, Tony, now, you have to make yourself presentable for us!" He looked in her direction with a question in his eyes, and she pointed at the bathroom door. "Go take a shower, and scrub yourself all over. And when you get back, you can lose the shorts."

"But..." he started to protest, and she interrupted him imperiously.

"No buts, baby! You agreed to play by our rules, remember?" Her flashing eyes dared him to disagree. And to her delight, he only smiled, and executed a small mock bow in her direction. Then, doing the same to Nicole, he slung the shirt over one shoulder and strode into the bathroom, where the two women soon heard the shower running.

"I don't believe this!" Nicole said, softly, her pleasure already building. "This is so hot! I don't believe this is working!"

"I told you, didn't I?" Eve reminded her, smoothing down her skirt. "Now come on, let's set the scene, girl, before he gets out."

They hurriedly went through the loft, arranging furniture and supplies, and lighting candles so that they could lower the lights. By the time the sound of running water halted, they had created a scene of elegant and spacious invitation. Candles lined the windows and glowed from darkened corners. The curtains around Nicole's sleeping space were drawn back, and the low coffee table was pulled closer to the windows, where it held more candles, the can of toys, and the piles of silken scarves and rolled belts they had brought out earlier.

Tony stepped out of the bathroom, his wet hair curled tightly around his head, and a towel wrapped around his narrow waist. He was still smiling, or so it seemed. He walked over to the candlelit corner of the room, where the two women waited for him.

"What's your pleasure, girls?" he asked, and then grinned mischievously.

"Oh, it's still girls, is it?" Nicole noted, putting one hand on her hip. "We'll change that...boy." She turned toward the coffee table and picked up one of her old belts. "Drop that towel, and let's see what you REALLY got, Tony-baby."

He unknotted the corner and let the towel drop, and exposed a rampant cock, extremely ready for action. It thrust out and up between his legs, the tight curly hair at its base still moist from the shower. Nicole took one look at it and then at Eve, who pursed her lips appreciatively.

"That's a nice piece of goods you got there," Eve admitted, moving closer. "But you know, it's all in the way you use it."

"Use me," Tony offered, "and you'll find out whether I'm worth it."

Nicole shook her head. "This guy is unbelievable! He's too arrogant for a slave." She looked at him, at his readiness, and again at the belt in her hands, and then made her decision. "You have to be punished first, sweet-cheeks." If he was disappointed, his eyes or his cock failed to show it. She pointed at the loft bed ladder. "Get yourself up against that thing. Put your hands up over your head! Yeah, like that. C'mon, Eve, give me a hand. Let's tie this arrogant stud all the way up!"

Giggling, the two women maneuvered Tony to the ladder, where they used the scarves to tie his wrists, forearms (Nicole paused to run one finger admiringly along the line of his bicep), knees and ankles to the frame and rungs. Soon, he looked like a handsome package of flesh, neatly wrapped up and ready to be presented.

Nicole picked up the belt again. "You know what this is for, Tony, right?" When he didn't answer, she swung it, hard, against his cheeks, making a loud "crack!" sound that made both women startle. Tony hissed once and flinched. "Uh..." Nicole lost her voice suddenly, afraid of the sound and effect of what she was doing.

Immediately, Eve stepped in and smacked Tony on one cheek with her palm. He groaned and shifted backward in his bonds, and the two women nodded to each other.

"It's to teach you respect," Eve said, smacking him again. She stepped back and let Nicole take another swing, a little softer this time. And so they continued, alternating between Eve's fast and steady hand-spanking, and the harsh punctuation of Nicole's belt swinging, which improved as they went along.

Tony jerked against his bonds from time to time, his body twisting attractively against the ladder. Eve found herself liking the feeling of impact she was delivering, and took a few extra seconds with each smack to give his buttocks a tight squeeze. Finally, when they thought he had enough, she dipped her hand in between his spread legs and found the first disappointing thing about him.

Oh!" She said, drawing back. "He lost the boner."

"What do you expect?" Tony gasped, turning his head. He had taken the punishment rather stoically, making no sounds but sighs and an occasional groan. "It's kind of hard to keep one of those when you're having your butt beat on." But even through his complaint, Eve could see an element of enjoyment. His eyes glittered as he spoke.

She put on a stern look. "Well, there's only one solution for that. Let's turn him around, Nicole!"

In a few minutes, the move was completed, and Tony had his back to the ladder, his arms and legs tied again to the frame. The two women came up close to him, and ran their fingers across his body, playing with the sparse hair on his chest, tweaking his nipples, and tracing patterns across his body. He moaned, gasped in ticklish laughter, and strained against his bonds again, as their fingers played closer and closer to his cock, fully limp just a moment ago, and now coming back to interest and life.

After exchanging glances and making a mental count, Nicole and Eve brought their mouths up to his nipples, where they engulfed them and began to lick, nibble, suck and chew. The sight of the two of them and the delightful sensations they sent through his body made Tony almost lurch against the scarves holding him prisoner. His knees bent slightly and his hips thrust at nothing, banging his sore ass against the ladder.

"Oh, God, oh, Jesus," he hissed, his head leaning back. "I can't stand it! Let me go, I need to get my arms around you!"

Nicole laughed as she let go of his nipple with a slurp. "Not yet, stud. We're not finished tasting you!" She ran her tongue down his chest and flicked it in and out of his belly button, and giggled as his cock seemed to inch its way further up. She looked up at Eve, still playing with his chest, and said, dramatically, "I gotta have this!" and then she swept her hot mouth over his straining manhood.

Tony jerked in his bonds like he had been electrocuted. "Oh, yeah!" was all he managed to get out in between gasps. His hands closed into fists, but Eve's colorful scarves and Nicole's tight knots held him to the sturdy ladder. He tried to thrust at Nicole's engulfing mouth, but found that she easily moved back to control his depth (and her pleasure), and his return against the ladder's plain rungs was invariably harsh against his recently beaten ass cheeks.

"Come on, baby, just a little deeper," he pleaded, squirming. "It's so nice...you're so good...let me go, and we'll do it right..."

"This is right for me, stud," Nicole said, drawing her mouth away. "This way, I get to control how much I want...and when." She licked the tip, and looked up at him. Then, she turned to Eve. "You know, Eve, it's not right that he should be able to look at me while I'm playing with his dick. You wanna do something about it?"

"Sure thing, honey," Eve replied, going to the side to fetch another scarf. "Say good night, little boy, mama's pulling down the shades!"

"Oh, no, please...don't blindfold me! No, I mean it!" Tony turned back and forth between the women. "Please! I won't look...I mean, I won't look down! You're so beautiful, how can I want to lose the sight of you? I won't call you girls...I'll only look where you tell me!"

"Talks a lot," commented Eve, as she tied the scarf around his eyes.

"We can gag you too," said her friend, examining Tony's glistening erection. The blindfold did not seem to affect his arousal. She immediately leaned forward to take his succulent flesh into her mouth again, and swirled her tongue around the head.

"I hope you're getting enough for a while," Eve said, going over to the table and pulling a wrapped rubber from the can. She examined the brand and then fished for another one, one with little bumps and ridges all over it. "'Cause it's my turn to play with our new toy."

Nicole glanced to the side and nodded, and attacked Tony's cock with renewed enthusiasm. He groaned again, and actually whimpered when she suddenly pulled her mouth away and left him, wet and exposed.

"Oh, don't worry, little stud, we're not going away," Eve said warmly, tearing the package open. "We're just changing tactics with you." She placed the condom over his cock and slowly, firmly, rolled it all the way down, her fingers forming a circle of pressure that smoothed it over his erection.

He gasped and said, "Yeah, do it, do it, I'm ready..."

Eve made a snorting noise. "He's ready? Honey, I'm more ready than you'll ever be!" She slipped her dress open, revealing her nude form before his unseeing eyes, and moved up against his body, touching him with her own, teasing him. Nicole went into the kitchen and brought out a footstool, which she placed between his spread legs, and Eve mounted it, so that she was now at the same level he was. Carefully, she hooked one leg behind him, her ankle resting on one rung of the loft ladder, and then slowly lowered herself down on his dick, Nicole helpfully holding it for her.

"Now, don't go jerking and jumping, stud," Eve warned, as she settled. "Because if I fall, we're gonna say good night and show you the door. You just be a good boy and stand still while I use that pretty cock of yours." Taking a firm grip on an upper rung, she began to ride him.

Nicole watched from below, a big smile on her face. They had done it in this position before, using the ladder, but never with a guy who couldn't move. Eve's eyes rolled back as she took all of him in, and rocked against him for her own pleasure.

Her body shuddered as she moved herself back and forth over his cock, taking him in and letting him go, using him to stimulate her and fill her, and then drawing back to teasing distances. He groaned and gasped and strained even more against his bindings, and then began to actually growl with passion.

"Yeah!" he exclaimed, his hips thrusting as far as they could. He struggled to get more of his cock into the temptress who was so ruthlessly riding him, and his voice was harsh and low. "Do it ! Come on, take it! Ride me, goddammit, yeah, do it..!"

Eve laughed as she continued to use him for her pleasure, and then began to concentrate on finishing the deed. She clasped one arm around his neck and bent his head toward the swell of her breast, and clung to him in an even more crushing position. He opened his mouth eagerly to kiss and nibble at her, finding her nipple and taking it between his lips. She gasped and shifted to take him into her at an angle that would best serve her, and began a final, rhythmic pounding against his body, a sheen of sweat growing on her back. She gripped the ladder tightly and pulled and held, and began to feel the waves of ecstasy growing inside of her. She opened her eyes for an instant to see the bowed head of the man she and her roommate had literally captured for their pleasure, and it was like setting a spark to gasoline.

"Mmmmm!" Eve shook with the start of her orgasm, and her body began to tremble. "Oh yeah, you stud! Come on, stud! That's it, come to me!" She writhed and bucked over him, finally taking him to the root, her womanly folds engulfing his length and pulsating around him in a way that he found impossible to resist.

With a howl, he came as well, his own body caught in as contorting a position as hers, his head arching back away from her as his cock shot forth its own tribute. When she sagged against him, they were both panting, their chests rising and falling with a harsh regularity. She slid down from her perch and took the towel that Nicole had thoughtfully fetched for her and began to rub the warm, soft cotton over her body, wiping away sweat. (Both hers and his.)

Tony shook like a dog in his bonds, his muscles glistening and tightening. "That...oh, god, that was nice. But you gotta let me down, girls, my hands are killing me...please?"

Eve nodded weakly as she sat down on the couch. "Go ahead," she said, leaning back.

Nicole began to untie the scarves, letting Tony massage his wrists, and then she took the blindfold off. The big man blinked and wiped at his eyes and grinned at the sight of Eve, half collapsed across the couch.

"You look like you had a good time," he noted. He stripped the used rubber, which had been tenaciously clinging to his softened dick, away, and wiped himself down with another towel. "I wish I could have seen it, though. You girls are tough."

Eve laughed. "You know, Tony, you never learn! What did we tell you about calling us girls?"

Nicole joined in the laughter for a moment, and then looked stern. "Apparently not enough!" she announced. "And on top of that, he came without permission. And without fucking me!" Tony shrugged.

"Give me a little while and I'll be happy to take care of you," he offered. "Give me a kiss, and it'll be sooner."

Eve whistled softly from her seat on the couch. "He is a smart-ass, isn't he?" she asked. Nicole nodded in agreement, and then looked at her friend with a meaningful expression on her face. Eve nodded back. "Yep. I think it's time for the secret weapon!"

"What's the secret weapon?" Tony asked, stretching.

Within minutes, he was stretched out on his back on the coffee table. A pillow propped his head up, while the two women secured his wrists and ankles to the table legs. The table wasn't very long, and his ass was at the very edge. The way his knees were bent up exposed the crinkled, star-shaped hole nestled between his smooth but lightly bruised ass cheeks. As Eve amused herself by lightly teasing his nipples, Nicole went to their condom can and drew out what looked like a strap on dildo. Then, she scooped up the warm container of lubricant and strolled back to where their evening's entertainment was enjoying the tugging and pinching that Eve was doing to his nipples.

Nicole held the dildo up and showed it to him. His eyes widened, but instead of strapping it on herself, Nicole turned it around and showed him that the dildo was actually hollow! In silence, she squirted some warm lube into the hollow shaft and then, picking up his interested-but-not-yet-hard cock between her fingers, she stuffed it into the dildo. He gasped and jerked as the thick, warm glop inside rushed to embrace his organ. Eve helped Nicole tie the bands around his thighs, holding the fake cock in place, with the real thing trapped inside.

"I don't believe you're doing this," Tony choked out. "Can't you wait until I'm ready? Don't you want the real thing, baby?"

"Who needs the real thing?" Nicole asked, pulling her dress up over her head. The garters were a stark black against the lightness of her skin, and they framed her dark triangle of curly hair perfectly. She took a squirt of the warm lube in her fingers and worked it all over the extended dildo, and Tony gasped again, because he could just barely feel the pressure of her fingers through the device. What he really felt though, was the motion of it when she pulled at it and then stroked it down. She grinned and swung a leg over the table to stand astride him. Luxuriously, she opened herself with her own fingers and slowly settled down over the dildo.

Her weight settled over him for a moment, and she ground her hips down. Her eyes closed and she gave a low "mmmm" sound as the dildo filled her. She smiled, opened her eyes to look at him, and then reached up to caress her own breasts. Easily, she began to ride it, and him.

"I don't believe this," he groaned, stretched out beneath her. "I'm being raped!"

"You sure are, sugar!" Eve agreed. She tweaked his nipples, and slapped at his chest, a flurry of light, stinging blows that made his breath come in short gasps. "And we're not finished with you yet!"

Nicole began to rock and plunge with a greater urgency. Watching Eve have her way with Tony the stud had been a really good warm-up, and she was hotter than she thought. She lowered a finger to her tender clit and began to flick it in the way she liked, and gasped at the surge of pleasure that washed through her.

Inside the hollow dildo, Tony began to feel its tightness as his cock responded to the welcoming depths of the toy and the prewarmed lubricant that was already beginning to be forced out along the base. All along the sides of the thing, he could feel the double pressure of the dildo and the gentle pulsing from Nicole's hot pussy. Despite the soreness of his butt, he began to fight his bondage again, to try and thrust up at her. His small success increased her pleasure tenfold.

"That's it, my stud," she panted, grinding down into him again. "Come on up to get me. Lemme see that pretty body struggle."

"Bitch!" Tony spat, finally, his belly tight with tension. The two women laughed, and Eve slapped his cheek smartly.

"Such language!"

"I think it's time to put something in that mouth of his!"

"I have a better idea," Eve said, grinning. She lifted one long leg and straddled the table over his head, letting him view her still glistening pussy, the pink flesh open in her arousal. "Let's put that tongue to good use, boy."

As she lowered herself, Tony went to work on her soft folds with an ardent fury that spoke about his own passion in a way very similar to the now fully erect cock entrapped in the dildo Nicole was earnestly fucking.

Both women used their own fingers to send them onward to the final reward of sex, and used Tony for stimulating amusement. Bound beneath them, he was the perfect sex toy, controlled by them, for them, and utterly available and willing to please.

Nicole's breath changed first, and she cried out as she came. "That's it! That's it! Oh, baby, it's so hot...fuck! Fuck!" Her hips pounded against him, and the pressure inside the dildo became too much for the man. His own muffled exclamations made vibrations of pleasure in Eve, and he thrust his tongue into her as deeply as she would allow, the only penetration he could really do. Because Nicole was fucking him, taking her pleasure from him. Even as his manhood began to shower the interior of the dildo with his own form of warmth, there was no doubt about who was in charge.

And as Nicole settled back to catch her breath, Eve found her own rhythm and sighed as she came again, perched over Tony's face, her fingers busy on her clit, his tongue awash with her ripe juices.

The three of them panted as well as they could, and Eve stood up to let Tony breathe normally. Inside the dildo, Tony's cock, again depleted, shrunk into temporary dormancy, but the dildo remained firm and erect and lodged in Nicole's tight pussy. In time, she also stood, and took herself off of it, and the suction it created over his cock made him actually whimper.

"Well," Nicole said, sitting down at last, "I guess you were right, Eve. He is kinda into this stuff."

"Huh?" Tony questioned, looking at her. "Into what?"

"You know. Bondage. SM. Sex games. Like in that movie."

He looked at her innocently. "What movie? I never did this stuff before in my life." There was just a hint of a smile on his face again.

Eve looked at her roommate with thinly disguised glee. "I think he's lying," she announced. "He should be punished for that. Terrible thing, lying."

"Absolutely," agreed the bound man.

The three of them finally collapsed in laughter.

Chapter Seven:
Helping a Buddy Out

Greg and Alan rode the train to their Queens neighborhood. The two of them had known each other from college, and roomed together for the ease on their wallets. But no one could deny that they were good friends, despite being room-]mates. They had separate rooms for privacy, and separate shelves for beer and a "no surprises" policy for parties, guests and their cable bill. (That was after Greg piled up almost fifty bucks worth of pay-per-view movies in one month.)

Greg was loud and obnoxious, but Alan could do a fair imitation of him when the situation called for it. They both dated around, and Greg had a "kind of steady" girlfriend as well, but neither was in a rush to settle down with anyone. They had a good life, full of bachelor comfort.

And, in a lot of ways, they had each other. If the girls weren't cooperating, they could go out to a game or a movie or something, or rent a couple of movies with lots of explosions and very little plot and top of an evening with some porn flick with lots of blonde babes.

And it was the ritual of watching porn together that led to jerking off in front of each other, and then finally "helping each other out" from time to time. Each guy would lend a hand to the other - literally - for the novelty of a foreign touch. There were a few times, especially when more than a few beer bottles lay scattered throughout the apartment, when one or the other actually got a mouth in on some action, but neither one really thought about it. They were young and horny. There really wasn't much to think about there. It wasn't like they were in love or anything. They were just being good guys, helping a buddy out.

Of course, it helped to be turned on first. So when they climbed the stairs to their apartment, still insulting each other, their parents and girlfriends, their pets and taste on clothing and art, Alan stalked into the living room and noisily pulled open the storage case where they kept their videos. As he rummaged through it, he called out, "Sure you don't wanna watch this? How about the one with the cheerleaders instead?"

Greg snorted as he shucked his jacket and sneakers. "Fuck that. It would take every one of the Cowboys' cheerleaders to get a boner out of me tonight. Man, I'm never gonna get that stupid movie out of my head! Y'know, you have some seriously bad fucking ideas." He turned to his own room and slammed the door behind him.

"Well, fuck you too," Alan muttered, pulling *Sorority Babes III* out of the case and popping it into the VCR. He hit the fast-forward to get past the credits and plot, and stripped off his shirt. Although he was considered the quiet and gentle one of the two, he was well built. He still lifted weights at a local gym, and played football whenever he could, out in the park. He knew that the beer he drank went straight to his belly. In the mirror, he could see the start of a problem there, but he was confident he could manage it. He kicked off his shoes, unbuckled his belt, pulled open his fly and prepared to enjoy the erotic antics of a bunch of girls at a college dorm that looked suspiciously like a cheap rented house in Las Vegas.

Minutes passed, and the movie got into its "all action, no plot" phase, and he was still waiting for some reaction from his dick. But somehow, it just wasn't working. The girls on the screen were pussy lapping, and he kept imagining spanking them. They were playing with their fingers and some vibrators, and he kept wishing they would tie each other up.

"Maybe Greg was right," he murmured to himself. "Maybe that movie does affect the brain." He pressed the fast-forward button again, and tried another part of the film, a part that never failed to get a riser out of him. He stirred all right...but it wasn't because of the shower scene. It was the thought of using all that soap as a lube and forcing one of those babes to bend over and take his stiff one right up her crack. Maybe swatting her butt while she took it, making her squeal...

This is not working, Alan finally realized. He hit the off switch and didn't even bother to take the tape out of the machine. I can't even concentrate. Sighing, he walked toward his room, thinking about just doing the deed on basic fantasies, and skipping visuals all together. Because sick or not, he was still kind of horny! It was just that his dick wasn't cooperating.

But as he passed Greg's door, he thought he heard something.

He paused to listen, and then easily identified the sound coming from Greg's room. It was his bed, the frame a little lopsided, knocking against the wall. Long nights spent listening to each other between the wall had given them easy ways to tell when the other was jacking off. And Greg, with his wild pumpings and thrashings, was much easier to identify.

283

Alan felt a grim triumph spread through him. Ha! He thought, standing in the hallway, dick in one hand. So it didn't turn him on, huh? It was just a stupid fucking movie? Well, who's in his own room wanking away while I can't even concentrate on a dozen blonde babes galore on the tube? And what the fuck was all that shit about, dissing me and making fun of me just because I admit I liked the stupid thing?

What a jerk, he thought, turning toward his own room. Even though I came out and fucking asked him to get off with me, he has to pretend he's not turned on and go off by himself. What kind of a friend is that? Then, Alan halted in his tracks.

Why should I let him finish, he asked himself. Let him wrestle with a limp one for a while. He deserves it! But wait...maybe I can really get him. Don't I have a camera with some shots left over from the Halloween party we went to? Yeah! And it has a flash, too. I'll open the door, and get a snapshot of him pulling his dick. What a hoot!

He slid into his bedroom and got the camera and pushed the button to charge the flash. The light thumping continued from Greg's room, and when the little light went on, Alan threw open Greg's door, making it slam into the wall, and immediately snapped off a shot. The sound and the light startled Greg so much that he actually fell off the bed.

Because Greg wasn't in his usual "flat-on-your-back" position. He had been kneeling on the edge of the bed, a pillow under his belly, one hand clutching the pillow to him, the other one presumably holding onto his dick. He was totally naked, his hairy butt displayed for one startling moment to his roommate before shock took over and he tried to get up too fast.

"Stupid fucking movie, huh? Didn't turn you on one fucking bit, did it?" Alan repeated, still amazed at what he'd seen. He raised the camera and got another shot of Greg sitting on the floor, a pillow next to him.

"You asshole!" Greg retorted, rolling over. "I coulda got killed! What the fuck are you doing with that fucking camera?"

"Taking pictures of a pervert," Alan retorted. "At least I wanted to jerk off the regular way. What the fuck is that, with your ass up the air? I never saw such stupid shit. What's the matter? Were you getting off on being the slave, or the master?"

"There better not be film in that camera!" Greg said as he began to get up. He actually sounded nervous, and Alan took a step back and dropped the camera out in the hall. Then, he threw himself into the room and kicked the door shut behind him. Greg tensed for a moment at this odd intrusion, and then tried to get up. In an instant, Alan was on him, pushing him back against the bed with a strength and force Greg knew from football.

What was going through Alan's head was too complex for him to sort out all the way. All he knew was that he had endured his friend's ribbing all the way through the movie and all the way home, even to the point of actually believing that he was wrong for liking the stupid movie, and here was Greg jerking off all alone while he couldn't keep a hard-on in the living room with those babes for company. He held his friend down in a pin and said, "You know, you are too fucking much. I practically begged you to come on and do the right thing and party with me, and you called me a pervert! Well, what are you, pal? I guess you're just another pervert, right?"

"Get the fuck off me!" Greg yelled, struggling. But Alan pushed into him again and refused to let him up.

"No way, man, not until you make like you're sorry." He pushed harder with his shoulders, squashing his roommate against the bed, and Greg snarled, trying to push back.

"You son of a bitch, get off me!" he shouted, fighting. Alan held on, though, and the two of them seemed to be at an impasse. Greg tried to struggle again and again, but Alan just allowed his weight to keep him down. Together, they panted from their exertions, and slowly, their eyes met.

"All right, all right," Greg finally growled. "I'm fucking sorry, OK? Get off me!"

Alan pulled himself up and back, but as he did so, he kicked away the pillow that was still wedged between Greg's thighs. And revealed something very interesting.

Greg still had a hard-on!

And so did Alan. He stood, breathing heavily for a moment, as Greg scrambled to get up. Then, he swept down to pick up the pillow.

"So what the fuck were you doing, pervert?" he asked, tossing the pillow into Greg's chest. The dark-haired young man snatched the pillow angrily.

"Come on, admit it, asshole. The movie made you hot! So how come all that bullshit about me being a pervert and everything, huh? At least I was honest about it."

"OK! OK, you're right, OK? Jesus, what do you want from me?" Greg exploded, now blushing. His boner still hadn't decreased, not in the slightest, and both of them were aware of that. Alan decided to push him even further.

"I want you to do the right thing, buddy."

"Fine! No fucking problem, man," Greg seemed relieved for some reason. "Let's go get that videotape, OK?" He started to move toward the door, but Alan stopped him.

"No, let's do it here. And I wanna see you get off first." He pushed Greg in the chest, back toward the bed. "I wanna see you get off just the way you were doing it when I came in."

"Aw, come on, Al, give me a fuckin' break," Greg complained. "That was private. Let's just go and take care of things the normal way, OK? We'll watch the babes video, have a couple of beers. OK?"

"No, man. I wanna see you on that bed again, with your butt up, just the way you are in the picture. If you do it, I'll give you the roll of film, and you can do whatever the fuck you want with it. Piss on it, make it into Christmas cards, or whatever. But I really wanna see you get off like that. I'll help you out. You gonna do it? Or are we gonna say good night and I keep the pictures?"

"You son of a fucking bitch!" Greg declared, clenching his teeth. "I don't believe you're doing this!"

"Believe it, or say good night, hotshot." Alan stayed still for a moment, and then turned toward the door.

There was a long moment as he reached for the door handle and a number of scenarios passed through Greg's mind. Finally, he spoke up.

"Fine, man, just fine. Leave it to my buddy to come up with fucking blackmail. You wanna watch my asshole while I jerk off? Hey, it's no problem, man." Angrily, he turned toward the bed and pushed the blankets back. Alan turned back with an expectant grin.

Greg took a deep breath or two and then got up on his knees on the bed again. While his back was straight, Alan asked him, "What part of the movie are you thinking about?"

"Jesus! Gimee a minute to clear my mind, OK?"

"Yeah, OK, OK." Alan pushed aside some laundry and a near empty box of cookies and sat down on the room's only chair. He had a great view of Greg, as the young man began to stroke his erection back to fullness, his eyes closed. As quietly as he could, Alan began to pull his belt through the loops on his jeans. He moved very slowly.

"I'm thinking about that mama in the high boots and those stockings," Greg said, after he got into gear. "Her fucking legs went on forever. And those tits!"

"Did you like it when she wrapped her legs around that guys' head?" Alan prodded, three more loops to go.

"Uh...yeah, sure. She could wrap her legs around my face anytime, you know?" He changed the position of his hand and began to compress his erection with his fingers, one finger pressing at a time, like he was trying to milk his cock to bring forth its essence.

"Yeah, you liked it all right. You liked that part when she almost smothered him, too. I remember watching you when that happened. I bet you'd get off on being some kind of slave, huh?" The belt was free. Alan doubled it and held one end in his right hand and stood up.

"What's your fucking problem, man?" Greg started to complain, opening his eyes. He was surprised not to see Alan in the chair, and he turned his head to look for him. At that moment, Alan took a swing with the belt and caught Greg once, hard, across his hairy ass.

Greg immediately dropped his dick and tried to get up, but Alan was relentless. He struck his roommate again and again, across his ass and thighs, and when Greg tried to move out of the way, Alan reached out and caught a handful of his hair and pulled his head up and back. All the while, the belt rose and fell, leaving broad, red lines all over Greg's body, hitting his legs, his waist, his back, and then back to his ass.

Greg screamed out his rage, and caught hold of the hand Alan had knotted in his hair. But Alan tightened his grip, and the pain of having his hair pulled actually shocked the punished young man. "Goddamn it, you motherfucker, let go of me! Shit! Ow! Goddamn!" His litany of profanity became more imaginative, and then alternated with threats. He tried to kick backwards, but the belt caught his calves and feet until all he could think of was pulling away. Finally, the threats lessened, and his cursing became more limited, and his thrashings on the bed became much more an attempt to pull in his more vulnerable spots, his legs and arms.

"Jesus, Al, stop! Please..." he finally sputtered, his voice quavering. And to his continued surprise, Alan stopped, and pushed his head down to the bed, keeping his ass elevated, the way he was when Alan had first burst in the doorway.

"All you had to do was say please," Alan said, out of breath from the energy expended to physically chastise his friend. "Now, you get to jerking off. It should be better for you now. You got marks all over your fucking body, just like the guy in the movie. Come on, pervert. Make it hard again. Get yourself off, or we'll get a picture of you like this, too."

"Man..." Greg's voice sounded almost weak, and he groaned as he shifted on the bed. "I can't..."

"Yes you can, fucker," Alan declared. "And you will. Or I'll add some more marks on top of those, OK? Come on, you love it. You're just too chickenshit to admit it. Get your hand on your dick and start dancing, Greggie, or I'll make you dance for me. Got it?"

There was a long moment where Alan thought Greg would defy him, but amazingly, Greg's hand crept between his legs and began the motions to make his somewhat softened dick come back to life.

"This is why you were so afraid to admit you liked the movie," Alan said, wiping some sweat off his forehead. "You didn't just like the damn thing, you loved it. But you wanted to be the slave, not the fucking mistress, or whatever. Some big macho guy, huh?" Alan kept a tight watch on Greg's busy hand, and was gratified to see the jerking motions going faster as he spoke. It only confirmed what he was saying.

"So you're gonna get yourself hard for me, and then you're gonna let me figure out what to do next, OK? You listening, Greggie?"

"Yeah, yeah!" Greg quickly answered. "Whatever, Al, just keep that fucking belt off me, OK?"

"No deals, brother!" Alan gave Greg one fast crack across the ass with the belt, and Greg almost fell forward. But he held himself, groaned loudly, and kept on pumping.

After a while, Alan looked a little closer, and asked, "Well? Are you hard yet?"

"Yeah," his aching pal said, with a slight edge to his voice. "Lemme cum, OK?"

"Nah, I told you I'd help you out, and I will." Alan stripped off his jeans and sat down on the chair again, the looped belt held loosely in one hand. "Get up."

Greg got back up on his knees and then slid carefully off the bed, his body aching with every movement, a deep heat rising in particular along his ass and thighs. He faced Alan, his erection in one hand, and looked entirely like he was awaiting orders.

"Get down there and get me harder," Alan said, pointing between his legs. His penis was not exactly at its full size, lying half limp in his tangle of dark curls. "On your knees, Greggie boy. And make it feel good."

Greg snarled for a moment, but Alan just shrugged and started to get up, the belt swinging in his right hand. Then, Greg dropped, avoiding Alan's eyes, and reached out for Alan's dick.

"You son of a bitch," he said, his voice low.

"Yeah," admitted Alan, sitting back again. "I can be. Come on, get me up."

Greg dropped his own cock to tend to Alan's, and their history of helping each other out gave him the knowledge of how to do it right. Alan liked it hard and slow, to a steady, long tempo. As he worked, he shivered from time to time, the after effect of the beating he had taken.

Alan rose in response, both to Greg's ministrations and to the effect this experience was having on the young man. This is fucking hot, Alan admitted to himself, easing back and enjoying the massage of his manhood. And as for how Greg was feeling? Well, the erection he had achieved at Alan's demand was still hanging between his legs, even without attention.

Soon, Alan felt about ready to get to the main attraction. He stood up, shaking Greg off, and pointed at the bed again. "Get up," he said, reaching down to help Greg. Then, he pushed the shorter man toward the bed, but stopped him before he got on it. "Wait right there," he said, looking around the room again. What he needed was hanging from a hook on the back of the bedroom door.

He pulled the cloth belt from the waistbands of a robe that Greg never wore. Something he got for Christmas years ago, but kept around for any sleep-over girlfriend who might want to shower the next morning.

Then, he pulled one of Greg's hands behind him and looped the belt around the wrist. Greg resisted, pulling away, but a knee in his back easily pushed him down to the bed, and once one wrist was secured, it was easy to grab the other.

"What are you doing, man?" Greg demanded, shaking in anger. Alan neatly wound the belt around the two wrists over and over again and then in between them before tying several knots.

"I'm adding to your fantasy, Greggie. Get over on your back, and I'll bring you off." Alan rose up to allow Greg to turn, and was rewarded by the sight of Greg's only-slightly-disturbed erection. "You're getting off on all this, Greggie. You lied about the movie, but you can't lie about this!" Alan reached and slapped Greg's dick, making it spring toward his stomach, and making Greg almost double over in shock and pain.

"Shit!" was Greg's only reply, because what else could he say? Despite his protests, his body betrayed him, and he strained against the cloth belt, his face flushed with humiliation. And it was about to get worse.

"This is the final deal, buddy. I'm gonna take your dick in my hand, and get you off, just the way you like it," Alan said. He swung his legs over Greg's torso, facing Greg's dick and taking hold of it as he described. His ass was almost resting on Greg's chest.

"But, unless you want it to take all night, you gotta get me off too." Alan slowly raised his butt, allowing his dick to point down, and in then inched his way backward.

"No fucking way, man!" Greg screamed, his friend's cock and balls almost dangling over his face. He turned his head to avoid them, and rocked back and forth to try to fight. Alan just grinned and picked up the belt again, and laid into the fronts of Greg's thighs, until the man started to cry out in pain and stop struggling.

Then, Alan dropped the belt again and slapped at Greg's dick, over and over. That was followed by a long squeeze of his balls, and then a tickling run of fingers all along the shaft, ending with a sharp tug on the head.

"This could go on all night," Alan mentioned, scratching his fingernails on the sensitive underside of his friend's dick. He slapped it again, feeling Greg jump beneath him. As he pulled out a few pubic hairs, he raised his ass again, and presented Greg with the vision and scent of his cock. "All you have to do is get me off. And get this, buddy...I promise I won't cum in your mouth!" With a laugh, he grabbed hold of Greg's dick, pumped it, about a dozen times, really hard, and then slapped it back and forth with his fingers. Then, he went back to tickling it lightly.

Greg was seeing things through a red haze. His ass was on fire, his thighs felt absolutely scorched, and his dick...! His dick felt alternately like he was ready to shoot gallons and gallons of cum, or he was gonna die. And above him loomed Alan's thick cock and loaded balls. If only he had his hands, he's be pumping away like crazy, but he didn't, and Alan was fucking torturing him! He couldn't take it any more! Anything for some relief!

Alan gasped as Greg's mouth took in the head of his cock. Deep inside, Alan figured Greg would never do it, not unless he was drunk or something. But the hot warmth that engulfed him was real, and he shifted to push more of his dick into the young man's mouth.

Then, remembering his bargain, he reached down and took firm hold of Greg's dick and began to frig it the way Greg liked it, easy, but very fast. It was so hot, thinking of Greg tied up like this and sucking his cock! Well, not actually sucking, but at least holding his cock in his mouth, breathing around it, licking it, making it feel real nice.

OK, Alan thought, spitting on his hand for lubrication. You make me feel good...it's time to get you off. He increased his speed and a little pressure, and felt the churning of cum before it appeared. And when it appeared, it gushed! Greg's hips thrust up as he spurted, sending loads of white fluid up and around Alan's fist, shooting it out in spurt after spurt, more juice than Alan had ever even seen coming from one guy. As he came, he moaned and made sounds that Alan knew were his usual curses, this time mumbled around a thick cock in his mouth. The vibrations the sounds caused brought Alan really close to the edge himself.

And when Greg fell backward again, his muscles relaxed, Alan scooted off of his face and out of his mouth, and turned around, again straddling Greg's chest but facing him. His own hand dropped to his dick, wet with Greg's spit, and he began the series of slow, hard draws that would bring on his own cum. In no time, his jism was pumping out onto Greg's chest, mixing with the hair and glistening in little opaque droplets. A few drops spilled down and ran across his neck.

The two men panted, and were silent for a while. Alan moved first, getting off the bed and pushing Greg over to untie him. The knots were hard to untie, but soon the belt came off in stiffened loops.

Greg didn't say anything, just turned toward the wall and lay still. Alan picked up his jeans and belt and opened the door. In the hallway, on the floor, was the camera he had dropped not a long time ago. He picked it up and tossed it into Greg's room, aiming for the bed.

Alan went into the bathroom to wipe himself down, and then to his own bedroom, satisfied, but disturbed. What was gonna happened tomorrow? Would Greg pretend it never happened? Would he move out? Would they fight about it? Should he apologize?

He lay down on his own bed, in the dark but over the covers, and thought for a while. He was honestly surprised when Greg walked into the room. He thought he would at least have taken the night to think about things.

Greg stood in the faint light by the door. "Uh...you awake?" he asked, softly.

"Yeah."

"I just wanted to tell you somethin'," he continued. "Uh...I'm sorry about ragging on you, man."

If someone had dropped an anvil on his head, Alan couldn't have been more surprised.

"And...and..." Greg wasn't finished. "If, uh, you wanna keep the picture, I guess its OK. I mean, if you can't trust a buddy, who can you, you know?"

"Wait a minute," Alan said, as Greg put the camera down and turned to leave. "You know that if I have that picture, I can, well...do this again."

There was a pause. And then, "Yeah."

"Tomorrow, if I want to."

"Yeah." There was no pause this time.

"Even now, if I want to."

"Yeah." A sigh.

"Well...go to sleep, man. Apology accepted. And we'll talk tomorrow."

"OK, Al. See you in the morning."

As Greg left to go back to his room, Alan lay back in satisfaction. Oh yeah, you'll see me in the morning, he thought, gently fingering his limp dick. When my stiff one is ready for some more relief.

After all, he thought, finally flipping the covers over his nude body, what are buddies for?

Chapter Eight:
Master of the Evening

Mark often went to the movies by himself so that he could have a chance to enjoy a film before taking a woman to it, and spending an evening paying attention to her. He had a feeling, from all the office scuttlebutt and the reviews, that this particular film was definitely going to be one to take someone to if you thought they might get into a little kink. But you never know when some woman would take this kind of thing wrong. So, he put it on his "preview" list, to check out whether or not it should be in his next scheduled dating agenda.

The house was crowded. Every showing was sold out. He bought popcorn and a large Coke, and settled into a middle row as the seats around him filled. A pretty, dark haired girl sat next to him, and she also seemed to be alone, and Mark didn't mind one bit. They smiled briefly at each other, the way that strangers did when circumstances put them together, and they turned their attention to the screen as the lights went out and the title rolled.

Ten minutes into the film, Mark was already amazed. This was no standard art film! Unlike all the others he had seen over the years, with weird plots and strange settings and brief, occasional scenes of slightly depraved sex, this one was nothing less then a catalog of kink! The audience was hushed, with that slight undercurrent of rusting that meant that people were shifting in their seats. Ahead of him by three rows, a couple was already making out. But all around him, including the dark beauty beside him, people's eyes were glued to the happenings on the screen, captured by the hypnotic eroticism on display there.

Mark actually found himself flinching at the part with the piercing. Did people actually do that? But as he shifted to regain his hold on the popcorn, he felt that peculiar sensation of being watched. He glanced around and found that the dark haired girl beside him was looking at him. He looked back and smiled again, as he became comfortable, and she did an astonishing thing.

Carefully, so that he couldn't help but notice, she unbuttoned the top three buttons of her blouse and leaned back.

Mark sat there for a second, waiting for her obvious invitation to clear his awareness. He was hardly a man to lose a good opportunity when it came, but this was NOT the way these things usually happened. He glanced back at the screen and then casually draped an arm around her, allowing his fingers to drape against the hollow of her shoulder, touching warm, bare skin. She eased up close to him, and turned slightly in her seat so that his fingers could touch her breast, and then she lay one cool hand against his thigh.

This, Mark thought, as he grinned in the darkness, is too much. This is my lucky, lucky night! Forget seeing the flick first and then choosing some woman to go see it with. Before the first fifteen minutes of the movie, some woman comes on to me!

He relaxed and flicked his fingers downward until they found her erect nipple. As the actions on the screen changed and intensified, his fingers began to experimentally pinch, pull, twist and tug at her nipple. With every harsh twist, she seemed to melt more and more into him. With every tight pinch, her hand grew more bold in his lap. Soon, her mouth was moaning little moans of pain into his ear, and her hand was caressing a hard-on the likes of which he hadn't felt...well, since Linda did that thing with the ice cubes and coffee.

At one point, he finally realized that what she was getting off on was the brutality and the pain. He began to just clamp down on her nipple, holding it as tightly as he could for as long as he could, while she squirmed slightly and tried to keep what he was doing as unobvious as possible. Then, he left that nipple and boldly pushed her skirt up, to the astonished but pleased attention of the man sitting to her right. When she didn't move to smooth it back or brush his hand away, Mark sent his fingers into the hot, wet delta between her thighs and discovered that she wasn't wearing any panties.

And during the infamous orgy scene, he finger fucked her, steadily, in rhythm with the fucking on the screen, and her gasps melded into the sounds of pleasure coming from the grand speakers all around the theatre. The man sitting to her right didn't know what to watch, the show on the screen, or the one next to him.

When Mark wanted to watch what was happening with the movie, he made her massage his stiff organ while she licked her own juices off his fingers. And when he had enough of that pleasure, he slipped his fingers into his Coke and pulled an ice cube out. For the rest of the movie, he amused himself by applying ice to her nipples and sticking pieces up her hot snatch. Her juices flowed over his fingers, and by the time the credits were rolling, they were locked in as close an embrace they could get into while in two seats at a theatre.

Their mouths and tongues devoured each other, and their arms locked around their backs in the kind if passion usually considered part of a honeymoon weekend. They heard the muted laughed of some other theatre goers as they passed them by, and then Mark broke the embrace and looked at her in the full light for the first time.

"I'm Mark," he said, softly, with a smile.

"Thea," she gasped out. "What you did was hot. I loved it." The words came out in a rush, and she kissed him again.

"Come home with me," Mark suggested. "It's a little more private, and we can really get to know each other."

She grinned, a wild, hot, crazy grin, and said, "Let's fuck right here, right now."

"You're nuts...!" Mark started to laugh, and then realized that she was teasing him. Teasing him by being demanding, by demanding something impossible. His mind seized upon all the clues she had given him, from her casual invitation to her pleasure in being pained, to her wild request to be screwed in a half-empty theatre, and he caught hold of her arms.

"I think I phrased that wrong," he said, holding tightly onto her. "You're coming home with me. And I'm going to get to know you better. And you're going to do some things for me."

She tossed her hair back, not fighting him. "Like what?" she asked.

"Like suck my cock. Like show me your body. Like anything I want you to do. Coming?" He stood up, pulling her with him, and she pulled herself into his arms for another kiss. He broke this one like the last one and laughed as he reached for his jacket. When she picked hers up, he dragged her out of the theatre and pulled her down the block. But he couldn't make it to the corner. Turning, he pushed her against the side of the building and pushed her legs apart with his knee, and kissed her, hard, raping her mouth with his tongue.

She melted under him and returned his kiss with passion. When he started to lift her skirt and show off her legs to the people passing by, he felt her tremble with pleasure and moan consent into his ear. She liked it. She wanted it. When he called her a slut, she moaned and caressed him with such fervor he thought he was going to come in his pants. He drove his hand between her legs and brought his fingers back literally dripping with her pleasure, and instead of letting her taste it from his fingers, he wiped it across her face, leaving her to recover while he hailed a cab.

In the cab, they resumed their impassioned embrace, and he opened her blouse all the way so that he could his hands on her twin globes. The cab driver paid no attention, and Mark wondered how much he could push this woman, who seemed to like being shown off. He whispered in her ear, "Do you think the driver knows what a slut you are? Shall we show him? Show him your tits! Go ahead, do it!"

She moaned, turned to kiss him, and then took the sides of her blouse in her own hands. Slowly, she parted the garment, and turned to face the cabbies rearview mirror.

The man looked into the mirror three times before he assured himself that it was no accident. His eyes kept glancing back to the road and the other cars, and he waited until they were at a red light to speak. "Nice pair, lady," he said.

Mark laughed. "Yeah, aren't they? Isn't she a little slut?"

The light changed, and the cab pulled forward into traffic again.

"If you say so, buddy," the driver said. He seemed glad when they reached their destination, and took the cash tip instead of Mark's offer of a copped feel. When Mark and Thea got out of the cab, they crushed each other in a laughing embrace, and he led her to his building at a pace that was almost a run.

They were insatiable! Waiting for the elevator, in the elevator, outside his door, and into his hallway, they were all over each other. But once inside, as he reached to turn on the lights, he finally pushed her away.

"Now we're on my turf, babe," he said, looking at her. She was disheveled, hot, and the look in her eyes was as wild as it had been in the theatre. "This is gonna be played my way."

If anything, his words and attitude thrilled her even more. "What do you want?" she asked, breathlessly.

He shrugged his coat off and sat down on his couch. "I want you naked," he said. "I wanna see what a slut looks like."

She shivered and pulled off her own jacket, and then allowed the fallen halves of her blouse to follow. She did have a nice pair, Mark thought. Small enough to cup in your hands, with big, pointy nipples. The skirt fell off almost as easily, and she stood before him in stockings and a garter belt. The dark triangle of hair between her legs was diamond shaped...a nice shaving job. Mark immediately wondered what it would look like bare.

He stood suddenly. "Wait right there!" he ordered, as he ran to his bedroom. In his closet, up on the shelf, was his instant camera. He checked to see if it was loaded, and discovered that he had plenty of film, and an extra pack besides. When he came back in the room, she was still standing there, and her eyes lit up at the sight of the camera. He raised it and shot a picture of her, that surprised look on her face.

"Come on, pose for me! Show off what you've got. Hold your tits together!" Mark moved in closer, and Thea responded by gathering her breasts in her hands and holding them together. She leaned forward and pouted as she did, and Mark snapped off another shot. The photos fell to the floor as he took them.

"That's right, that's my little slut. Show off for me...now show me your ass! Bend over, like you're gonna get it right up the ass, that's it. Now spread your legs!"

Her shapely ass, framed by the garter belt, invited his touch. Before he took the picture, he moved up beside her and pinched her butt, sharply, all along the bottom. Then, he pulled gently on her curly hairs to fluff them out a little, and smacked her rounded cheeks to bring up some color. She whimpered delightfully and shook her ass back at him, and he hit her harder. She gasped, and said, "Oh, please, no more, take the picture..."

Mark immediately stopped and leaned back to get his shot. It looked so good, he took another and then slid to the floor underneath her, between her spread legs.

"Come on, bitch, open up for me. Spread those pussy lips wide, or I'll whack you again. Dance a little for me. Make it good!"

Thea obligingly opened her lips with her fingers and displayed her intimate charms to Mark and his camera. She glistened with moisture, and as she ground down in a dancer's move, he got off another shot, and then dropped the camera. He reached up with his fingers and slid two of them neatly into her.

She moaned and sank down onto them, twisting and turning her torso in order to get them into her. She was so open and wet that he immediately slipped another finger in, and she gasped, and bent over. "Oh, yeah, Mark, oh yes!" she cried, as she took them in. "Oh, do it baby!"

He finger fucked her for a while, enjoying the view and the sensations, and then pulled his fingers out. He rolled to his feet as she moaned her disappointment, and held one finger up at her. "Wait right there, babe. I think I got something you'll like better up there." And he dashed into his tiny kitchen.

When he came back, he was holding a cucumber, which he dangled in front of her nose. "This is going up that hot snatch of yours, you slut, and you know who's gonna get it there? You are!" He took her by the arm over to his coffee table and forced her onto it, on her back. He wrapped the fingers of her right hand around the thick vegetable and picked up the camera again.

"Let's see you fuck yourself, baby," he said, raising the camera. "A slut like you shouldn't have any problems fucking for the camera! Get it in!"

Thea arched her back and eased the tip of the cucumber into her cunt. It stretched her, but its rounded tip slid in gently. She panted and moaned again, as she gradually worked it into her. Mark danced around her, snapping off pictures of her with the cucumber at different angles. He was aching to replace the vegetable with his own boner, but he waited, and finished the pack of film. Then, he moved between her legs, pushing her thighs apart to open her even more. Her breath came in a harsh, shallow rhythm, and he could tell she was close to coming.

"You love this, don't you, you slut?" he demanded, lifting her legs up. "That's it, get that in there. You just love fucking yourself in front of me. It gets you hot doesn't it? Tell me what a slut you are. Admit it."

"Yes, yes," Thea moaned, her head tossing back and forth. "I am a slut...your slut...I need to be fucked, I need it so bad..." Her body shuddered, and she began to tense. Then, suddenly, Mark plucked the cucumber out of her hand and pulled it out, covered with her juices. She opened her eyes in shock, and he grinned.

"I'm gonna shoot my load before you do, slut," Mark said. He wiped the cucumber off on her belly and thighs. "Look at you! Filthy bitch...all covered in your own slime. Let's get you cleaned off!" He pulled at her garter belt and dragged the stockings down her legs, stripping her completely naked.

With that, he pulled her to her feet, and dragged her, stumbling and out of breath, to his bathroom. He turned the shower on, and pushed her in. The water was cold, and she screamed as it hit her body. He pointed to the soap. "Start cleaning yourself off, bitch!" When she reached for it, he adjusted the water to a more comfortable temperature, and began stripping off his own clothing. She lathered herself up, turning and posing for him, and she smiled like the wanton she was when he exposed his substantial erection. He climbed into the shower with her as she rinsed off, and had her soap him up. Then, after he rinsed, he brought her mouth to his chest.

"Lick me!" he ordered, over the sound of the shower. "Lick my entire body! All over!"

And she did, starting with his chest, nibbling on his nipples, washing his underarms with broad strokes of her tongue, wiping it across his back, and legs, teasing the crack of his ass, and then swiping across his balls. He groaned in near agony! He couldn't take it any more!

He took a firm hold on her head and thrust his cock into her open mouth, past her tongue and into her throat. She closed her mouth around his manhood and he felt a deep tug on it as she embraced the length with her throat muscles. Was there nothing this woman couldn't do?

He twisted his fingers in her hair and thrust into her, again and again, pulling further back, using all of his control, until he couldn't stand it any more. Feeling the eruption in his balls, he pulled his dick out and shot his come right across her face, splattering her forehead, eyes, nose, and cheeks. The sight of her face dripping with his offering was almost too pleasurable to bear, and it was almost a relief when the shower wiped it all away.

She clung to his legs, and he cradled her head while the warm water washed over them both. When they finally regained their breath, he turned the water off, and helped her out.

"I'm not finished with you yet," he said, handing her a towel. "Don't dry between your legs."

When they were both mostly dry, he took her back into the living room and put her back on the coffee table, with a towel under her. He went back into the bathroom and came out with shaving cream and a fresh razor. She looked genuinely concerned for the first time, as he knelt down between her thighs again.

"Don't you like the design?" she asked hesitantly. He looked down between her legs and nodded. It was very nice, the way she had it shaved, in that cute diamond shape.

"Yeah. But I think anything that makes you more naked will help matters, you know?" He brandished the can. "Any objections?"

She hesitated for a moment, but then grinned, and leaned back. He lifted her ankles and said, "Hold them. Keep yourself wide open while I do this. I want you to feel open and vulnerable every minute." She shivered and obediently took hold of her ankles, and he sprayed the shaving cream into his hand.

At the first touch of the cool cream to her sensitive lips, she trembled, but held her position. He used the tips of his fingers to gently massage the rich foam into her hair, and around it, using it as lubrication to tease her. He got to know the folds of her skin, and the areas that she liked touched, and he pinched and prodded to get reactions whenever he felt like it. Even when the foam started to subside, he didn't stop his groping, but added more, and began again.

"How would you like it if I did this while a crowd of my friends watched?" he asked, watching her reaction. She arched, shook her head in pleasure, and he felt her tremble beneath him. "I think you'll have to shave every day, if it gets you this hot," he joked. "But then, what doesn't get you hot, you slut? I bet you'd really like to be stripped and shaved in front of an audience, wouldn't you?"

She groaned, and her legs shook, her hands still locked around her ankles. Finally, Mark wiped his fingers off an picked up the razor. With agonizingly slow and careful movements, he proceeded to shear her of all her pubic hair, baring her delicate flesh to the cool air. Inch by inch, he exposed her mound, stripping away the last covering she had, until it gleamed a bright pink, and the last of the hair was gone. He rinsed the area with a damp towel, wiping away the last traces of soap and any stray hairs, and then, quickly, dived in!

The petals of flesh guarding her cunt opened as his lips and tongue assaulted her. She cried out, an incoherent cry of pleasurable anguish, and he reached out to brace her thighs in the air, pushing her back. His mouth wanted to take on all of her. He wanted to let his tongue dart in to sample her, wanted his teeth to tug on the lips and the hood which guarded her center of pleasure. She shook and impossibly thrust back at him, inviting him the way she had been doing all night, until he felt he was buried in her, in her taste and scent, and the wonderful feel of her bare skin against his lips and his cheek.

He ate her like a man gone mad, thirsting for something withheld. He licked at her, teased her and washed her with his tongue, until he felt the unmistakable thrustings and rhythmic breaths that signaled her journey to orgasm. Then, as before, he stopped and drew away. He picked up the camera, and popped in the new film cartridge. "Don't let those legs down yet," he cautioned. "I want some memories of this too!" She tightened her hold and almost cried as he took his time, walking around her and taking shots from all angles. He stood over her head, his cock dangling over her mouth, as he aimed down between her legs, and she opened her lips for him. But he only teased her with it, allowing her to lick the tip a few times before her finished his shoot and told her to put her legs down.

She twisted on the table, clamping her legs together, her hand snaking down to that neglected nub, now twice thwarted from her pleasure, but Mark stopped her. "Oh no, not yet, my sweet slut," he said, pushing her hand away. "I think I wanna come again before I let you do that. If I let you do that at all. Maybe I'll just fuck you and throw you out. Maybe I'll shove that cuke up your cunt again and send you home with it. You'd like that, wouldn't you?" He reached for his coat and pulled a condom out of the inside pocket.

Thea moaned at each suggestion, and nodded, and then whimpered. "Oh, god! Oh please, don't do that, I'll do whatever you want, but let me come! I need to come so bad!" She arched her back, welcoming him, and he chuckled.

"Oh, yeah, I'm gonna fuck you," he said, tapping her leg. "But I want a change of scenery. Turn over, get your butt up in the air. Make like a hungry little bitch for me."

Eagerly, she got up and turned over, resting her elbows on the table, and sticking her delectable ass out at him, wiggling it a little. He grinned, and stroked her thighs, and spanked that available rear until it turned pink again, and it matched her freshly shaven pussy. Then, he unwrapped the condom and slipped it on, welcoming the tight feel of it. With one more moment to arrange his position, he aimed it at the entrance to her cunt and thrust in.

She squealed as he opened her, and thrust up and back. In answer, he pulled back and plunged into her again, and again, just like he had invaded her throat a short while ago. But her pulsating pussy walls enveloped him in a softness that was absolutely unbelievable, and he gasped at each new entry into paradise.

Between her own natural lubrication, his spit, and the extra lube on the safe, she was absolutely flowing with wetness. As he slammed into her, they could both hear a distinctive slap, and the droplets splattered the inside of her thighs. She cried out and moved beneath him, and actually screamed when he pulled completely out of her and then plunged forcefully back in. She cradled her head in her arms as he thrust against her.

"Oh yes, oh yeah," Mark chanted as he thrust. "Oh, this is so good, you are such a fucking slut, you love this don't you? You love it!"

"Fuck me, fuck me...yes! God, yes, that's it, do it!" Her own replies were as tortured as his chants, bursting out with exhaled breaths, her whole body reacting to the building pressure between her legs.

When he pulled out again, she was ready for the return thrust, but instead, he pulled her ass cheeks apart with his hands and pressed up against the tight brown hole he exposed! She screamed again, and thrust back, and in a moment, his well-lubricated cock had slid neatly into her hot, tight back passage, and she couldn't hold back anymore!

As he began to move back and forth, she felt the first stirrings of a good come, and she threw her head back. "Yes! Fuck my ass, pound me, fuck me, do it, finish me!"

He felt her tight ass muscles contracting against his cock and let it all go. His hips moved faster and harder, and as she came in a shuddering, shattering, orgasm, his cock felt like it was literally being milked of his come. He spurted deep into her, his hips grinding against her butt, his hands locked around her hips.

She came once, twice, and then, as he leaned into her and eased her down, he found her center with his fingers and returned her favor by milking one last orgasm from her sweaty body. His cock shrunk and he withdrew carefully, and lay beside her on the floor, both of them covered with a sheen of sweat. She turned toward him and rested her head on his chest, her dark hair spilling out over him, and he stroked it, admiring it again.

They didn't speak for a long time.

Finally, he groaned and sat up, leaning against the couch. She pushed herself up and put her head in his lap.

"You were great."

"You are something else!"

They both laughed. He leaned his head back. "You are one hot lady," he said finally. "I never thought I'd meet someone like you at that movie."

"Hmmm. I was looking for you," she said softly. He looked back down at her.

"Huh? What do you mean?"

"That was the fourth time I've seen that movie," she replied, giggling. "You were the first guy to treat me right while we were in the theatre. Everyone else wanted to take me out to dinner and talk about things first. Or they thought I was a hooker, or playing some kind of trick on them. You just dived in." She grinned. "I like that in a man."

"Oh?" Mark couldn't help but smile. How couldn't he? He'd just had the best night in ages! He wrapped some of her hair in his hand and gently shook her head. "Well, because of you, I missed half the damn movie. So I think we should go back tomorrow night."

"Oh?" she replied, her eyes shining.

"Yeah. And this time, you'll blow me while I watch." He watched her for any sign of a negative reaction. Instead, she melted into him again and wrapped her arms around his legs.

"Oh yes," she said softly. "Yes, master."

Mark could definitely get used to this.

About the Author

Laura Antoniou's work has become well-known in the erotically alternative community as the creator of the Marketplace series (The Marketplace, The Slave, The Trainer, and The Academy), originally written under the name Sara Adamson. One Marketplace character also appears in her first book, The Catalyst, but she leaves the reader to figure that out. The only independently written Marketplace short story, "Brian on the Farm," appears in Lawrence Schimel and Carol Queen's ground-breaking anthology, Switch Hitters: Lesbians Write Gay Male Erotica, and Gay Men Write Lesbian Erotica (Cleis), which has been published in English and in German.

Antoniou has also had great success as an editor, creating the Leatherwomen anthologies which highlight new erotic work; By Her Subdued, a collection of stories about dominant women; and No Other Tribute, which features submissive women. Her nonfiction anthologies include Some Women, and an homage to author John Preston entitled Looking for Mr. Preston. Antoniou's books have been published in the United States, Germany, Japan, and Korea, to international acclaim.

Antoniou's short stories also appear in other anthologies, most recently in SM Classics, edited by Susan Wright; Things Invisible To See: Gay and Lesbian Tales of Magic Realism, edited by Lawrence Schimel; The Second Coming, edited by Pat Califia and Robin Sweeney; Once Upon a Time: Erotic Fairy Tales for Women, edited by Mike Ford; Ritual Sex, edited by Tristan Taormino and David Aaron Clark; and Best Lesbian Erotica 1997, edited by Tristan Taormino. Antoniou was also a columnist for Girlfriends magazine from 1995-1997, the submissions editor for Badboy and Bi-Curious magazines from 1995-96, and was a regular contributor to The SandMUtopia Guardian.

Antoniou is currently finishing the sixth book in the Marketplace series, entitled The Inheritor. She is also currently working on a collection of her short stories, and a new book titled Serious Player.

Web page: www.iron-rose.com/marketplace

Books from Mystic Rose

SCREW THE ROSES, SEND ME THE THORNS
The Romance and Sexual Sorcery of Sadomasochism
by Philip Miller and Molly Devon

The Bestselling guide to sadomasochism by two experienced players. This popular book strips away myth, shame, and fear revealing the truth about an intense form of eroticism too long misunderstood and condemned. It is fully indexed and includes over 225 photos and illustrations, a 250-plus word glossary, as well as appendices with contacts

DHAMPIR: CHILD OF THE BLOOD   by V.M. Johnson

In Dhampir, Child of the Blood, the myths come alive, as Johnson passes on to us the history, legends and wisdom of The Clan. Frank, explicit letters from a mother to a daughter about life and survival as members of the vampyre Clan of Lilith.

The Marketplace Series by Laura Antoniou

THE MARKETPLACE
"Compelling, charged with electricity . . ."   - Kitty Tsui

The first volume in the landmark Marketplace trilogy, the series that set the standard for contemporary SM erotica. After Sharon, Brian, Claudia, and Robert are accepted for training by Marketplace representatives, they struggle to overcome their shortcomings: pride, selfishness, immaturity and perfectionism.

Who among them will survive the training meted out by the rigorous and unrelenting Chris Parker? And who will uncover the truth of his or her own sexual need to submit?

THE SLAVE

"There's a new voice in S/M fiction these days, and none too soon . . . Thank goodness Sara Adamson has exploded onto the scene!"
- Kate Bornstein

The second volume in the Marketplace Series, The Slave describes the experiences of Robin, an exceptionally sensitive submissive who longs to join the ranks of those who have proven themselves worthy of entry into the sexual training ground of the Marketplace. Follow Robin as she is educated in the arts of submission and service by the meticulously ethical Chris Parker, the person in whom she will confide her deepest sexual secrets.

THE TRAINER

"This is domination and submission at its best - a very well-written work that holds from page to page . . ." - Shiny International

In the third book of Sara Adamson's Marketplace Series, would-be trainer and spotter for the Marketplace, Michael LaGuardia, learns there is more to the art of commanding respect than meets the eye. Moreover, iconoclastic master trainer Chris Parker doesn't seem to appreciate Michael's potential. What can he do to get his attention? What does Michael really want from Chris? And when will Chris finally divulge his long-hidden secrets?

THE ACADEMY

The fourth book in the Marketplace series! Taking up where The Trainer left off, as Chris Parker and dozens of other Trainers journey to Okinawa. This book explores both the strict, hidden order behind the men and women who train the exquisite Marketplace slaves and the mysteries behind Mr. Parker himself. The Academy is a full length novel incorporating independent short stories written by Guest Authors. Karen Taylor, Cecilia Tan, Michael Hernandez, david stein and M. Christian delve into the world of the Marketplace and turn up tales of power, sex, and surrender, the kinds of stories Trainers tell each other to inspire, teach. . .or warn.

THE REUNION

More from the characters we have come to love as book five of the Marketplace Series reunites Chris Parker, Robin, and others in a castle in Ireland. Once again Antoniou brings us a compelling novel bursting with raw sexuality, set within the hidden world where slavery is absolute and personal honor is valued above all.

Order by mail at:

Mystic Rose Books
P.O. Box 1036/SMS
Fairfield, CT 06430

Or online at WWW.mysticrose.com

___Dhampir: Child of the Blood
by V. M. Johnson $8.95

___Screw the Roses, Send Me the Thorns
by Philip Miller & Molly Devon $24.95

___The Academy, Tales of the Marketplace
by Laura Antoniou $13.95

___The Marketplace
by Laura Antoniou $13.95

___The Slave
by Laura Antoniou $13.95

___The Trainer
by Laura Antoniou $13.95

___The Reunion
by Laura Antoniou $17.95

___The Catalyst and Other Works
by Laura Antoniou $15.95

___Shipping   (add $3.75 per book shipping)

___Total (check enclosed)